From the Top Plates Up
A Production Roof Framer's Journey

Will Holladay

W&H Publishers

Dedicated to the only carpenter who walks on water
– Our Lord Jesus Christ –
and also to my bride
– Mariela –
I am everything I am because they have loved me

Disclaimer of Liability

This book is the historical account of the roof framing career of Will Holladay. Because the author may describe using tools and techniques that are extremely dangerous does not indicate that the reader should do likewise. By mentioning them the author only seeks to be honest in the portrayal of the events, processes, and methods he used throughout his life. Without exception, always follow a tool manufacturer's operating instructions and comply with the current safety codes or regulations applicable to your activity, both on and off the job. The author and publisher do not approve of the violation of any safety code or regulation.

The author and publisher hereby fully disclaim liability to any and all parties for any loss, and do not assume any liability whatsoever for any loss or alleged loss or alleged damages caused by the reader's use or interpretation of the information found in this book, whether such errors or omissions result from negligence, accident, or any other cause that may be attributed to the author or publisher.

Illustrations by Jim Goold
Photographs by the author except as noted
Various versions of the Holy Bible are used in quotations:
American Standard Version (ASV)) – public domain.
International Standard Version (ISV) Copyright © 1995-2014 by ISV Foundation.
   All rights reserved. Used by permission of Davidson Press, LLC.
King James Version (KJV)– public domain.
New International Version (NIV). Copyright © 1973, 1978, 1984, 2011 by Biblica, Inc.™.
   All rights reserved. Used by permission.
New King James Version (NKJV) Copyright © 1982 by Thomas Nelson.
   All rights reserved. Used by permission.

ISBN: 978-0-945186-09-0
Library of Congress Catalog Card Number: 2017916828
Printed in the United States of America

W&H Publishers
whframingconsultant@gmail.com

Cover photos
Upper: Holladay Flyiing Sevice (1992)
Lower: Stacking a custom home, Medford OR (1997)

Contents

Books by Will Holladay

A Roof Cutter's Secrets to Framing the Custom Home
The Complicated Roof – A Cut and Stack Workbook
From the Top Plates Up – A Production Roof Framer's Journey
The Carpenter Patriot

Videos by Will Holladay

A Roof Cutter's Secrets – live workshop
Roof framing for the Professional – The Essentials
Roof Framing for the Professional – Advanced Topics

Foreword
By Rick Tyrell and Shone Freeman

Rick Tyrell

Having spent more years in the construction field than I can count both as a high-end custom home builder and contributing author to various construction trade magazines, I have gained a great deal of respect and admiration for Will Holladay's work. In just reading any of his books or articles, it is obvious that Will is innovative. His approach and techniques have lifted roof framing to a new level. As I read this book, *From the Top Plates Up*, I found myself fascinated not only by Will's journey as a framer, but also by his journey as a person. In the end, his personal journey becomes as interesting as his professional journey. You certainly will enjoy the book and I recommend it highly.

Hidden in *From the Top Plates Up* I found three themes. The first is that Will's decision to stay as a "bags on" lead carpenter all his life rather than move up the ladder into a "bags off" supervisory role has been bittersweet. The second theme is that if you spend your whole life pounding nails, there will be a physical cost. Are you ready to pay it? The third theme is that every carpenter must master problem solving or else be doomed to mediocrity. Things drawn on paper or punched into a calculator can look good and make sense but making it work in the real world is where the rubber meets the road.

Will has been a pioneer in roof framing. From sharing production roof-cutting methodology to inventing labor-saving tools like the Headcutter and the Seat-cut jig, Will has helped more carpenters than he will ever know. As for me, his classic book, *A Roof Cutter's Secrets*, is what I always reach for when working on any framing project.

In *From the Top Plates Up*, readers will find a journey that shows how one can build on opportunities in spite of setbacks. As a result of the book, you will most likely find yourself reflecting on your own journey just as I did. I think that those of us in the construction field owe Will a debt of gratitude for sharing his knowledge and experience. For if I have learned nothing else from Will, it is that the road to riches is not found writing construction books.

Rick Tyrell is owner of DSR Design Build (MA and SC). He is also a contributing author to Fine Homebuilding, The Journal of Light Construction, *and* Design/Build Business *magazines.*

Shone Freeman

When I started out as a young carpenter some 30 years ago, I had no idea I would end up the founder and president of one of the most successful custom home framing companies in the San Francisco Bay Area. Aside from the support of a loving wife, one of the most important things I did to accomplish this was to surround myself with many talented people in one form or another. One of these people was Will Holladay. I first heard of Will in the early 1990s on account of his book *A Roof Cutter's Secrets*. In my quest to become a better, smarter carpenter I devoured that book. It was a technical treatise. In this book *From the Top Plates Up*, Will shines a light on the other side of the building equation – the practical side. It is filled with the real-life advice one might expect to hear an old time master carpenter share with his crew. It is entertaining and informative at the same time. Most definitely a book every carpenter should read.

As the result of a simple letter that I sent to Will, we became friends. To know him has been an avenue to connect with those who were part of the framing generation that came before me while also helping me grow in the trade that I love. Having framed a bit in the housing tract environment, I have always wished that more was written about what is was like in the earlier tract days. Reading through *From the Top Plates Up*, I was pleased to find that Will dedicated a whole chapter to a nostalgic look at the heyday of production roof framing. The book pays tribute to so many values that are foundational to success on the jobsite, in business, and in life. Stories of hard work, humility, camaraderie, innovation, discipline, passion, and persistence are just some of the things that you will find in this book.

If you have ever packed lumber in the rain, smashed your thumb, hurt your back, or stacked roofs in 100° weather, you are part of the framer's brotherhood. Despite those miseries, there is nothing more gratifying than standing back at the end of the day, seeing a house erupt out of a hole in the ground. I am proud to be a part of this – something much bigger than just a job or a trade. *From the Top Plates Up* helps bring that to life.

Shone Freeman is president of S.R. Freeman Inc., a large custom home framing business serving the greater San Francisco Bay Area

Preface

I have led a tough life and I have lived it at full speed. I never backed off the accelerator, and, as I look back, I realize I have seen and done things that few others may have experienced all together in one lifetime. This is not to brag or anything like that, but only to say it has given me a unique perspective on life compared with many of my peers. After reading this book, many of you will undoubtedly come to the conclusion that I am crazy. I can reassure you that you will not be the first to think so – I have heard it all my life.

Whereas *A Roof Cutter's Secrets* and *The Complicated Roof* were immensely demanding and arduous books to write being of such technical nature (thank God I will never have to do them again), *From the Top Plates Up*, while still grueling, was certainly gobs more fun to write. This book is a sharing of many of my memories as a framer – the good and the bad, lessons learned and lessons I should have learned, as well as my points of view on a variety of subjects. Consider it to be like a grandpa sharing stories of his past with the extended family as they gather around the fireplace on some special occasion. Because one's memory fades with age, I wanted to get as much as I could recorded on paper before I too must follow in the footsteps of all those who have gone before. May this book provide helpful insights to those of you "still in the game," or stir recollections for those like me who have been forced begrudgingly to move on to a later stage of life.

Without a doubt, the Lord has blessed me in uncountable ways with experiences that few have had while also providing a platform from which to share them. He has impressed upon my heart that they were not meant only for me, but also to be passed along. Therefore, I would be totally remiss if I failed to do so. The Lord did not make any of us a bucket just to receive good things, but rather He made us a light to shine forth. "People don't light a lamp and put it under a basket but on a lamp stand, and it gives light to everyone in the house" (*Matthew* 5:15).

I suppose that as we see the light at the end of the tunnel of life arriving, we want to make sure we have done all that we can do to make this world a better place. I pray in some small way I have done my share. Although I have fallen short of the Lord's will in many other areas of my life, I pray that at least here I will have completed it. When they throw my ashes into the wind I only hope it can be said that the world is a better place because I passed through.

Each one of us has a story to tell – this is mine.

My best to each of you,
Will

1

One Swing, one Nail – the art of the hammer

If I tell you I'm good, probably you will say I'm boasting.
But if I tell you I'm not good, you'll know I'm lying. – Bruce Lee

The hammer has been a mainstay of rough carpentry for centuries, but during my lifetime its importance has slid into a secondary role behind that of the pneumatic nail gun. As a result, I find that fewer and fewer of today's carpenters can really swing it efficiently. Here are a few thoughts on the subject from an old, way-over-the-hill framer.

Like some of you, I have been swinging a framing hammer for a long time, reaching as far back as my childhood. I grew up on a little farm in Southern California, and like all farm boys, I learned to use carpentry and mechanical hand tools at a young age. While the city kids were learning to skateboard, play the piano, and shoot hoops, we were learning to shovel manure, shoot rifles, and build things. Two of those skills helped me to be successful at my first "paid" construction job. During summers in high school, I worked as a laborer for a spec builder in Santa Barbara. You know, I was that young buck the contractor sent around to do all the dirty work that no one else would ever dream of doing. I moved lumber and supplies, shoveled sand for slabs, and dug lots of trenches. I was the forklift, the backhoe, the loader, and the tractor-scraper on the job.

One day I was given the opportunity to build a large wooden planter using railroad ties along the front of a custom home we were building. This was my first chance to demonstrate to the boss that I could do something other than work a shovel. I had a blast putting it together and the boss saw that I could handle a hammer and handsaw fairly well, so soon afterward my responsibilities also included nailing tasks. On subsequent jobs I became the one who nailed off all the roof and floor sheathing (no wall sheathing in those days, just let-in braces). These duties provided me with lots of nailing practice and soon I sounded like a machine gun with only a slight pause now and then to reload my fingering hand. Needless to say, nail-gun usage was not all that common yet. When I moved back to the Southern California area early in 1974, I was a decent framer who was able to put boards on a mark and nail them off, but I lacked any real knowledge in home building. Two years in the Orange Coast College construction technology program changed all that, and I walked away from there with lead carpenter skills. I could easily run a job since I was now able to read and draw plans, calculate lumber lists, layout, etc. One of the Orange Coast College instructors, Hank Resse, whose framing career had been abruptly cut short by a leg injury, taught me the fundamentals of production roof framing, and he coached my hammering skills to a higher level. He knew I was headed into the booming housing tracts of the Eastern Los Angeles basin to frame and wanted to make sure I would do well. He had been a stacker and groomed me to follow in his footsteps. He would share stories and tricks from his "piece" framing days in the tracts; and was so good with the hammer that many times he would flip the hammer around to nail with the claws just to break the monotony.

Whereas Hank typically swung a 22-ounce smooth-face straight-claw Plumb hammer and had no problem sinking a 16d nail in one pop, I being a young "macho" guy had purchased two milled faced 28-ounce Vaughan straight claw hammers with 18-inch handles after seeing that all the "cool" tract wall framers used them. Originally, I had even thought of getting the 32-ounce version (even more testosterone), but when I heard that the carpenters' union wouldn't allow them, I settled on the "smaller" version. From what I was told, the union's restriction against the 32-ounce framing hammer had been implemented after a couple guys had broken a leg from a swing that went awry. Who knows if they were pulling my leg or not, but since I was planning to work in the housing tracts, I went for the 28-ounce version to avoid union scrutiny. In the end, it was a fairly good choice for me personally, because I have used it for everything from wall framing to roof stacking. Little did I know that those two hammers would stay with me through my whole career. Only my roof cutting dado saws are older by manufacturer date. **(fig 1-1)**

Most would say a 28-ounce hammer is too heavy for stacking and I would tend to agree, but, after mine were modified to my liking, they felt more like a 25-ounce than a 28-ounce and are superbly balanced (I will describe my personal modifications farther along). Carpenters who have tried my hammer love its feel. I must add that when I first started piecemeal stacking in the housing tracts, I did use a 22-ounce milled face Plumb hammer on Hank's recommendation, but soon discarded it for my beloved 28-ounce because I found that the 22-ounce was way too light for me. A 25–ounce probably would have been a better choice to stack with, but since I had the

28-ounce versions already, I just stuck with them rather than go buy more hammers.

While Hank was hell with a smooth face hammer, I was/am absolutely miserable. If I used a smooth face hammer, I bent nails right and left or sent them shooting off into outer space. The reason behind this is that, ever since I was a young boy, I have used a milled face hammer and have done only rough carpentry work all my life. With a milled face hammer, one doesn't have to hit the nail "straight on" to sink it like you must do with a smooth face. Since the milled face grabs the head you can contact the nail head at many degrees off "straight on" and still sink the nail, no problem. I had become very competent at sinking nails when striking them from odd angles as long as I was using a milled face hammer. The ability to off-angle nail well was a big plus for me as a stacker since the majority of my nailing was just that. Now, after half a century of doing what some might say is a "bad habit," my swinging style is permanently embedded in my subconscious.

In the early 1970s, the striking surface of the milled face framing hammers were hardened to a high Rockwell hardness, so that the corrugation would hold up well even when being used against metal nail-pullers (cats-paw)

1-2 Side comparison: a 28-ounce straight claw framing hammer (left) versus a 28-ounce rigging axe (right)

1-3 Face size comparison: a 28-ounce straight claw framing hammer (left) versus a 28-ounce rigging axe (right)

and the like. At some point in the late 1970s or early 1980s, the hammer manufacturers decided to lessen the face hardness on their milled face hammers so they would deform a bit when struck against another metal tool. It was done for safety's sake, since there had been some serious eye injuries that were caused by small chips of the struck device/nail flying off to embed itself in folks' eyes. I suspect, while the change may have come as a recommendation from the fledgling OSHA, it was most likely done for liability protection reasons. Flying particles only happened with milled face hammers, since smooth face versions don't normally shred off pieces of the struck device/nail. Good reason to always wear safety glasses.

Many guys in the tracts liked to wall frame with the Vaughan 28-ounce rigging hatchet, because it had the largest diameter face and was really well balanced. **(fig 1-2)** With the big face, it was hard to miss the nail even when you were exhausted from pounding nails all day. While the big face was great

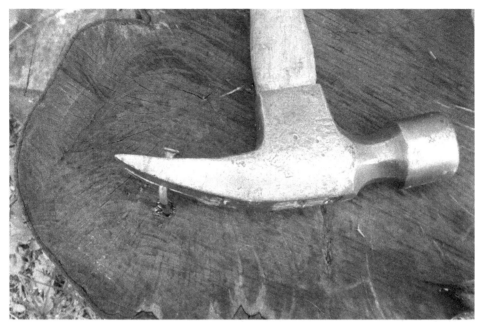
1-4 Use the side of the hammer head to pull nails

for wall framers who sank end-nails all day long, the big face was somewhat of a detriment for roof stackers like me, who sank lots of toenails in tight corners, etc. **(fig 1-3)** Although the hatchet blade was very helpful during plumb and line to pry over the bottom of a diagonal brace, the downside was that it was difficult to yank nails with the nail-pulling slot on the hatchet blade edge if the nail head was flush or embedded in the wood. Not that you should be going backward and pulling nails, but occasionally "stuff happens." If you had a straight claw hammer, you could simply flip the hammer around, swing and catch the flush or embedded nail head with the claw (in a chisel-like manner), and then lever the hammer handle sideways to pry the nail. **(fig 1-4)** I not only grew very adept at this, but also at flicking out nails once the head was exposed with a super powerful swing of the claws. The split between the claws would grab the nail shank and the sheer force of the swing would yank it right out. Stubborn nails might take an extra swing, but this saved tons of time screwing around to remove a nail that had been poorly placed. Just make sure no one is behind you, since the nail will be sent flying like a bullet. With practice, the nail-puller becomes only a backup for the most stubborn or difficult positioned nail-pulling situations.

The blade of a rigging hatchet is also harder to use as a chisel-like device compared with straight claws. Although I knew guys whose rigging ax skills were phenomenal, I still find that, in the simple mechanics of it all, the claw did a better job performing the job of a 2-inch chisel. Not that it couldn't be

1-5 Using a straight claw hammer to chisel out a let-in brace notch

done, mind you, just that with the hatchet you have to chisel at times with a sideways swing and, depending on your position relative to the wood, it may be a bit more cumbersome. Just imagine chiseling out a let-in brace notch with a hatchet compared with a claw when wall framing (those rare situations where you can not fit the Skil 77 in sideways to make a plunge cut). **(fig 1-5)** Chiseling with the claws mimics the normal nail-driving swing, so most have an easier time with it. A straight claw hammer definitely has an easier time disassembling wood that has been nailed together flat, since the claw can be swung and set like a wedge between the plates, and then the hammer handle levered sideways to pry the two boards apart just like what is done when removing a nail.

The Hart brothers were the first guys I know of to cut the ax blade off a rigging hatchet and weld on claws from a straight claw framing hammer. Since the hatchet blade weighed a bit more than a pair of claws, these combo hammers lost a couple ounces in weight down to maybe 25 ounces. Hart's hammers were so popular that soon they made their own hammer head forging rather than mating two different hammer halves. Thus, the large diameter face "California framer" style was born. Seeing the success Hart had had, many other tool companies followed suit and started producing a

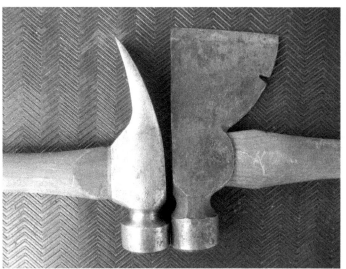

1-6 A Plumb produced "California framer" style hammer (left) compared to a Vaughan rigging axe (right)

similar style hammer within a few years. **(fig 1-6)** I have lost track of all the players in the hammer-making business nowadays, because I have never had to replace my +40-year-old hammers. They don't wear out due to their super hardened steel face. In all my years, I have only had to touch up the milled face a couple times. I didn't want to do that often anyway, because the face is only surface hardened and you would ruin the hammer if you penetrated this depth. I avoid using the hammer face against a nail-puller to extend their life and typically smack the nail-puller with the side of the hammer head. Many hammer companies have started making hammers from titanium, claiming they work better and are easier on the body, etc. Physics-wise all this may be true and I have tried one or two out of curiosity, but I still prefer my old steel hammers. I suspect this is most likely because my body is so accustomed to them that it just feels more natural rather than having to "break in a new horse." If you like them – great – use them.

Besides finding a head face diameter that suits your needs, I feel that the two most important things in a good framing hammer are weight and balance. Since weight × speed = power, it is possible to develop power equally whether it is with a light or heavy hammer if the speed is adjusted accordingly (wh KISS power formula. The "real" formula is a bit more complicated: $E = mv^2/2$, where E is energy, m is mass, v is velocity). Since each person is a different size and has different physical attributes, how each can best mesh weight versus speed will vary individually. Super simplistically, since I am no physicist like Albert Einstein, let's say that to sink a 16d nail takes 60 units of power. You could combine a 22-ounce hammer with 38 speed units to arrive at that 60 or you could combine a 32-ounce hammer with the lesser speed

1-7 The closer the hammer's balance point is to the striking surface the better

units of 28 to achieve that same 60 units of power. Comparing rifle cartridge ballistics would be another example of power variations based on velocity and weight. It should be noted that, in the "real" power formula, speed plays a bigger role in developing energy than does an increase in weight – something to keep in mind. After developing the required power to sink that nail, you must now consider how repeating that same motion thousands of times per day will affect muscle endurance and total body fatigue. Is a longer handle better or worse for you? That length affects speed generation. Will you be swinging a hammer mostly downward where gravity is helping in speed generation, or will you spend more time swinging upward where gravity will have a restraining effect? Hopefully, you can begin to see the wide number of variables that play a part in determining what is the best size hammer for an individual and its particular use. No one can say definitely that this hammer size or that hammer brand is best for you – it is something you will need to explore and determine by yourself. Whereas Hank worked well with the 22-ounce hammer, the 28-ounce was a much better fit for me. He was short and had less distance to accelerate a weight, whereas I am very tall and had gobs more arc distance to accelerate a weight. I was also a young highly trained competitive athlete and, as such, had much greater physical endurance than he did to swing a heavier hammer all day. Bear in mind that weight and hand grip can affect the possibility of developing tendonitis at the elbow (tennis elbow). Some guys may never develop tendonitis their whole career, while for others it may be a chronic problem. I have noticed that the older I became, the easier I would develop tennis elbow (outside elbow) or golfer's elbow (inside elbow) when I used my hands too much. Chalk one up for the pneumatic nail-gun.

Married in importance with hammer weight is hammer balance. Once again, I make the disclaimer that I am no physicist, but I can say that the closer the hammer's center of gravity (CG) is to the head end of the hammer, the longer the lever arm will be and the more kinetic energy will be concentrated on the striking surface. **(fig 1-7)** This explanation is kind of arcane, so how about if I try to explain it in another fashion. Consider hitting a baseball with a bat: in any given swing more force is applied to the ball if it contacts the bat farther out versus closer in. Farther out is when you see home runs. Not exactly a perfect parallel, but you get the idea – the closer the CG is located to the hammer head, the better. You would be correct in observing that the closer you hold your hammer to the end of the handle, the more speed and therefore more power you can develop. This is definitely true, but there are two other factors that come into play to explain why choking up on the handle a little bit is a much better choice. **(fig 1-1)** We will look at them a little further along.

Now let's talk about the body mechanics involved in swinging the hammer and how one can better this aspect. Whereas in boxing and baseball, power is developed starting in the legs and accelerated with a torquing rotation of the hips using the core, striking power for the downward hammer swing is developed primarily using the core with the legs serving more as a stabilizer rather than a force initiator. When wall framing in the bent-over position, the stomach, hip flexors, and latissimi dorsi (lats) pull the body down in the power stroke of the swing, while the buttocks, hamstrings, and back return the body to the starting point for the next swing. The shoulders and arm muscles continue to accelerate the movement initiated at the core and serve as the mechanism to transfer the total combined momentum to the hammer. Sorry to upset those of you who think hammering is an arm exercise requiring big guns. If you are only using your arms to swing the hammer, you will not develop the speed you could, since the arm has a relatively short arc having the pivot point located at the shoulder joint compared with the near twice the arc length when the pivot point is the hip joint. The force generated using your arms alone will be far short of what could be developed if you incorporated your core. Besides that, you will tire very quickly since you are concentrating the total workload on the arm and shoulder muscles. During a hammer swing, the core doesn't move very far in most cases, but its movement is the key to powerful swings. The role of the shoulder, arm, and wrist is to continue to accelerate the core's generated forward rotation movement until contact is made with the nail. As you may have surmised, the longer the acceleration arc is, the more time there is to accelerate a hammer and, likewise, the higher a speed it can attain. As in cracking a long bullwhip, the farther a point is located out along the whip's length, the faster it is traveling. Therefore, taller guys with long arms have a distinct advantage over shorter guys when driving nails, given that both individuals are generally of the same strength. I rowed a bit of crew when younger and the physics involved was somewhat similar. Rowing leverage is such that the taller guys could develop power easier than shorter guys. The taller fellow's oar has a longer arc in the water with which to accelerate and transfer his power. I am not saying you can't be an excellent framer if you are shorter, I'm just noting how physics play an important role in developing hammering power.

At times, you will be required to nail from a position other than the downward stroke of standard western style wall framing. In many of these positions, you will find that you still incorporate your core. Consider the task of nailing rafters to a ridge board located at shoulder height: from this standing position you will contract the core while pushing slightly off the hammer side leg to make a quick twisting movement at the hip in the manner of a boxer throwing a hook and send the hammer whipping forward in a sideways arc. Bruce Lee was an icon of my era. He would demonstrate a 1-inch punch at martial arts conferences where he would send an audience member flying. The power he generated for this punch all came from a quick subtle hip twist.

Therefore, exercises that strengthen the muscles of the core (stomach, hips, buttocks, hamstrings, and back) will certainly help better your swing. This reminds me of a time many years back when I was visiting the Los Angeles County Fair. Walking around, I saw a participation event named "Kill the Giant." They had a huge +/−30-foot-tall one-dimensional giant with a 2-inch pipe running vertically from the ground up his front to the head. At the very top of the pipe was a bell. Located around this pipe was a doughnut-shaped weight. At the bottom was a tiny teeter-totter apparatus upon which this doughnut sat. Striking the teeter-totter with a sledge hammer sent the doughnut weight shooting up the pipe. If you hit it hard enough, it would reach the top and ring the bell, signifying that you had killed the giant. If you did that, you were awarded a prize of some sort. For a price, you had 3 swings with the sledge hammer. I spent some time watching as huge professional football types tried their luck with no success. I was ready to walk away when my wife prodded me to go do it. I thought to myself that I would be an utter fool to try seeing as how these big gorillas couldn't do it. What chance did a guy weighing some 100 lbs less have at success. But not to be berated by the wife for failing to even try, I paid my fee, grabbed the sledge, and swung – Ding! Swung again when the doughnut was back down – Ding! Swung my last time when the doughnut was back down – Ding! I rang the bell 3 times! What those big bruisers couldn't do in all their effort, I had done on every swing. It surprised me to no end. It was at that very moment when I realized that body mechanics was the key in developing speed and power. It easily trumped size and strength. Having spent many years refining that same exact downward striking motion while framing, in the end, I had developed true "giant killing" power. This simple lesson I have carried all my life.

Every swing you ever make needs to be a relaxed, fluid, ever-accelerating movement. If the body is tensed, your performance will suffer. Bear in mind the importance of the wrist flick (for lack of a better name) at the end of the hammer swing. Your hand and hammer handle should not be frozen together to form a solid plank, but rather the wrist rotates to create a second short whip at the end of a long whip. I am sure many of you know what a martial arts nunchaku is (made famous by Bruce Lee in the movie *Enter the Dragon*), and how by just adding a simple joint in the middle of a solid staff, the swinging force of the staff is magnified many times over. That little wrist flick will do the same and multiply the speed that has been developed up to that point. Remember, I mentioned earlier that it is better to choke up slightly on the hammer handle versus holding it on the very end. The simple reason is that it is easier to make the flicking motion if the hand is positioned about one-third the distance up the handle from the end versus being situated on the very end. So the overall swinging arc length lost by choking up slightly on the handle is more than compensated for by creating a much improved wrist flick. To do a good wrist flick, your hand must not have a death grip on the hammer handle (more on handle design coming up). This is an error I often see. During the cocking part of the swing, your grip should be such that the thumb and forefinger are somewhat firm around the handle, while the three other fingers are in a half-open palm position. As the hammer rotates through the flick to the striking position, the thumb and forefinger release their grip on the handle, allowing the smallest three fingers and the base of the thumb to take over as the grasping section. **(figs 1-8, 1-9)** You do need strong hands and fingers to do this properly, and, for this reason, you will find that good framers will always have a very firm handshake. If your hands are weak, you will lose your hammer. By using your hand in this fashion, you will find that the wrist flick motion can achieve an arc range of 110° or more. If you keep your hand in a fist around the hammer handle you will be limited to about a 40° maximum of wrist flick arc. Choking up on the handle slightly is what allows you to control the back-and-forth motion. This cannot be done on the end of the handle where you are hanging on for your dear life. Bear in mind that I have been writing about framing hammers with 16- to 18-inch handles, not your homeowner tack hammer. In addition to facilitating a good wrist flick, choking up slightly on the hammer handle exponentially increases target accuracy since the tail of the handle extending past the palm permits the hand to more easily guide the hammer head to the desired point of contact.

1-8 Applying the wrist flick to your hammer swing – part 1

1-9 Applying the wrist flick to your hammer swing – part 2

There are a bunch of excellent framing videos by Larry Haun on YouTube. Take a look at them sometime and notice where both he and his brother Joe hold their hammers and how they use their core when they need to add real power to their hammer swings.

Hammer handles are super important because they not only absorb shock from the blow, but they also affect the whole balance of the hammer. I prefer wood over fiberglass, steel, titanium, or whatever. Not only does it do an excellent job absorbing shock, but, from my experience, wood is the lightest of all the other materials used in handles, which, in effect, automatically moves the CG closer to the head. Therefore, wood-handled hammers end up being much better balanced than hammers with other types of handles. Wood also has the added benefit to me personally in that, with it, I can easily reshape the handle to a design of my liking. Whereas one must treat a wooden hammer kindly, you can certainly throw the train at a fiberglass- or steel-handled version and see little damage. So the moral of this story: It is best to stay with an indestructible style of handle if you are into demolition work, or you will spend a lot of time replacing handles.

Only rigging hatchet hammer handles seem to be designed to help your wrist flick. Most claw hammer designs I have seen are so thick in the middle that you have to grip them firmly all the time or risk losing them. A thick handle that fills up your whole hand is anathema to getting the most out of a wrist flick. Since I have never found a wood claw hammer handle to my liking, and a rigging hatchet handle won't fit my claw hammer's head forging,

1-10 The strongest hammer handle wood grain direction parallels the hammer head

I started modifying the commercially available hammer handle variant. What I do is rasp (followed by sanding) off the wider part in the middle so they run straight from where the neck narrows down after leaving the head forging to where the handle flares out at the butt. Basically, I get rid of the "beer belly" in the middle of the handle that you are supposed to grab. This not only facilitates the process of flicking the hammer, but, by removing material from the handle, you have now moved the CG even closer to the hammer head, improving its balance somewhat.

Moving on now to talk about hammer care. In general, besides a light application of WD40 to a steel-hammer head if it will be taking a short siesta during the winter, the hammer requires little maintenance. Occasionally, over time, one will have to replace a wooden handle, sharpen the claws, or remill the corrugated face. But if you pull nails by levering the hammer handle to the side (or using a nail bar), hit a nail-puller using the side of the hammer head, and stay away from chiseling concrete with the claws, these tasks will be infrequent.

When changing out a broken hickory hammer's handle select a replacement where the grain is super tight and parallels the head's face-to-claw direction for the greatest durability. **(fig 1-10)** When I go looking for a hammer handle in the hardware store, I line up all the available handles so I can see the butt ends and compare to see if any fit these parameters. Often none do and I must go elsewhere to look, but sometimes I am lucky and find more than one that fits the bill. When that happens, I always grab two so I will have a spare. Simple instructions on how to install the handle usually come with the handle itself and it is not that complicated of a procedure.

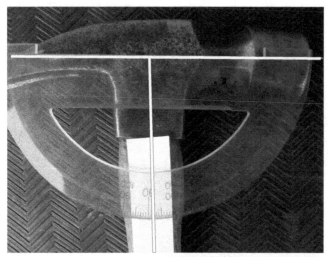

1-11 A 2° downward hammer head cant better aligns the striking surface for bent over framing

1-12 I use an extra steel wedge to cant the hammer head

Cut the old hammer handle off where it enters the hammer head casting and, with the casting fixed firmly in a vice drive, drive the remaining wood handle part out the top. Next, drive the hammer head onto the new handle by striking the butt end of the handle held vertically against the floor, cut off the excess running above the forging, and install the wood and metal wedges. Some guys throw a little epoxy in the hammer head before jamming it in the new handle. While that certainly can't hurt, it does make it a bitch to swap out the handle the next time around, because you will need to heat up the hammer head to break the epoxy's grip. I always keep a few extra metal wedges around, since I always drive one steel wedge into the face end of the hammer head casting's opening to tilt the head about 2° down from perpendicular to the center line of the handle. **(figs 1-11, 1-12)** I put the second

1-13 The correct cant should align the hammer head with a flat surface when positioned as shown

steel wedge in the middle as given in the instructions. While many hammers don't come from the manufacturer with toe-in, this small rotation allows the face of the hammer to match the arc of your swing and contact the nail square on. A good way to test if your hammer is set up correctly with the $2°$ toe-in is to grab the hammer in a normal grip and put the face of the hammer and the fist holding the handle against a vertical wall to note if the hammer head face parallels the wall. If it does, you have the correct toe-in. **(fig 1-13)**

Keeping your claws sharp is a good habit, because this allows you to be ready when you must chip some wood away or need to grab something and move it around. Many times, rather than reaching down to grab a header from the ground with your bare hands, you can simply swing the claws to embed them in the material and now you have a solid handhold without having bent down. Anything to save your back. This same embedding swing works great to extend your reach so you can grab something like a block of wood that is out of reach when you're running blocks. Using a rigging hatchet in this "hay hook" style works equally as well but, in either case, the claws or blade need to be sharp or the strike will either just bounce off or not penetrate deep enough to be of any use. To sharpen the claws, use a small 4½- to 5-inch disk grinder to touch up the top and bottom of the claws only enough to give them a sharp edge. Do it too much, too often, and your claws slowly disappear. **(fig 1-14)**

1-14 Sharpen the hammer's claws from the underside using a small grinder

1-15 Re-mill a hammer's corrugated face using a thin steel cutting blade mounted on a small grinder

To remill the corrugated face I install a .06-inch cutting disk on a disk grinder and, with the hammer head firmly clamped in a vise, run the cutting disk lightly down the existing grooves to slightly deepen them. I typically just momentarily hit the trigger, release it, and then touch the spinning blade to the face, dragging it quickly toward me. Practice the procedure on something of little value first before you try it on your beloved hammer face and end up ruining it. **(fig 1-15)** Of course, you can always drop your hammer off at a saw shop to have them touch up the hammer head face professionally, but since the advent of the throwaway carbon-tipped saw blades, most saw shops have disappeared.

Folks who use rubber-gripped metal or fiberglass handles don't have to worry much about slippage caused by a sweaty hand, but guys like me who work in hot climates and use wood handles, will most certainly have to deal with it. What I do is rub down the handle with surf wax. This seems to resolve sweaty hand slippage. I suppose you could use wide receiver's football gloves or these thin special-coated work gloves to accomplish the same thing, but I can't speak with any authority on this, since I have never tried them when hammering. Anyway, you have a few options.

Many of the newer hammer styles all incorporate a nail-setting groove on top of the hammer head. It was an excellent invention by some smart

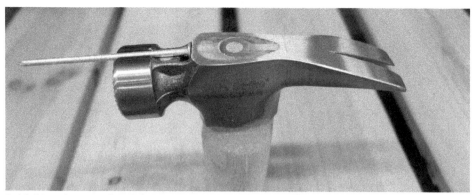

1-16 Many hammer heads have a groove to hold a nail for out-of-reach nailing

1-17 A nail-holding trick for wood-handled hammers without a nail setting grove.

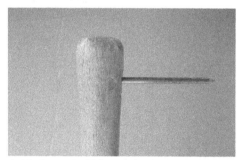

1-18 An angled ³/₈-inch hole creates a pocket to hold a 16d sinker

carpenter. **(fig 1-16)** When you can't set a nail at a high or far-off spot because your nail-holding hand just won't reach, you simply place a nail in this groove with the pointed tip facing out and then, with the swing of the hammer, set the nail. Since the hammer handle gives you a good 16- to 18-inch extension to your arm (depending on your hammer size), this works great. Unfortunately, many regular-style wood handled claw hammers (like mine) don't have this cool improvement, but you can modify them easily enough to do nearly the same thing (although not quite as efficiently). What I started doing some 35 years ago after seeing a similar thing on a steel Eastwing hammer was to drill a ³/₈-inch-diameter hole about ³/₄-inch deep into the side of the hammer handle about 1-inch in from the butt end. The hole is drilled to incline at about a 10° angle toward the hammer head so that, when it is complete, you can place the head end of a 16d sinker full depth in the hole and it will sit perpendicular to the center line of the hammer handle. **(figs 1-17, 1-18)** Now, grab the head of the hammer and carefully swing the handle to set the nail. Because the butt end of the hammer is super light compared with the hammer head, the nail sometimes doesn't stick well and it takes a few attempts before you actually can get it to

1-19 A 6-inch spike serves as my nail-set

1-20 A Vaughan square ended cat's paw does double duty as monster nail-set

stick in place. Many times I don't swing the handle to set the nail at all but rather just reach up to place the tip of the nail where I want to drive it and then strike the handle right behind the nail holding socket with a short piece of 2×4, a nail-puller, or a borrowed hammer using my free hand.

Two last-minute hammering tidbits that jumped into my mind before I conclude: I always carry a 6-inch spike to use as a long nail-set for those super-tight areas where you can't reach very well with your hammer. **(fig 1-19)** If that doesn't have enough reach and you carry a Vaughan nail-puller (cats-paw), flip it around to use upside down as a nail-set. Might save you from having to climb down and get your pea-shooter (a.k.a. slide hammer) out of the truck. **(fig 1-20)** The other tidbit is to make a saw kerf mark on

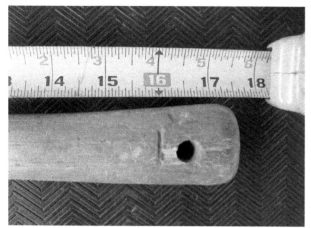

1-21 Mark your hammer handle at 16-inches to aid in nailing sheathing

your wood handle at 16-inches measured down from the top of the hammer head. Now, rather than having to pull out your tape and tie up two hands to measure layout for nailing off a sheet of plywood, you can keep the nail-gun in one hand, grab your hammer with your free hand, and use it as a guide to find the next 16-inch OC support member. **(fig 1-21)**

The nail-gun has done much to alleviate the physical wear and tear of swinging a hammer. By using a nail-gun, a carpenter can work faster and last longer without tiring compared with a hammer swinger and it saves one's joints in the long run. In things like wall framing, overhead soffits, nailing off sheathing, it is unrivaled. Some may even stack roofs using a nail-gun, but I still prefer to do this with "hand drive" 16d nails. Personally, I find that the hassles caused by the air hose running across my work area, or being forced to work one hand down at times, or the nail-gun's inability to suck two pieces of wood together, outweighs its benefits up in the air. One thing I have noticed is that many folks who grew up using the nail-gun since birth never learned "economy of nailing." What I mean by that is that because a nail-gun shoots nails by just a tiny movement of the finger, many develop the habit of overnailing everything (to the point of spitting the wood sometimes). Guys that grew up swinging a hammer were accustomed to making every nail count and, when they transitioned to nail-gun style nailing, they generally continued with that good habit.

A man may fail and fail many times, but he isn't a failure until he blames somebody else for pushing him. – James Burroughs

2

My Two Best Friends – the Skil 77 and a Homelite chainsaw

My best friend is the one who brings out the best in me. – Henry Ford

Like most framing carpenters, I have a fair selection of power tools for various occasions, but, in reality, the ones that I always pull out on any given day are only two. Although most guys would say that an air compressor and nail-gun are their two top essentials, for me it has always been my Skil 77 and a chainsaw.

THE SKIL 77

When I was an apprentice carpenter in Santa Barbara, CA, the builder supplied all the power tools. We only had to show up with our personal hand tools (hammer, tape measure, nail bags, etc.). I bought my first $7^1/_4$-inch worm drive, a Skil 77, together with a 100-foot twist-lock extension cord while at Orange Coast College in 1974 to use on all my side jobs. When I ventured off to work in the Los Angeles housing tracts, I would use this Skil 77 together with a regular blade to cut all my hips, valleys, jacks, and gable studs, or with a sidewinder blade installed to gang-cut all the common rafter ridge-cuts. **(figs 2-1, 2-2)**

When I started piecemeal stacking in the tracts I purchased a Skil $6^1/_2$-inch worm drive. Its lighter weight was a huge benefit over that day's 16-lbs Skil 77 version. The super lightweight Mag 77s (11.5–12.5 lbs) wouldn't come along for decades. As a stacker, I didn't really use the saw for much – a special 2×6 frieze block here and there, or 2×4s for ridge bracing and purlins. These were all flat face cuts, so the saw's bevel rarely left 90°. I removed the lower guard on the Skil $6^1/_2$ inch rather than pin it back; therefore, a $7^1/_4$-inch blade would

2-1 An old 7¼-inch sidewinder blade mounted on a Skil 77

2-2 Using the sidewinder to help make the plumb-cuts on common rafters

fit on it anyway if I needed more depth. Removing the guard helped lighten the saw a bit more (OSHA was barely in its infant stage at this point). I would never recommend that anyone ever remove some safety device, just noting in truth what we did. But if one considered that the chainsaw has always had a +16-inch fully exposed blade and is totally legal, we didn't think a guardless Skilsaw was any less safe. In reality, learning to operate a tool in a safe manner has always been the best protection against injury (see *wh's 10 Commandments of Skilsaw Use* a little farther along).

One modification to the Skilsaw that all we stackers did right off the bat was to exchange the manufacturer's short 8-foot power cord for a 60- to 75-foot, thin plastic-sleeved, 14-gauge power cord (not SJO rubber – plastic slides better). **(fig 2-3)** The reasoning behind the factory-issued short cord on any tool was to act as a backup in case your trigger ever got stuck in the "on" position. If that were to happen, one only needed to quickly reach over and disconnect it from the extension cord. A short cord was a nightmare for a stacker, since the connection was always getting stuck on something as you dragged the cord across the rafters or CJs when moving from one area to another up top. This was dangerous as heck since you would be walking the rafters with your saw in one hand and, all of a sudden, the cord end gets stuck, possibly causing you to lose your balance. A long cord helped eliminate getting snagged as often. The thinner sleeved power cord also made the saw lighter to handle and move around, rather than having to pull some fat cable all over the place. We would also cut a tennis ball in half and install it in front of the plug to smooth out the twist lock plug's catchy leading edge. **(fig 2-4)**

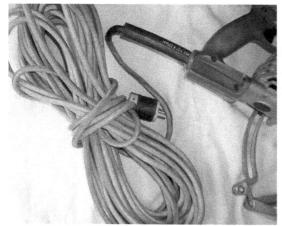

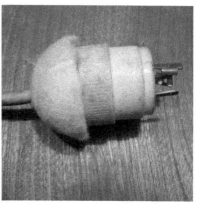

2-4 Half a tennis ball helps keep a cord's plug from getting hung up on sharp edges

2-3 I have a 60-foot-long cord on my Skil 77

2-5 A Skil 77 mounted on a self-designed swing-table base

2-6 Plunge-cut hanging a Skil 77 in the days before saw hangers

Today's Skil 77 is hard to beat for hard-core framing. I have tried just about every other worm drive brand available and nothing can equal it when you sum up all the pluses and minuses. For most folks, a Skil 77 would last decades, but I typically went through a Skil 77 in a year or two. Their short life with me was because I pushed the saw long and hard, gang-cutting rafters versus the intermittent cross-cut use of a regular carpenter. The Skil 77 isn't made to run constantly under load like a lumber mill but rather depends on a little time between cuts to cool down. Maybe a 20% duty cycle or on 2 minutes of every 10. If you overheat the armature, the saw will grow old long before its time. By far the most difficult cuts for a Skil 77 are 45° cheek-cuts on jack rafters and the ganged seat-cut pass when mounted on a swing-table saw base. **(fig 2-5)** The motor is just not designed to handle that much binding type resistance.

2-7 Install an aftermarket saw hanger if your worm drive doesn't have one

2-8 I used the Makita 16-inch beam saw to substitute for a band saw on occasion

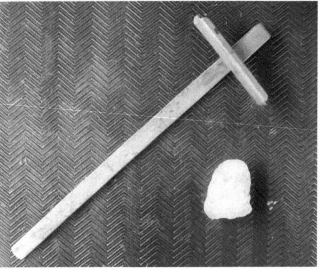

2-9 Paraffin wax and a rip guide are two useful saw accessories

The invention of the saw hanger was a great help to joisters and stackers. Before they came along, we would plunge-cut bury the Skilsaw blade into the top of a nearby rafter or CJ lengthwise to "hang" it. **(fig 2-6)** The first saw hangers appeared in the late 70s and were a simple bent metal-strap replacement handle that had a +/-5-inch prong-like hook welded on. A similarly shaped cast aluminum unit was next, and finally we saw the current day compact stowaway saw hanger produced by Toolhangers Unlimited and others. **(fig 2-7)** It hit the market back in the early 90s (if my memory serves me correctly). Saw hangers now come as standard equipment on most worm drive saw models.

I have never been a fan of sidewinder-designed saws (helical drive with the blade on the right) since they lack the torque or durability for true heavy-duty framing use. Some guys swear by them, but I have found that most of these folks are either left-handed individuals or grew up using them. I can say that they are a bit lighter than a worm drive saw, but this one advantage doesn't outweigh all the negatives, at least in my mind. I did own the sidewinder-designed 16-inch Makita beam saw for a while, but it got very little use. I felt it was so underpowered that I rarely had the patience to pull it out and dribble along at snail speed making a cut. I mostly kept it around to help out when we were assembling big 6x exposed trusses or to put a quarter round on an exposed 6x beam tail that, for some reason, wasn't cut on the band saw at the lumber yard. **(fig 2-8)**

In the mid-1990s, DeWalt invited a few carpenters and builders to come to Orlando, Florida, and try out some of their new line of jobsite power tools before they hit the market. I was somehow included in that group, probably because I was a presenter at *JLC* Live conferences and they hoped to get some positive professional reviews. In their lineup along with various other power tools was their first worm drive circular saw model. They were proud of the 15-amp motor and its compact lightweight plastic body, etc. I gave the saw a good workout, cutting 2×6s and plywood, but I was not that impressed. I found that the motor had less power than the standard 13-amp (at the time) Skil 77, the operator had a poor view of the cutting line, the plastic body would probably not be able to take the heat from heavy-duty roof cutting, and the saw-foot was chintzy. The saw-foot also swung to 55° off vertical, something I have always hated. While going over 45° makes sense on a swing-table saw whose sole purpose is to make very shallow-angled seat-cuts, going over 45° on a standard circular saw is utter nonsense in my opinion. There are two angles that a carpenter uses 99% of the time in framing; they are 0° (or perpendicular to cutting surface) and 45°. Square cuts are used on just about everything up to the top plates, while 45° cuts are used from the top plates up on things like cheek-cuts on hips, valleys, jacks, fascia joints, etc. I personally dislike having to mess around to find these two angles – I want to flip the saw's bevel adjust to each extreme and

2-11 Position material so the cutoff will fall freely

2-10 Use silicone spray as a
blade lubricant

know that I have these two angles without ever stopping to verify. Anyway, to finish my DeWalt story – I didn't give their new worm drive a good review for the reasons I mentioned, so I never heard from them again. I did see that they have since redesigned their worm drive more in line with a Skil 77 or Milwaukee 7¹⁄₄-inch.

Two great Skilsaw accessories to keep handy are a simple rip guide and some paraffin wax. **(fig 2-9)** They are worth their weight in gold when you need them. I always store a piece of wax in my nail bags for all types of friction-reducing applications from moving beams around on racks to jamming something in a tight fit. Rub a little on the bottom of the saw-foot and you have just knocked down a major source of resistance when cutting. That, together with a squirt of silicone spray on your saw blade every now and then, and you will have gone a long way to lighten your saw's motor load so, not only will it cutter faster, but it will also live longer. **(fig 2-10)** This takes for granted that you always run with a sharp blade. Skilsaw did come out with a little plastic base that snaps onto the saw-foot to protect the wood surface during cutting. Haven't tried it, but if it is made from Teflon it would be ideal for gang-cutting.

Operation-wise, I believe it is always a good idea with any power tool, and especially circular saws, to ask a veteran operator to share some usage tips

2-12 Never lift the front of the saw-foot during a cut

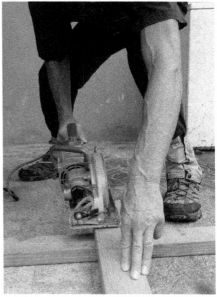

2-13 Sustain a board to be cut in front of the saw. Brace the saw-holding arm's elbow to your body

and comment while you use the tool for the first time. Injuries most often occur as a result of poor usage habits, and, in the case of a circular saw, it can cause major physical damage. Developing good operational habits from the beginning is much easier than overcoming ingrained bad habits. I have seen some gruesome Skilsaw accidents. The most common cause of injury is getting cut from saw kickback. There are several situations that can cause this to happen, and they must be avoided like the plague. Here are the safety tips that I like to stress with my crew:

wh's 10 Commandments of Skilsaw Use

1. Never cut in the middle of a board that is supported at both ends, but rather cut in such a manner as to allow the cutoff piece to fall free. This will prevent the blade from binding. **(fig 2-11)**
2. Never allow the front of the saw-foot to raise off the cutting material. The back of the saw-foot can be raised without adverse effects, but raise the front and the whole saw will be in your lap in a microsecond and there is nothing you can do to stop it. **(fig 2-12)**
3. Never back up a running saw in an ongoing cut in the attempt to readjust the cut slightly. Rather, let off on the trigger and allow the blade to stop spinning. Then reposition the saw and begin anew.
4. When you are ripping a board lengthwise or making a longitudinal plunge-cut one-handed, sustain the board with your free hand in front of the saw. NEVER

2-14 Immediately following a cut, set your saw on the ground with the blade pointing away

hold any board behind the saw. If at all possible, use two hands on any plunge-cut. **(fig 2-13, 2-6)**

5.   Release the trigger before the end of the cut so the blade will come to a stop just as the cut is finished. This takes some practice to get the timing down, but, in effect, you are using the last little part of the cut to slow the blade's rotation down to a stop. If you misjudged the trigger release timing, and the blade is still spinning at the end of the cut, do not move the saw until the blade has come to a dead stop. You can press the spinning blade slightly against the cut wood piece to help slow it down like a brake pad slows a wheel disc.

6.   When finished using the saw to make a cut and the blade is stopped, immediately set it on the ground with the blade directed away from you. **(fig 2- 14)** On joists or rafters – hang it immediately a safe distance away after use.

7.   Never carry the saw with your trigger finger on the trigger. Keep your index finger outside the trigger guard until you are ready to use the saw. Carry it just like one carries a loaded cocked rifle or pistol. **(fig 2-15)**

8.   Don't press the saw's trigger until the saw's foot is resting solidly on the work with the blade positioned a mere 1/4-inch or less from making contact with the wood.

9.   When making a rip-cut, come from the direction that will place the wider 3 1/2-inch side of the saw-foot on the fixed part of the cut wood, while the smaller 1 1/2-inch side is over the cutoff side. **(fig 2-16)**

10.   Always brace the elbow of the hand that is operating the saw with a knee, hip, or stomach in such a manner that, if the saw were to kick back, it has nowhere to go. **(fig 2-13)**

Skilsaw maintenance is often overlooked. Since worm drive saws are nearly bulletproof, most folks never touch them until something fails. The most common failure is the switch going bad, and it always happens at

2-15 Keep your forefinger off the saw trigger at all times, except when cutting

2-16 Always work with the wide side of the saw-foot supported by the work

the worst time. If you have the slightest glitch with the switch, change it out immediately. Don't wait, that glitch is a forewarning of coming doom. Switches do not heal themselves. A spare switch is something a carpenter should always keep in his tool box. It takes about 5 minutes to swap out, and you can easily order one on-line from www.ereplacementparts.com.

A quick side. – It is true that, when working up high solo with a long cord, your options are very limited if the trigger gets stuck in the "on" position, but I still believe the benefits of the long cord far outweigh this single negative. I have always been able to get a stuck trigger to flick off by quickly snapping the trigger, but a friend of mine was up on the rafters cutting the tails for fascia when his saw stuck "on." He couldn't get it to flick off, and no one was around to disconnect his power cord from the breaker box so he just chucked the saw. It shut off when it hit the ground. He figured that he can always buy another Skilsaw. So keep an eye on the switch for the first sign of a hiccup.

The most overlooked maintenance item I see is the lack of checking or changing out the gear oil. Try to create a habit of checking the level and color of this oil on a monthly basis. I have never seen the oil level go down unless there is a leak in the shaft seal under the blade mount. Normally, you would spot a leak there long before the oil level ever becomes dangerously low. I suggest that a framer change the gear oil yearly, but this really depends on saw use. If the oil color seems to be getting darker , dump it and go for some clean oil. Just as in your car – clean oil helps the moving parts wear less. You don't need to buy that special Skilsaw gear lube unless you really want to. Some good-quality manual transmission or differential 80 to 140 wt. gear oil works fine and that is what I have always used. If you work in a super cold climate lean toward using a thinner oil. Likewise, if you work in

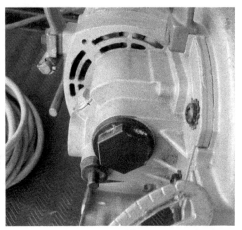

2-17 Change the saw's carbon brushes when they wear down to less than ½ inch in length

2-18 I remove the Skil 77's front ventilation dust cover

hotter climates or push the saw hard, go for a thicker oil. Multiviscosity gear oil is good option for variable climates.

Another maintenance item to keep an eye on is carbon brush wear. Just as you monitor your car tires' tread wear, do the same with your saw's brushes. To check the carbon brushes, just screw out the plastic retaining plugs, pull the brush out, and verify its length. Once they start getting down to much less than ½-inch long, it's time. **(fig 2-17)**

Keep the motor housing free of saw chips and carbon brush dust by using compressed air at the end of the day or at least every week to blow the innards clean. Direct the air nozzle in from either the front or back ventilation windows and go until no more junk comes out. One of the modifications I do to my Skilsaw is to remove the little plastic umbrella cover in front of the front ventilation window by the gear housing. **(fig 2-18)** It allows better access to the front ventilation window and, with the old style of saw hanger, it broke off anyway. Keeping the motor housing clean of junk allows the motor's fan to do a better job cooling the armature. Heat is the biggest enemy of your saw's longevity. If it gets too hot inside the motor housing, the coating on the armature windings melt, and the copper wires begin to short out. When cutting, don't bear down so heavily on the saw that the rpm fall off much. Not only does the blade need speed to cut correctly, but you need to keep the internal fan at high rpm to keep the armature cool. If your saw is down on power, and the brushes are making big bright arcing sparks, know that your armature is most likely "fried," especially if your brushes are in good shape. If you are working the saw hard, feel the motor housing every now and then. If it starts to get hot to the touch, run the saw without a load for a few minutes so the fan will blow fresh air over the hot armature to cool

2-19 A hose clamp on the electric cord inside the Skilsaw handle keeps pressure off the connections

2-20 Use the top handle to hang a Skilsaw when lowering it using the electric cord

it down. Then, let the saw sit for a while until it is only lukewarm and the latent heat has dissipated. Treat your saw just like you treat the turbocharger on a car motor – when you finish running it hard and know the turbo is red hot, permit the engine to idle a while so everything can cool down gradually before you kill it. Otherwise, all that built-up heat will just stay right where you don't want it and could possibly damage the unit.

Another modification I do to a Skilsaw, in addition to the ones I mentioned earlier (installing a long, thin power cord and a saw hanger), is to install a tiny hose clamp on the power cord just inside the Skilsaw cord clamp section of the rear handle. **(fig 2-19)** The Skilsaw cord clamp works OK, but it doesn't put as much compression on the thinner cord as I desire, so the clamp provides double security by serving as a knot in the cord to stop any pulling force from transferring to the electrical wires inside the handle. This is super important when you lower the saw to the ground from up high by using the power cable as a rope. I have done this all my life, so I can testify

2-21 A Skilsaw handle is weak at the cable exit so I tie-wire the two halves together

2-22 Cross-cut 2×4s and 2×6s by eye using the buck-saw method (drop-cut and push)

it does no harm whatsoever to the Skilsaw. If you want to try it, lower the saw-foot until the blade is at its shallowest depth (little to no blade below the saw-foot), then take a loop of the power cable just aft of the rear handle and run it forward over the top of the saw to pass under the top handle and hook this loop on the angle adjust lever or the rafter hanging hook if installed. Now, when you lower the saw, all the weight of the saw is hung off the top handle via the power cord. **(fig 2-20)** I believe that the Skil 77 is somewhat deficient in the number of screws joining the two handle halves near the cord clamp area, so I cross-drill and tie-wire the handle halves at the cord exit. **(fig 2-21)** I also at times install a short piece of ½-inch fuel-line hose in lieu of the flimsy Skilsaw cord guard, which I feel does a poor job of keeping the saw cord out of the way. **(fig 2-3)** Look at the burly wire-type cord guard they used to put on the old barrel saws. **(fig 6-9)**

Four cutting techniques that I feel a good saw operator must learn are to square cut 2×4s and 2×6s by eye; to use the Skilsaw to make plunge-cuts safely; to feather the trigger; and to power plane using the blade. To square-cut by eye takes practice. You must become adept at visualizing a right angle between the left side of the saw-foot and the far top edge of the board to be cut. To cut a 2×4 in this fashion, place the front of the saw-foot on the far edge, while the rear of the saw-foot is held high so the blade is above the board surface. The saw blade is then aligned over your cut mark, the saw-foot is positioned to 90° by eye, and the cut is made in a buck-saw fashion (drop-cut then push to finish). **(fig 2-22)** For a 2×6, the same technique holds true, only the front of the saw-foot is set with a little less of

2-23 Always keep forward pressure on the saw when plunge cutting

the front of the saw-foot sitting over the edge. Remember you must always keep the front of the saw planted firmly on the board (*wh's 10 Commandments of Skilsaw Use*).

Plunge cutting is similar to this chop-saw style of cross-cutting, only you are burying the blade in the middle of a board instead of starting the cut at one edge (cross-cut) or a board end (rip-cut) and then pushing the saw forward as needed. I use this technique a lot when I am notching something whether it be a let-in brace or plating a wall that has a plumbing waste line sticking up through the floor. **(fig 2-23)** Keep the front of the saw-foot always planted firmly on the material and start with the rear of the saw-foot raised so the saw blade is 1/4 inch above the material. Then press the trigger switch on and slowly lower the blade into the wood at the desired location. Always keep some forward downward pressure on the front of the saw-foot in any cut. When the blade is buried and the saw is sitting flat on the saw-foot, push the saw forward as needed for length.

Feathering the trigger is foreign to most guys. I developed the technique without even realizing it. Only after an experienced framer observed me doing it and asked about it did I even recognize that it was unknown to others and begin to share it. Technically, the Skilsaw trigger is a momentary on/off type switch and not a variable speed switch, but, by massaging the trigger so it cycles on and off through a cut, one can vary the rpm and the overall cutting speed so it performs similar to a variable-speed switch. I don't always want the saw running full bore, so by cycling it I can adjust it to what I want. It kind of goes along with the method I spoke of in *wh's 10*

2-24 "Brush" plane to the left with the bevel adjustment set to 45° and the blade at minimum depth

Commandments of Skilsaw Use, where one comes off the trigger application far enough in advance of the end of the cut, so that the blade comes to a complete stop just as the cut is finished.

To power plane using the blade of the Skilsaw, set the depth adjustment to its shallowest position and then swing the saw's bevel over to 45°. With the saw in this configuration, place the front of the saw-foot on the surface as you did for a plunge-cut and hold the rear of the saw-foot up so the blade clears the material by 1/4 inch. Looking straight down, you can see where the blade will touch the wood, so align this point over the area you want to plane down. Move the saw-foot slightly to the right of that area and press the trigger switch to lower the blade slightly while swinging the rear of the saw-foot to the left in the clockwise direction. You can only plane 2 to 3 inches at a stroke so, when you have reached that limit, release the trigger, lift the blade slightly, and reposition it back to right where you began, then do the whole thing over again, lowering the blade a bit deeper on each successive pass. The front of the saw-foot stays in one place like a pivot point with the rear of the saw-foot making a small arc. Because a Skilsaw's saw blade inclines upward to the left, this is the direction you will always be brushing. Do not try to go back to the right against the blade, because it can be dangerous. I have seen some folks brush with the Skilsaw blade set at 90° degrees (vertical blade), but at 45° there is less risk of kickback, plus you can see what you are doing, since the motor body is off to the left side, out of the way visually. **(fig 2-24)**

THE CHAINSAW

Having exhausted what comes to mind on the Skilsaw, let's now move on to the controversial chainsaw. For me, there is no controversy; it is a vital tool that is second only to my Skilsaw in total use time. I have had a chainsaw at my side since ever since I started framing custom homes. When I worked for Hal Benhardt in the late 1970s, we often did the house foundation in addition to the framing. It was one way we could control the accuracy of the measurements and levels, etc. On one job, the power hadn't been installed yet and I didn't want to wait around for this or head off to rent a generator, so I started using my chainsaw to cut all the 2×12 form boards to length. Since that day I have never looked back. I would never again use a Skilsaw on foundation work, heading out joists, cutting headers, etc. The chainsaw is amazingly versatile tool, and, for concrete form work, eliminates stretching a power cord back to the power pole some 100 to 200 feet away and having it get in the way of everything. While some people may believe an individual who uses a chainsaw to frame is a "wood butcher," know that I, a chainsaw framer, have been credited with some of the cleanest framing work many have ever seen. Therefore, a chainsaw is not the tool of a sloppy carpenter unless that carpenter is a sloppy carpenter from the start. Only then does it amplify your sloppy work by making it more obvious. It is true that to become an expert with a chainsaw in framing takes time. Don't expect to pick it up and instantly make perfect cuts. But this is the same with any tool. Notice how I said "expert with a chainsaw in framing." This is because using it in framing is a different skill than using a chainsaw to cut firewood or fell trees. In both of these two areas it is uncommon that you will find an individual who has developed the trigger control and ability to follow a line dead-on by eye. It is just not required in their work. But this is exactly what you must learn if you decide to use a chainsaw in framing. Whereas a lumberjack or firewood cutter buries the blade and goes full throttle, learning to feather the power and balance it with cutting speed is the task of a carpenter when applying it to framing. While most carpenters are accustomed to their Skilsaw being either on or off, the chainsaw can be used like a variable speed drill to suit the situation. The coolest part about a chainsaw is that it is so much more powerful than a portable electric circular saw, it has a cutting depth many times over the largest circular saw available, and it requires no long extension cord to use.

A chainsaw will make quick work of cutting headers, beams, Trus Joists, etc. without even the need to unstack and reposition full-length pieces like you must do for a circular saw or beam saw. If, for example, you ordered out 16-foot-long 4×12s for headers, just jump up on the freshly dropped lumber package, layout your headers back-to-back adding in for the thickness of the chain on each dimension, pencil in a square-cut line across the face and down each edge, and then simply cut everything right there as it lays. You

2-25 The Homelite Super EZ was a great all around framer's chainsaw

could jam a thin piece of wood under where you plan to cut to avoid any "overcut," but as you get real good with the chainsaw, the thin protector piece of wood becomes irrelevant, since you have developed so much control that you can make the cut with barely a scratch to the wood below. If the saw's bar won't reach across the beam laid flat, stand it on edge and cut it from top to bottom. The small cut pieces are then carted off to be used. Saves your low back. In the same line of thinking, packaged Trus Joists should be gang-cut to size right after the load is dropped before breaking the bands and moving them anywhere. In this case, you will have to use the Headcutter chainsaw base with the saw mounted in the vertical position like a jigsaw to make the cut, but we will get into that subject a little further along.

A chainsaw can be substituted to do the work of a sawzall if the wood is clear of nails or can be cleaned of existing nails. You can even get a carbide-tipped chain to avoid the occasional time when you didn't see that one last hidden nail. A chainsaw in wood will do the work of a sawzall in a fraction of the time. And unless you are running a cordless sawzall, using a chainsaw saves you once again from the hassles of stringing out an extension cord, etc. Learn to use the top edge of the chainbar to make cuts in addition to bottom edge, since this method will come in extremely handy in overhead pickup work where you can't position the saw to be able to cut in the standard downward chopping manner. Most folks are so conditioned to using the chainsaw in a certain fashion that it would never enter their minds that the top of the bar can also be used as well. One time, I went to help a friend who was putting the final touches on a huge, open 25-foot × 25-foot Hip roofed cabana shade structure. He had built it in the true Polynesian manner using

2-26 The Homelite XL Automatic is another of my framing favorites

round poles and palm tree fronds. For some reason that I can't remember now, an overhead installed pole needed to get cut and he was contemplating how to do it. Now you must understand that this friend of mine was a +40-year chainsaw expert. Not only was he a lumberjack, but he also rough milled the fallen tree trunks into workable beams. In other words, he was extremely skilled with a chainsaw. I suggested that he make the cut with a chainsaw to which he looked at me like I was stone crazy. He responded that to make the cut he would have to invert the chainsaw and as such it couldn't draw gas. I didn't say a thing in response but went over and grabbed the chainsaw out of his hands, cranked it up, and made the cut using the top of the chainbar. He stood there totally astonished, since he had never heard of doing that before. Now, he has a cool new trick in his bag. Isn't it funny how easily we all get tunnel vision. When you use the top edge of the chainbar to cut overhead, be sure the tip is clear or you can get some dangerous kickback when you are in a very weak stance. Aside from that caution, you will find there is little difference between using either the top or bottom edge of the chainbar, except that, on the upward cutting stroke, your arms support the chainsaw and supply all the cutting force, whereas in the standard downward cutting stroke, the weight of the chainsaw itself helps make the cut. This "top of chainbar" technique would play an important role in the development of the Headcutter as I explain a little further along.

The best choice for normal framing is what is classified as a "limbing saw." You want something that is small to fit into tight areas, lightweight so it can be easily handled, powerful so it never bogs down in a cut, and has a 16-inch bar. I found the Homelite EZ to be the best in all these categories. **(fig 2-25)**

2-27 Using the chainsaw to detail cut glulam beams in Bend, OR

Unfortunately the EZ is not manufactured anymore, but having its cylinder placed horizontally (versus other units that utilize a vertically positioned cylinder) made it super compact. It weighs in at +/−11 lbs, has a 41-cc motor, and comes with a 16-inch bar and a $^3/_8$-inch pitch chain. Another feature the EZ has that I like is manual oiling in addition to automatic chainbar oiling. Another favorite model of mine is the Homelite XL Automatic. **(fig 2-26)** It is a little smaller and less powerful than the EZ, but it none the less is a great saw. The XL uses the smaller toothed .325-inch chain on a 14-inch bar, but it still handles most jobs with ease.

I won't delve into how to use a chainsaw properly because there are many great resources available to do that, but rather focus more on applying the chainsaw in framing. The one caution I will share is to "avoid at all costs touching the top quarter of the chainbar tip to anything." If you do, this will cause a very dangerous kickback, and you could face a spinning unguarded 16-inch cutting chain coming toward you at mach speed. Nowadays, most larger chainsaws have an anti-kick chain brake built in to help avoid this

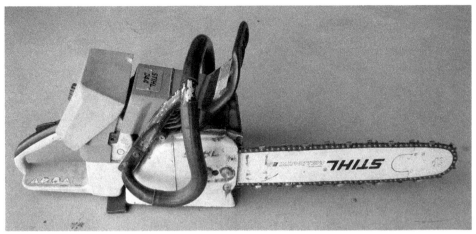

2-28 The Stihl model 044 is a perfect size to use as a rafter-milling saw mounted on the Headcutter

hazard, but limbing saws generally do not. In framing, most of the cuts can be made without the need to embed the chainbar. For cross-cutting (or vertical cutting with the Headcutter), the blade should extend a few inches beyond the far side of the work. The 16-inch bar works well for almost any beam you will ever need to cut on the job. If the beam laid flat is taller than the bar is long, simply stand the beam on edge and cut from top to bottom as mentioned before. I have cut some monstrous glulam beams with a Super EZ. In one custom house in Montecito, Santa Barbara we had a roof glulam that spanned 100 feet from one end of the building to the other. It was a 5 feet tall and 11^1/$_2$ inches thick. Others at a shopping center we built in Bend, Oregon, were near 3 feet tall. **(fig 2-27)**

In the late 1990s, I picked up a Stihl 044 chainsaw when I was in the process of inventing the "Headcutter" (bigfootsaws.com). For this project, I needed a powerful saw that could stand up to the rigors of heavy duty milling. The 5.1 horse power power-head of the 044 filled my needs to a "T." **(fig 2-28)** I had bought my 044 from a guy who had been a lumberjack in Oregon, and he had modified it by installing a ¾ wrap handle and Max-Flow air filter. Both of these modifications I would highly recommend to anyone (www.baileysonline.com). The saw ran so smoothly that I quickly fell in love with it. I replaced the 36-inch chainbar with a 16-inch sized version and kept a spare 20-inch bar on hand for when I needed more length. The Headcutter application uses the top edge of the chainbar as the cutting surface; therefore, the cutting chain removes material in a downward direction. This is opposite to all other chain-type cutting devices like Mafell's electric chainsaw, the Prazi Cutter, etc., that cut in an upward direction towards the saw-foot, duplicating the rotation of a circular saw. By using the top edge of the bar, the chips are

2-29 Using the top edge of the chainbar allows good visibility to follow a snap-line

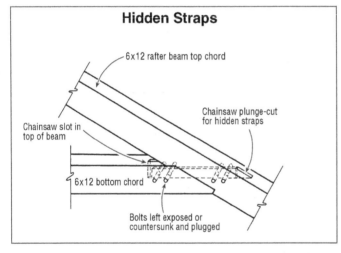

Hidden Straps

6x12 rafter beam top chord

Chainsaw plunge-cut for hidden straps

Chainsaw slot in top of beam

6x12 bottom chord

Bolts left exposed or countersunk and plugged

2-30 Hidden metal connections on exposed beam work often requires plunge cutting with a chainsaw

thrown away, allowing full visibility of the milling cut-line at all times. **(fig 2-29)** Unhappy with the flex in a standard laminated chainbar, I switched over to using solid chainbar versions that are much more rigid. This change helped improve the precision of milling ridge-cuts on racked common rafters.

There are lots of different chain types one can use in cutting operations, but I found that Granberg's (granberg.com) style of ripping chain provided the smoothest cut for the milling operation of the Headcutter. Their ripping chain has a continuous sequence of two modified scoring cutters followed by two clearing cutters. The clearing cutters top edge is only 10° off perpendicular versus the 35° off perpendicular for a normal chainsaw chain. Since a ripping

2-31 Dadoing a little groove with a Skilsaw can make starting a chainsaw plunge cut easier

2-32 After the chainbar is embedded past the tip, bring the chainsaw to vertical and press downward

chain only takes small bites of wood compared to other chain variations, the rpm can stay high, which helps achieve a smooth cut. The cut is so good that often it is difficult to distinguish between a cut made by the Headcutter utilizing this chain versus a similar cut made by a regular circular saw.

In addition to making standard cross-cuts with the chainsaw, I feel it is beneficial for a framer to learn to make plunge-cuts. While not an everyday occurrence, this cut is required to install ¼-inch-thick hidden straps in things like beam trusses. **(fig 2-30)** It can be a dangerous cut to make, so you must be very careful to only work the bottom quarter of the chainbar tip until you are well into the slot where any kickback bucking from touching the top quarter of the chainbar tip will be confined inside the slot itself. So, as you raise the chainsaw bar from horizontal to vertical, work the tip in a drawing motion to keep the pressure on the lower quarter of the bar tip as long as possible into the cut. Before you crank up the chainsaw, make a small ¼-inch-wide starter groove by plunge-cutting the Skil 77 blade repeatedly if the wood is super dense. **(fig 2-31)** This groove will serve to keep the

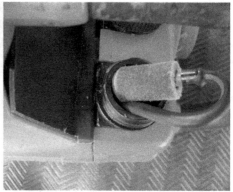

2-33 Keep the air filter free of saw chips

2-34 The fuel filter is located on the pickup tube inside the chainsaw's fuel tank

chainbar on course as you initiate the plunge. The chainsaw bar's position during the starting phases of a plunge-cut mirrors a slowly rising draw bridge – going from a near level position at the beginning to vertical as the slot deepens. Once the bar is vertical and the saw's bucking has calmed down push the bar straight in like a drill press. **(fig 2-32)**

One last little technique that comes in handy is "brushing" or "power rasping" material by using the chainsaw bar. Just like the Skilsaw, the chainsaw can be used to plane down some material by brushing the chainbar right and left while lightly goosing the throttle. I use this technique instead of a chisel to make a small indent in mudsills when the anchor bolt is so low I can't get a nut and washer on it. I also use it for a myriad of purposes when doing beam work. It makes quick work for things like cleaning out notches or slightly concaving the ends on a post so the edges will be tight. Use the bottom part of the chainbar tip to "brush" and only gently feather the throttle. If you get really good, you may be able to moonlight as a chainsaw statute carver.

Maintenance on a chainsaw is a bit more involved than an electric circular saw, since it is a small gas engine with points, plugs, condenser, fuel tank, fuel lines, etc. On-site maintenance is generally limited to tensioning or swapping out a chain, cleaning all the wood chips and bar oil buildup from the chain sprocket area, keeping the air cleaner dust free, and checking the in-tank fuel filter for cleanliness. **(figs 2-33, 2-34)** I use compressed air and brake cleaner to keep my chainsaw clean. Air pressure blows away all the saw chips and dust, while brake cleaner washes away oil residue. Occasionally, it is a good idea to pull the plug to inspect, clean, and gap. **(fig 2-35)** If the center or ground electrodes seem to be wearing down or the plug has some years on it, it is time to replace the plug. There are a variety of things that can go wrong with a chainsaw, but I find that if a chainsaw starts acting

2-35 Clean and gap the spark plug as part of regular preventative maintenance

2-36 Idling speed and the high- and low-speed mixtures are adjusted using a small screwdriver

up for some reason that cannot be quickly diagnosed by a layman, it is best to drop it off at a saw shop. Of course, if you are a small-engine guy, then by all means go to it.

I have gotten fairly proficient at adjusting the carburetor's high and low jets, which I feel is a good skill for a chainsaw operator to learn. Different models have different setups, but usually there are three screws. **(fig 2-36)** One is the idle-speed adjust, another is the idle-speed mixture, and a third is the high-speed mixture. Clockwise or threading the jet screw in is leaning the mix, whereas counterclockwise or screwing the jet screw out is enriching the mix. On the idle-speed screw, clockwise or in is higher idle rpm, whereas counterclockwise or out is lower rpm. I find that working to lean the mix until the saw starts to stumble, then enrichening it slightly, works best as a general procedure. Everybody has a different method. With the saw warmed up and the rpm screw adjusted so the chain clutch is below its activation speed, turn the low-speed mix screw in until the rpm start to fall off, then enrich it 1/4 turn. Try the throttle and see if it accelerates off idle OK. If it stumbles, enrich it another 1/4 turn and try again. Continue this procedure until the saw accelerates smoothly off idle. You will need to go back and forth between adjusting the idle speed and mixture screws because messing with one affects the other. To adjust the high-speed mixture, go full throttle (in a short burst of less than 10 seconds long) and slowly turn the high-speed jet screw in until your rpm peaks and starts to fall off, then enrichen it 1/4 turn or so until it is smooth. That leaves it at just slightly rich of peak. Some folks prefer it a taste richer. You can tell a lot by the exhaust smoke. If there is little to no smoke on full throttle, then it is very lean and you might want to come out a taste more with the high-speed mix screw lifting its tapered tip farther away from the jet's aperture, which allows more fuel to get by. If

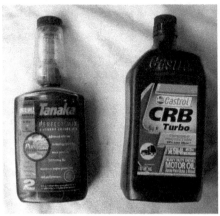

2-37 I use Tanaka's perfect mix 2-cycle oil for the gas mix and 50 wt reg car oil for the bar/chain oil

2-38 Lube the chainbar tip daily

2-39 Tighten the chain when cold so that, only by a firm pull, will you expose a full drive link tooth

2-40 Changing a chainsaw starter cord can be tricky if you have never done it before

you have a ton of smoke at full throttle, then it is rich and you can screw the high-speed mix screw in a bit, shrinking that gap.

I run Tanaka 2 cycle oil in my gas mix. It is a "perfect mix," meaning that it works in any chainsaw no matter what mixture ratio the chainsaw requires from 16/1 up to 50/1. Just 2.6 ounces to a gallon of gas, and you are all set. I don't have to fret about which of my chainsaws requires what ratio. I also only use 100 LL (low lead) aviation fuel in my mix, preferring to avoid car gas with its lower octane or added alcohol. I go by the airport and purchase what I need. For bar oil, I most often just use plain old 50 wt engine oil (the thick stuff) – the same oil I keep on hand to feed my truck engine. **(fig 2-37)** Not only is it cheaper, but I avoid having to keep a bunch of different oils around. Remember, I am a Keep It Simple, Stupid (KISS) guy. Yes, of course produc-

2-41 A modified Headcutter chainsaw base can easily gang-cut any size seat-cut required

tion chainbar oil clings a bit better to the chain, so if you are a perfectionist you may want to stay with the pricier stuff.

On a daily basis, lube the chainbar tip (unless it is a solid bar that has no sprocket) and check the chain tension. **(fig 2-38)** The chain should be tensioned "cold"; in other words, before the saw has been used for the day. Tighten the chain until, when you pull hard on the cutting chain at mid-bar, you can almost expose the full drive link. **(fig 2-39)** Once the chain warms up, it stretches out and will hang down to almost expose the drive tooth. This procedure works well for the bar lengths I use (16- to 20-inch).

Occasionally, you will bust your pull cord and have to replace it. After years of use, pull cords start to fray and weaken. Swapping them out can be an interesting endeavor depending on the model, but nothing you can't overcome. If you are not that mechanically inclined, have someone show you how the first time through. **(fig 2-40)**

Chainbar wear is another issue to keep in mind. If you keep flipping the chainbar from top to bottom each time you change the chain this will help the bar wear evenly. **(fig 2-25)** When the chain groove wears to the point you can wiggle the tooth side-to-side easily, it's time to order up a replacement bar. Like chainsaw-operating techniques, how to sharpen chains can usually be found in the operator's manual, so I won't waste any time on this. Although I know how to sharpen a chain, I rarely do it, preferring to quickly swap to a sharp chain and keep right on going. I have four or five extra chains on stand-by. When I am getting down to the last one, I simply drop all the dull chains off at a saw shop and pick them up the following afternoon all sharpened up.

So to sum it all up, with a Skil 77 and a chainsaw I can take on just about anything that comes my way. Not only do they serve standard carpentry purposes of cutting individual members for floors, walls, ceilings, and roofs, but these two saws are the only tools needed to production-style gang-cut rafters. With the chainsaw mounted in a modified "Headcutter" base, gang-cutting both the common rafter head-cuts and seat-cuts are a whiz.

The Skil 77 is used for the heel-cut. No more need of the antique dado saw to gang-cut birdsmouth notches. The chainsaw with a short bar mounted will make seat-cuts that my old dado saw can only dream of doing. **(fig 2-41)**

> *Never explain — your friends do not need it and your enemies will not believe you anyway.* – Elbert Hubbard

3

The Minimalist – "simple" and "speed" both start with an "S"

It is not a daily increase, but a daily decrease.
Hack away at the inessentials. – Bruce Lee

Many know me as a guy who follows a Keep It Simple, Stupid (KISS) philosophy both on and off the job. I only invest time in learning things that will help me produce more or do something faster. I don't waste time learning a bunch of junk that I will never see or use in my lifetime. I don't need to know everything – just everything I need. What I do know I try to condense down to as few steps or calculations as possible and have them down cold. There are lots of guys who know more about weird roof situations or fancy roof math than I do. Good for them, it doesn't bother me in the least. Let them be the roof gurus – I suppose it keeps them out of trouble, but that knowledge really does little good in the modern world of framing. I get paid by what I produce not by how much useless information I know. Besides, I have too many other interests in my life to spend every waking moment drooling over some eccentric roof situation. Is roof framing "the means to an end" or "an end to the means?" Think about it. The world is so full of God's treasures, don't miss them.

FIRST-TIER TOOLS

Just as I like to keep my thinking simple, I like to keep my tools simple. I have always been amazed at what some framers carry in their tool bags. Many have three nail bags encircling their waist in addition to a hammer-carrying loop. To me they look like a Vietnam era SEAL on his way out for patrol. I, on the other hand, live at the other end of that spectrum and carry very little. It reminds me of a scene from *Rambo 2* where Sylvester Stallone parachutes out of a little jet over Vietnam with all kinds of unwanted high-tech weaponry and gadgets strapped to his body and hanging from a deployment bag. As he exits the aircraft, his string of equipment gets hung up on a part of the aircraft and he is being drug along by the jet. To extricate himself from this bad situation, he pulls out his trademark 10-inch survival knife and slices himself free from all the gear. The next scene finds him running through the jungle with nothing else except his two favorite weapons – his survival knife and his compound bow, having sacrificed all the other junk. My philosophy, like many of my habits and methods, dates back to my early days as a piecemeal stacker in the Los Angeles housing tracts. In those days, my nail bags consisted of a Nicholas model 444X single pouch on the left and a model very similar to the Nicolas 583 double pouch on the right. Both were leather, of course, and mounted on a 3-inch-wide leather belt. In the 444X, I carried 16d nails along with my hammer tossed in on top, upside down. As a stacker I never had any use for 8d nails, so I didn't carry them. The 583 positioned on my right gave me quick access to my carpenter's pencil, a razor knife, and a 12-foot tape measure in the main pouch, while my chalk line lived in the small outside pouch. This was everything unless the roof had gable ends, in which case I also carried along a little plastic 6-inch torpedo level in the main pouch. It would be used to set up the first gable stud in a run, and from it, I would mark layout. I suppose I was kind of like one of these modern-day super-lightweight backpacker types whose total pack weight for a 3-day jaunt is under 15 lbs. I carried the bare essentials and nothing more. Not only could I move around up top on the plates more easily, but I didn't get as tired since I wasn't lugging around a bunch of dead weight all day. The weight that I did carry was just nails and my hammer.

Some of you may ask, "Why such a short little tape measure, Will?" Very simply – it makes no sense to carry around a heavy 25- to 30-foot tape all day when you might only need it a couple times to measure for a special frieze block or to layout gable studs. Remember, all the rafters were precut, all the frieze blocks were precut, and all the gable studs were precut. We were only assemblers; our job was to nail things together. Through the early/mid-1970s, the typical tract home size might have been around 1700 to 2000 square feet, so even the ridges weren't that long, and these you always laid out on the ground before you stood them up anyway. At ground level you would have some second-tier tools like a longer tape measure and a try square stashed for things just like this. Vertical and sway bracing were installed by the scribe, cut, and copy method. We would simply eyeball the angle-cut needed on the bottom end and then hold it up in place to mark length, etc.

Others of you may say "Hey Will, how did you level the ridge without a long bubble level or something?" Those of you who have taken a roof-framing class of mine, seen my roof-framing video series, or read *A*

Roof Cutter's Secrets (RCS) will know that leveling a ridge board or setting a ridge beam using a bubble level is a no-no. Some may teach otherwise, but they undoubtedly fail to grasp the big picture of what is happening up in the air. If your outside rafter walls parallel each other "as they should" and your common rafters for the associated span are all cut the same length "as they should be," your ridge will follow the slope of your outside walls whatever that may be. If they happen to be level, then your ridge will be level; if not, then your ridge will plane with whatever they are. That is what is important. It is rare that any house's walls are "dead on" level all the way through but trying to set things level up in the air when the walls are not will only lead to greater stacking difficulties. Moral of the story – if you want a level ridge, make sure you do a good job "from the top plates down."

The razor knife was only along to sharpen your carpenter's pencil. Undoubtedly, if I had had one of these handy-dandy flat pencil sharpeners of today I would have swapped the knife out for one of them and saved some ounces. Yeah, of course, now and then, you might use the knife blade tip to dig out a splinter, but in that situation why not toss a safety pin in your bag instead. It would be lighter and do a better job. The chalk line was used to snap out frieze block runs on open eaves so they came out nice and straight (all California tract homes were open eaves), although I have to admit that many times I would forgo using it and just eyeball the blocks at 90° to the rafters (blessed with a darn good eyeball). "How did we pull the 90° line up to the top edge of the block without some type of square" you might ask? Well, with frieze blocks hung along the top plate in between all the rafters, we had improvised speed squares hung everywhere. Just grab one of these and place it up against the rafter tail with the top and bottom edges flush, then slide it up to butt the building and mark the inside edge of the block. Same held true if you wanted to mark a square-cut line across a frieze block or something – just use the square-cut end of another block as your marking square. **(fig 3-1)**

But in reality, most of the time, when trimming a regular frieze block down in size to use as a special, the square cut across the board face was just eyeballed or you paralleled the existing cut if it was close. **(fig 2-22)** Bear in mind that, in those days, a framer's typical "carry along" square included the sliding combo-square, a try square, or Squangle (roof cutters). All three of these squares were cumbersome and a real pain to carry in your nail bags, so improvising on the job was a better option. These squares with their sharp thin blades acted like a knife to cut you up good if you fell, so it was best they stayed among your ground support tools or what I call my second-tier tools: first tier being what you carry in your nail bags, second tier being what is quickly available in a stashed tool box (I used a 5-gallon plastic bucket), and third tier being tools that were kept in your truck to be pulled out as needed.

As a side note: Although it appears the 6-inch triangular square was invented in 1925 by Albert Swanson, it didn't really gain its all-encompassing domination as the carpenter's favorite carry-along square in California until the early 1980s when the nail bag manufacturers created a slot so it could be easily carried. Before that, the other squares named were carried not because of great affection, but because they fit into a special carrying loop or the little

3-3 Paraffin wax comes in handy for a variety of framing tasks

3-4 My right side bag is set up for efficiency and ease of access

metal combo square pocket that was a part of the older nail bags.

At Orange Coast College, Hank Resse had schooled me well on the danger of a stacker carrying his hammer in a loop behind his back. If you did happen to fall on your back and your hammer was positioned there, just imagine the type of damage the hammer head and claws can cause to your lumbar spinal region. It could be a paralyzing injury. So for all my years framing, I have always carried my hammer upside down in my left side nail pouch. There, it has less of a chance to do major damage in a fall. I carry it in my left side bag although I am right-handed, since I want my right side bag to remain uncluttered for fast unhindered access to my tape measure, pencil, etc. To reach across and grab it from the left bag is a natural movement – kind of like how the right-handed undercover cops keep their pistols stashed in an upside down holster under their left arm pit. You don't have to bunch up your arm to grab it like you do if it was on the right side hip. Just a few gunslinger tips. **(fig 3-2)**

When I production cut roofs, my nail bag setup stayed the same, except that I swapped out the 12-foot stacker's tape measure for a 25-foot-long version, and added in both yellow and red keel (crayons) in a single holder; a Squangle to layout head-cuts and birdsmouths; a little chunk of paraffin wax to grease the bottom of the various saw-foots **(fig 3-3)**; and a copy of *Riechers Full Length Roof Framer* (tiny rafter table book) to find rafter lengths. I also modified my right side nail bag by installing little pockets to hold my pencil, my keel holder, and my razor knife, so that it would be faster and easier to grab these items. As a roof cutter they got a lot more use. **(fig 3-4)**

3-5 Wax pencils are used to mark dark-colored wood where a pencil line is invisible

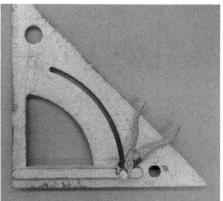

3-6 I secure the adjuster on my 12-inch Quick Square® using a pair of Channellock model 424 mini-pliers

In the earliest days, my keel holder was just a short 4-inch section of a standard garden hose that had a piece of red and blue crayon stuck in each end. In time, I switched over to a regular keel holder having a removable end cap. Since blue was my primary color, it was mounted in the jaw, while a short chunk of red crayon for corrections was hidden under the end cap.

"OK that's fine and dandy Will, but what do you carry in your tool bags today?" When I left the tract framing days behind to reenter the custom home building market, I changed what I carried slightly, but after that initial revision, what I carried stayed fairly constant over the next three decades as I moved through roles as a job foreman, a framing contractor, and a roof-framing consultant. Until the very end, I wore the same style leather nail bag setup that I had in the 1970s, but inside you will find that my old rafter table book went bye-bye and was replaced at first by a simple solar-powered calculator with a slide on/off protector. In 1997, after nearly two decades of this calculator being my mainstay, I discarded it in favor of a Construction Master Pro Calculator. I also added into my right side main nail bag a 60d spike to use as a nail set or open the nozzle of large tubes of construction adhesive, a 35-mm film canister containing two pairs of earplugs for when I need to fire up the chainsaw or do other noisy tasks, and a spare carpenter's pencil. I also upped my measuring tape size to a 30- or 35-foot model. I do not use these heavy "Fat Max" measuring tape versions, but stick with the slimmer 1-inch-wide version. I prefer to swap width for length if I will be carrying any extra weight since I have rarely if ever needed the 11-foot standout distance they advertise, but the added length over my older 25-foot tape comes in very handy during layout on these big custom homes. I did sew on a small nail bag to the outside lip of my 444X so I could carry along

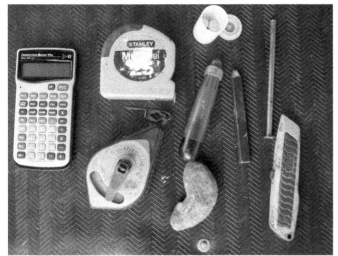

3-7 My first-tier tools are the ones I carry on my person

some 8d nails for tasks like snapping lines or positioning sheets of plywood. **(fig 3-2)** I swap out these 8d nails for 20d galvanized nails when it is time to run fascia. If it is hot, I will usually bring along a tube of lip balm. To layout on dark-colored Wolmanized wood, I toss a white wax pencil into my bags. **(fig 3-5)** When I layout rafters, I toss in a black wax pencil to help with layout marking and a mini pair of Channellock pliers to firmly tighten the thumbscrew adjuster on my 12-inch adjustable Quick Square®. **(fig 3-6)**

FIRST-TIER TOOLS

These are the tools that live in my nail bags day in and day out: **(fig 3-7)**

1. Hammer (not shown)
2. 30- to 35-foot tape measure
3. Carpenter's pencil (2)
4. Carpenter's marking crayon (keel)
5. Razor knife
6. Chalk line
7. Construction Master Pro Calculator
8. A piece of paraffin wax
9. 60d spike
10. Ear plugs in 35-mm film canister

Optional: lip balm depending on the weather.

You may ask why I never switched over to the lighter-weight cordura nylon nail bags if I am so fastidious about carrying the least amount of weight. Good question. I was truly excited when they first came out for just this reason, so I gave them a try. Unfortunately, I found the material's weave would grab and pull on my leg hairs since I always wear shorts. If you are a long-pants wearer, then this wouldn't pose a problem. Also, the first cordura nylon versions did not have a lot of rigidity in the bag's aperture, so it would not stay as open as I preferred. I notice that, in follow-up versions, they have addressed this deficiency by adding a stiffener around the bag's rim. I suppose when it came right down to it, I didn't find that the little saving in weight could compensate for the true comfort of good old "broke in" leather tool bags. Since our nail bags stay on all day, they best be super comfortable. I have maintained my leather bags for decades by keeping them clean and treating them with bee's wax (Sno-Seal). Warm them up first in an oven before you apply the bee's wax so it will easily soak into the leather rather than just sitting on the surface. Occasionally, if the leather dries out too much, I might apply a smattering of Neatsfoot Oil. The bee's wax makes them waterproof, so they handle drizzly days without a problem. **(fig 3-8)**

3-8 Applying Sno-Seal to your leather nail bags helps them last decades

I have read some articles by carpenters who favor attaching suspenders to their nail bags in order to transfer a portion of their nail bag weight up to their shoulders. While this might function if you work a stand-up job all day, like installing wall sheathing/siding or finish work, but guys who spend a good portion of their work day bent over at the waist like us stackers, or joisters, or wall framers would only find suspenders confining to their upper body movements and abrasive. Besides, why would anyone want to transfer some of the nail bag load to your shoulders when our hips are so much better equipped to carry weight and the spine itself remains free of unnecessary compression. Notice how nearly every outdoor backpack transfers the pack's weight directly to one's hips while the shoulder straps serve to do little more than stabilize the load front/back and side/side. Maybe one should really rethink why they need suspenders in the first place and strive to lighten their load instead. I personally have never seen a framer wear suspenders, but I did know of several finish carpenters who used them.

SECOND-TIER TOOLS

My second-tier tools are the various tools that I might occasionally need during the work day. **(fig 3-9)** They live in a 5-gallon bucket that I stash somewhere centrally located on the jobsite each morning:

1. Vaughan cat's paw style nail puller (NP12G)
2. A simple 3 beam laser level
3. Vaughan 18-inch ripping bar (RB18)
4. 6-inch adjustable Quick Square®

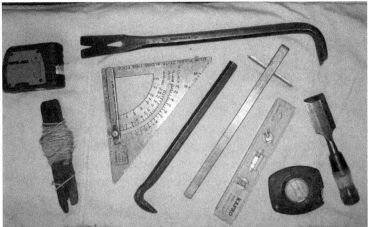

3-9 I stash my second-tier tools in a tool bucket near where I am working

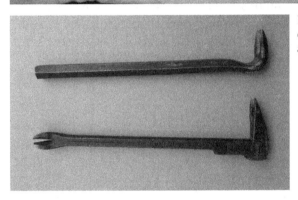

3-10 The squared ended Vaughan cat's paw nail puller can double as a long nail-set

5. A roll of string
6. Skil 77 rip guide
7. A torpedo level
8. Stanley 50-foot steel tape measure (never fiber – it stretches)
9. 2-inch wood chisel
10. A pair of work gloves (not shown)

While my Skil 77 holds first-tier tool status, my Homelite super EZ is a second-tier tool and sits on standby near the tool bucket. **(figs 2-22, 2-25)**

I prefer Vaughan's single claw cat's paw nail puller because, not only does it carry Vaughan's superior nail-biting jaw design, but it also can do double duty as a monster nail set. The double-ended clawed versions don't have this versatility. **(fig 3-10)** While the double-ended version may come in handy for some folks, I have hardly ever used a straight claw to pull a nail. Besides that, I feel that these double-ended claw versions are plain dangerous to carry. If I happen to stow one in my left side nail bag just to use on some little project, I now have a sharp pointed object sticking up that could open up my midsection big time in a fall. I don't have that problem if I toss a single-claw cat's paw in my nail bags. While you may like to carry yours hanging on your side or behind your back somewhere – not me – for the reasons I have already mentioned in regard to carrying a hammer there. Mine sits in the bucket until absolutely needed, and this was usually only when I had failed to somehow remove an errant nail with a hammer claw strike. You may even find that if you don't carry a cat's paw in your nail bags, your nailing skills might improve, since now you must really focus on what you are doing since your crutch is a few steps away. I remove the plastic handle cover from my single-claw cat's paw version so that when it is needed as a nail set, I can quickly place the squared off handle end on a nail head while striking the clawed end with my hammer to set the nail. This many times saves a walk to the truck to pull out my "pea shooter" or "slide hammer" as some folks call it. When using the cat's paw to either remove an errant nail or set nails, I try to use the side of the hammer head, if at all possible, to save the hammer head's corrugated milled face. While most of the time the claws on my hammer suffice as my chisel, there is that rare situation that because of the approach angle I cannot get at something with the claws of my hammer and need to resort to a formal chisel.

THIRD-TIER TOOLS

My third-tier tools always stay in the truck until needed. This group of tools is composed of a variety of portable electric hand tools and their accessories plus some miscellaneous items:

1. $1/2$-inch pistol grip drill (Rockwell 7514)
2. $1/2$-inch right-angle drill (Milwaukee 1001-1)
3. $4^1/2$-inch disc sander/grinder (Milwaukee 6145)
4. Sawzall (Milwaukee 6506)
5. $1/2$-inch router (Rockwell 6902)
6. Small jigsaw (Black & Decker U-153)
7. $1/2$-inch impact wrench (Black & Decker 2214-09)
8. Various combo wrenches
9. 36-inch framer's slide hammer (a.k.a. pea shooter)
10. 2×6 T&G application tool
11. Layout stick
12. Channel marker
13. 78-inch level (Sears Craftsman)
14. 24-inch level (Sears Craftsman)
15. 2-foot handled 5-lbs sledge hammer
16. Two pipe clamps (4-foot and 6-foot lengths)
17. A shortened framing square with stair dogs
18. A 15-inch Stanley FatMax 8 tpi/9 ppi handsaw
19. A 220 v/110 v outlet box with pigtail clamps
20. A Speed Fastener stud gun (model 825)

My roof-cutting saws plus supplies would be considered third-tier tools as well, and they include:

1. Modified Skil 107 with a 4-inch dado set **(fig 6-10)**
2. Skil 127 on a swing-table **(figs 6-9, 6-15)**
3. Stihl 044 on a Headcutter with five different chainbar lengths **(fig 6-16)**
4. Two 12-inch adjustable Quick Squares® **(fig3-6)**
5. A can of silicone spray to use as blade oil **(fig 2-10)**

While you may think many of my tools are antiques, and indeed they may well be, I have had no need or desire to swap them out for newer models. They are still running strong and doing the job as well as or, in many cases, better than the newer models. Most of my third-tier tools I picked up in the late 1970s when I worked as a framing foreman and they have stayed with me ever since. Aside from the occasional changing of armature brushes, all my tools have had the on/off trigger replaced at least once. While most carpenters nowadays like to use cordless power tools whenever possible, I am happy to stay wired up. Yeah, they may be a bit more inconvenient at times, but I will never have to worry about the tool's power winding down while I am working or having to take out a personal loan to buy their high-priced replacement batteries. I had a DeWalt cordless impact wrench for a long time. It was a member of my pickup truck's roadside breakdown mechanical tool kit. It came in handy to change flat tires, etc. It was a great help until the day the battery would suddenly no longer hold a charge and I had to get a replacement. Since I was in a third world country at the time, the impact wrench ended up sitting for several years before I was able to get a replacement battery. Of course most people don't live the crazy life that I do and a replacement battery would arrive within 3 days via UPS, but experiences like that have reinforced my affection for electric tools with a cord that connects directly to the construction site power supply. I do still own an older Makita 9.6v cordless drill. It is normally part of my aircraft mechanic tool kit (when the batteries are working). I got it to serve as an electric screwdriver for the opening/closing of access panels on an aircraft. With a #2 Phillips screw bit set in its jaws, it is just the ticket for the job. It works fine as long as you are very careful. One has to set the torque just right so that, when tightening the screws on reassembly, you don't damage the fragile Tinnerman® speed nuts. Most guys just set the torque setting super light and then hand tighten the last half-turn to snug it up. Some shops won't even let their mechanics use an electric screwdriver so as to avoid any possible damage. So, believe me, I know that cordless tools have their purpose, I just prefer corded tools when framing with the one big exception – a gas-powered chainsaw. It has no equal. Since I already have an extension cord out for my Skil 77 (we are inseparable), it is no big deal to tie in a drill or impact as the situation may require. Bear in mind that nearly all my portable electric hand tools have

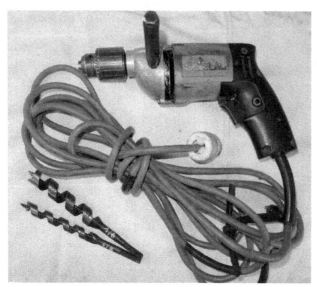

3-11 A good ¹/₂-inch pistol grip drill together with only two bits is all one needs to lay mudsill plates

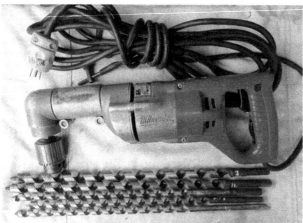

3-12 For beam work I use a ¹/₂-inch right-angled Milwaukee drill and 18-inch ship auger bits

been modified with the installation of a tool-mounted power cord at least 25 feet in length.

My ¹/₂-inch pistol grip drill's primary use is for making holes for anchor bolts in mudsill plates. **(fig 3-11)** The drill is typically paired with a ⁵/₈-inch short ship auger drill bit for ¹/₂-inch anchor bolts or a ³/₄-inch short ship auger drill bit for ⁵/₈-inch anchor bolts. I am not a fan of flat boring bits for framing, so I do not even own a set. I go ¹/₈-inch over the bolt diameter with the hole size when using these big square 2×2 inch and 3×3 inch bearing plate washers. While I have fried a ¹/₂-inch Milwaukee Magnum pistol grip drill inside of a year, my Rockwell drill has never failed me in over 3 decades. Too bad they aren't produced any more, they were geared much lower than the competition (+/– 300 rpm). Because of its hefty torque, the side helper

3-13 A small disk grinder is a very versatile tool to grind, cut, and clean jobsite steel products

handle is an essential. I also use this drill to tap and shoulder $^{1}/_{2}$-inch, $^{5}/_{8}$-inch, or $^{3}/_{4}$-inch lag bolts.

The $^{1}/_{2}$-inch right-angle drill's main purpose is to make holes for machine bolts in various types of beam connections. **(fig 3-12)** The right-angle drill is normally paired with 18-inch ship auger drill bits sized $^{1}/_{16}$ inch larger than the bolt's diameter. The drill works well to drill holes for bolts up to $^{3}/_{4}$-inch diameter; over that size, it is better to use a Milwaukee Hole Hawg® drill. Only a couple times have I had to install bolts larger than $^{3}/_{4}$ diameter, so the right-angle drill fills my needs just fine. The model I have spins at about 300 rpm, which I find near a perfect rpm for the auger boring of holes. I also use this drill to make holes for beam-to-post connections that require $^{1}/_{2}$-inch driven rebar pins.

I love my Milwaukee $4^{1}/_{2}$-inch disc sander/grinder. **(fig 3-13)** In fact, I have two of them. One is set up to grind or cut steel, while the other is set up with a wire wheel to clean. When I was a kid, the only steel we ever used on the job were nails and some joist hangers, but nowadays a carpenter has to be half steel worker with all the steel beams, moment frames, etc., they throw into the building designs. These versatile little grinders can be used for anything from knocking concrete off anchor bolt threads (if the foundation contractor was a slob), to cutting bolts, to prepping and finishing in welding. Occasionally, I will affix the grinder in my bumper-mounted vice to use it like a bench grinder. I keep a big rubber band around the motor body to serve as my third hand in these instances. I locate the rubber band over the trigger switch so it is permanently on and the turn the grinder on and off by connecting or disconnecting the tools power cable.

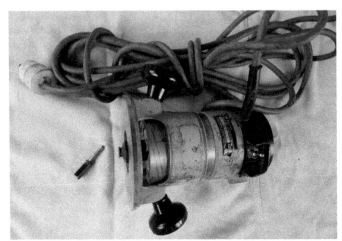

3-14 I use a router and straight-cutting bits to make beam pockets and recess beam ends

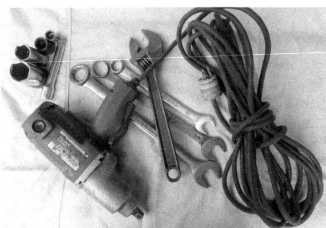

3-15 An electric impact wrench makes quick work of installing lags, bolts, and plate nuts

A sawzall is one of the least used of my second-tier tools. It may sit undisturbed for years without ever leaving the truck, but when it is called upon, it is indispensable. Where many folks use a sawzall to make headouts, etc., I use my Super EZ chainsaw. The only time my sawzall comes out of the truck is when it is needed to cut some nail-embedded wood that I felt was too risky to address without damaging the chainsaw's cutting chain. The need to pull the sawzall out is not usually a good sign since it shows we are going backward instead of forward. On remodels and additions, the sawzall is king.

The router is another tool that leads an easy life. **(fig 3-14)** It is only pulled out when there is a need to dado beam pockets in a ridge in order to receive rafter beams or to slightly recess the end of an exposed post or beam so it can easily be dressed up with a handsaw for a hair-tight joint (RCS, pgs. 207–208). I only have two bits that I use – either a $1/2$-inch or a $3/4$-inch straight-cutting router bit.

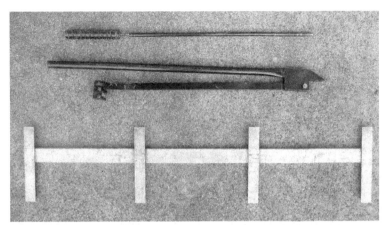

3-16 A slide hammer, a T&G decking installation tool, and a layout stick

My jigsaw has the same cushy life as my router and sawzall. Only on rare occasions, when a plywood plate radius is so tight that it can't be cut with my Skil 77, does she get the chance to earn her keep. The model I have is super simple unit. I feel it would be a waste of money to personally own one of these amazing high-end jigsaws since it would hardly get used.

An electric impact wrench is typically used on par with both of my $1/2$-inch drills. They are like two peas in a pod. Undoubtedly, if the drills are out for a task, so is the impact. The impact wrench sees time installing mudsill plates, assembling beam trusses, installing bolted hardware, driving lags, etc. While there are lots of fancier models available today that allow for torque adjustment, my old Black & Decker model gets the job done without a lot of fanfare. **(fig 3-15)** Its primary work partners are the appropriate sockets for tightening nuts on $1/2$-inch, $5/8$-inch, and $3/4$-inch bolts, or driving lags of the same sizes, and a set of matching combo wrenches to hold the far end of the any bolts being tightened. Every now and then the impact wrench gets the chance to install those short $1/4$-inch lags on stair tread angles.

The slide hammer (a.k.a. pea shooter), the 2×6 T&G decking installation tool, the channel marker, and the layout stick, all hold important roles but only the two layout guides see consistent use. Of these four items only the T&G tool must be handmade since the other three can be found commercially. **(fig 3-16)** Back in the 1970s, almost any framing outlet carried them, but nowadays you may have to look around a bit. Bigfootsaws.com is one option. You can make your own slide hammer by welding a 6-inch-long piece of #10 rebar to a 36-inch-long piece of $5/16$-inch steel round stock and fit this into to a $3/8$-inch steel pipe. The slide hammer can be fabricated to whatever length you want, but the bar should extend a $1/2$-inch past the pipe at full extension. To make a channel marker, I use a scrap of $3/4$-inch plywood together with a short chunk of 2×4. These two pieces are connected with a few wood screws.

3-17 While commercial corner tools are available I make my own on the jobsite

3-18 My old Sears 78-inch level never failed me over 4 decades of heavy use

(fig 3-17) See *A Roof Cutter's Secrets*, pg. 12 for more detail.

I hold my 78-inch level as one of my most precious tools. **(fig 3-18)** While many guys have changed over to using a laser to plumb walls when framing, there is absolutely no way they can match the speed which with I can do the same task using my long level when all the walls are standard 8-foot or 9-foot heights. For this task, which is its primary function, it is mounted it on a straight 2×4 of the appropriate length having a spacer strip of plywood on each end as shown in *A Roof Cutter's Secrets* (pg. 31). I walk to each corner and simply read the bubble. Since I am so familiar with the bubble's position in its vial, I know instantly how much the wall needs to move in what direction. There is no bending down to set the laser on the bottom plate and adjust it into position, etc. I can do everything I need from an upright walking position, which saves the low back. This is not to say the laser is not useful, I just reserve it for situations where it can speed things up not slow them down. On tall walls where before I used a heavy plumb bob to align, I now use the laser. To check the positioning of beams up in the air

3-19 I glue in all my bubble vials with Lexel or Goop

against my snapped-out floor drawing I use a laser. To check level in almost all situations, I use the laser. Only when it would be easier or faster to use my 24-inch or 78-inch levels do they become involved in a task.

I have always only used a Craftsman brand bubble level. Not only do they carry a lifetime guarantee, but they never fall out of adjustment as many other levels do. In the older Craftsman design, the bubble vial slots are milled into the level's aluminum rail so there is no adjustment. That is exactly what I want. The level is either good or bad. The only way the level will go bad is if the rail gets bent, and, believe me, that is hard to do since Craftsman levels can sure take a beating. Mine has fallen from the second floor of a house several times without ill effect (it wasn't me). I remove all the plastic vial covers and simply glue the bubble vials in place. **(fig 3-19)** It gives me a clearer view because, after time, the covers get all scratched up or break. To verify if the older Craftsman level was still good after such an act of violence such as a two-story fall, one simply sights down the rail to verify that it is straight end-to-end. If it is, then it is still perfectly good, it not, then it was probably time to get a new one since it was unlikely that you will be able to bend it back to its original perfect form. Only once in four decades did I have to replace my long level. I can't remember how it came to meet its demise, but I do remember going into Sears and ordering up four new 78-inch levels. When they arrived, I went in and chose the best of the bunch to take home. I try to treat my 78-inch level with the utmost of respect at all times. When she is not actively participating in plumbing walls, she lives well protected in the fortified bunker of my truck's 4-inch well casing pipe bumper.

My 5-lbs sledge is called on for tasks like driving stakes during concrete formwork to applying a little persuasion when something refuses to go where I would like it to go. The sledge has moved many a wall in, out, or end-to-

3-20 I keep a regular and a "C" styled pipe clamp ready for beam work and other tasks

end. I personally find 5 lbs to be the optimum size for a framer. I have used others that are bigger and heavier, but they seem like overkill. I do shorten the handle so the whole affair is 24 inches long. When I drive wood stakes, I always use the side of the head as the striking surface since this seems to work better. Maybe you have noticed that wood stakes tend to split after half a dozen strikes using the normal driving face, whereas, when using the flat side of the head, this seems to happen less frequently.

Pipe clamps have all kinds of uses when framing custom homes. Most often, I use them to draw two beams (or two anythings) together and straighten any twists in studs and joists. **(fig 3-20)**

I use my framing square for three things: stair stringer layout; on rare occasions to layout a monster hip/valley rafter birdsmouth; and as a straight edge to help draw out complicated roof connections on the ground or a sheet of plywood. I use my 12-inch Quick Square® to cut rafters, fascia, and joists. As most know, I do not use a rafter square for any rafter layout – that went away as soon as I learned production roof cutting in the 1970s. Timber framers are the guys that can really put a framing square through its paces and it is an essential to their trade. I started shortening my framing square up many decades ago. At first I cut the tongue down to 12 inches and the blade down to 18 inches, just so it would fit into a tool box on my truck's utility bed, but after doing that I found I liked it so much better that it became my norm. In my limited applications it was all I needed. Now, I see a couple framing square manufactures have started offering a shortened version sized similar to mine. A pair of stair dogs always lives with the framing square.

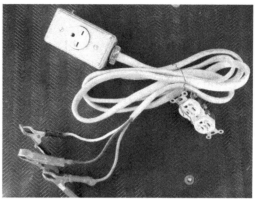

3-21 Recessing the middle of a beam end allows easy joint cleanup with a handsaw

3-22 220v/110v outlet box with pigtail clips for hot wiring direct to a subpanel

While fewer and fewer carpenters carry a handsaw in their tool box nowadays, I still rely on one when it comes to doing exposed beam work. In the late 1970s, I purchased a 16-inch Makita beam saw to make exposed cuts on 6× material that was used in fancy roof beam connections or exposed trusses, but found the thin blade flexed just enough so that at times it failed to give me the quality of cut I desired. I tried mounting a thicker blade in hopes that this would provide more rigidity but found the extra thickness was just too much for the saw's tiny motor. So I dumped the Makita beam saw in favor of using my faithful Skil 77 to wrap the beam with a starter cut and then finished the cut off with a few strokes of a handsaw. For most of my life, I used a standard 8-point cross-cut handsaw for this task but when these newer Stanley triple-ground tooth Fat Max versions came out in the 2000s I switched over to them. On the cut of a post or beam which is part of an exposed joint, I recess the interior section slightly using either a router (as described earlier), a chainsaw, or a circular saw so the outside visible edges are be the only part to make solid contact. **(fig 3-21)** With the interior section of a beam cut recessed, it only takes a pass or two with a handsaw to tighten up any unacceptable gaps.

One little tool that I haul around is a 220v/110v outlet box with pigtail clips. **(fig 3-22)** There have been many times when this rig has come in quite handy. It gives me the ability to tie in "hot" inside a breaker panel when my big dado saw or Skil 127 are popping the breaker because they pull so much amperage. If I bypass the breakers and go straight to the hot lines, I remove the problem but, of course, I have no circuit breaker protection. For certain, Occupational Safety and Health Administration (OSHA) would have a conniption fit if they ever saw me do it. I only use it as a temporary fix to keep the job moving along.

To attach interior framed walls to a concrete slab floor one needs a stud gun. While there are various models nowadays that use a .22 caliber load to drive a hammering piston, I still prefer the old high-velocity single-shot units because they can easily shoot into steel. I purchased my Speed Fastener stud gun in the late 1970s, and it served me well all my career. Rather than keep different load strengths around, I would only purchase the high-power purple loads, and, if I found them too strong for some application, I simply pushed the pin down the barrel a tad, enlarging the explosion chamber and thereby lessening the force applied. Typically, a purple load worked fine unless the concrete was green, in which case I would need to lighten the load using the "push pin down" method. If I had to shoot a 2× nailer onto a thick steel beam or moment frame, many times a purple load would not provide enough force, so I would double the load up. To do this, I put one .22 purple load into the breech plate, as is standard procedure, but then I would also place a second load into the barrel just above the loaded pin. While the second load would push the pin down the barrel a taste, it still nearly doubled the force applied to the pin. I wasn't worried about overstressing the gun, since there were single loads one could special order that were equivalent to double purple loads. I did remove the cover shield from the exit end of the barrel at times to allow the gun to function better in tight spaces. Removing the shield can expose the operator to muzzle flash particles, but if one is positioned well above the unit and the gun barrel is kept tightly pressed against the work, this should not create a danger. I liked to wire-brush clean and oil everything after a day of heavy use since stud guns seem to build up carbon residue quickly.

The roof cutting saws are detailed in other chapters, so I won't bore you by repeating myself except to note that the Stihl 044 is paired with a bar length depending on the rafter size and roof pitch.

CONTRACTOR TOOLS

When I was a framing contractor I also had a big 3-horsepower 30-gallon compressor wired for 220v that sat permanently mounted in the bed of my pickup truck. It could put out 120 psi all day long with enough air volume for 3 nail-guns. Since I only ran two Berryfast 16d nailers, the compressor just loped along. I always operate on the principle that no tool should ever be made to work at its maximum limit and always get something big enough so it has a lot of extra capacity built in. The Berryfast guns served us well. They were mainly used to nail off the roof sheathing or shear walls, but occasionally they would be called upon to help out on some pickup work like installing a soffit under the eaves or something similar. I never used them to wall frame or stack since I hate air hoses running all through my work area. Besides that, nail-guns will never suck anything tight like a hand drive does. I also mounted a Miller 200LE Onan powered welder/generator on a small trailer and would haul that baby to the job to either serve as an electrical

3-23 A telehander is a "must have" tool for the serious framer (photo courtesy Dave Saunders)

power source or to weld something as needed. When I shut down my framing company in the late 1980s, I sold the compressor, nail-guns, and the welder/generator so I could mount a camper and be lightweight in order to travel up/down the West Coast and work as a freelance roof cutter/framing consultant. To keep some power-producing and welding capacity, I replaced the big Miller welder/generator with a small high frequency unit, that was mounted in my truck's engine compartment and powered by an upsized 200-amp alternator. **(fig 4-5)**

While I had a some small step ladders and a short extension ladder, most of the time I built in such a fashion that ladders weren't needed. Going up/down ladders is a huge waste of time and contra to production methodology. When I frame a second floor, the stairs are up before the floor is even finished. An outside shear wall is normally nailed off before the wall is stood if it cannot be reached by standing on the ground. To get up on the top plates in order to frame the roof, I would many times make a quick walking ramp using a pair of long, stacked 2×12s if there was some way to do make it work. Anything other than a ladder. I also preferred to assemble some quick scaffolding to work a hard-to-reach high area rather than try to do something from an extension ladder.

My biggest screw-up in third-tier tools as a framing contractor was not getting a telescopic handler (boom lift or telehandler). If I had to do it over again, that would definitely be one of my very first purchases. **(fig 3-23)** While through my life we would use Genie portable hand crank material lifts for setting smaller beams or truck mounted telescopic cranes for setting

3-24 These guys welded up a lifting boom using a discarded antenna tower

big beams and rafter packages, we still did too much lifting by "back power" and my body has paid the price. It was way too late by the time Dan Daley showed me the utility of the telehandler in the late 1990s; my spine was already destroyed. A Gradall telehandler was one of the first tools Mark Monosmith (Salt Lake City, UT) got when he started framing and he uses it for everything. Even the walls go up by pneumatic power. Same with framing contractor Dave Saunders of Hyannis, MA, the master of prefabrication. He was such a skilled operator that Lull used him as their telehandler poster boy. Dan Daley even purchased a tower crane which he would set up on jobsites where access from all sides was limited or where the height of the lift was better accomplished by its amazing reach. I wonder if one of these mini tower cranes might have been the solution to move materials for homes built on lots too steep for a telehandler, like the Oakland Hills. Even on a limited budget, I have seen guys in poorer countries weld up ingenious little lifting rigs to help them move light materials around up high. **(fig 3-24)**

JOB CLOTHING

There is certainly no dress code for a framer, and clothing is as varied as there are different climates. I have worked in several climates and for each of them I dress differently. I don't like cold weather and thankfully I spent the vast majority of my framing career along the California Coast during the winters. Summers in the Los Angeles area are super hot, especially out in the east valley cities like Pomona, Rialto, Fontana, where I spent time piecemeal framing. Typically, we saw temperatures in the 100s during the day with smog that blew in from the west becoming so thick that, by 2 pm, my lungs hurt when I tried to take a deep breath. All the guys who worked in the tracts along with me wore shorts, no shirt, and for us guys up in the air (joisters, stackers, fascia hangers, and roof sheathers), tennis shoes. You lose about $2/3$ of your body heat from the waist up, so going shirtless allowed your body's radiator to be more efficient in the hot climate. Wall framers and guys on the ground might have worn a little heaver shoes but I can't rightly remember. In fact, in California I have never worn boots or long pants on a job unless I was in some muddy trench doing concrete formwork. If the dirt was dry I would be in shorts and tennis shoes just like usual. The shorts I wore were almost always some type of lightweight, loose-fitting, nylon running shorts or swim trunks. We were involved in an athletic activity after all, so it only made sense. On hot days, sweat would soak my shorts starting from the waist on down, so being made of nylon they would dry quickly. For me, athletic shorts were perfect because they were super flexible and had short leg lengths with wide openings so that as I climbed around on the roof they would never get hung up on my thigh when I brought my knee up. I hated that worse than anything. It was kind of like someone was trying to hold me back as I moved.

My work shoes were super, super important and I spent a good deal of time selecting them. They had to be light and breathable, and possess a sole that would grip under any condition. Weightwise the old backpackers axiom "for each 1 lb you cut off the weight of your shoes is like removing 10 lbs from the weight of you backpack" expresses my feelings about shoe weight. While you might not be hiking all day with a pack on your back, think about your nail bags strapped around your waist, and, at least as a stacker, we moved around a fair amount. Just being on your feet all day in shoes that weighed ¾ to 1 lb each is pure delight when compared to tramping around a jobsite in heavy work boots that weigh $2^{1}/_{2}$ to 3 lbs each. I don't know about you, but I find it rather difficult to be nimble like a squirrel up high when wearing work boots.

I would always try out any new work shoe to see if its sole will grab on wet wood. Since I would be walking across rafters, decking, or plywood up high, I had to have total confidence that the shoe's sole would grip on any surface no matter how steep and wet. I would look at cross-trainers, and trail-runner types at REI, Big 5, Great Pacific Ironworks (Patagonia Ventura), etc. My favorite work shoe for many years was the Montrail Vitesse. Unfortunately I have yet to find a replacement of its equal. Isn't that the way things always work – you finally find something that is perfect and then the manufacturer discontinues it. A poor gripping sole was the cause of a disastrous ground level slip I made in 2012 that resulted in major knee and ankle damage.

For most of my life I wore short athletic socks since they kept my feet the coolest. Obviously, in cooler climates longer tube socks would be a better choice. One problem we carpenters face with our shoes/socks, especially if

3-25 Hiking gaitors keep saw dust out of my shoes and socks

one does a lot of cutting as I do, is that they get filled with sawdust. When I would arrive home each night after a hard day I would sit outside for a few minutes and brush my shoes and socks clean with a bathtub scrub brush. I must have done that for 25 years until I figured out that if I just wore a pair of hiker's rock gaiters I could terminate this routine. Yeah, when I first started wearing gaiters on the job in sunny California I would get all kind of wise cracks from everybody like "Hey Will, are we expecting heavy snow today?" but as soon as everybody saw the benefit they eventually shut up. **(fig 3-25)** When I cut roof rafters I started wearing coveralls. They worked great with my gaiters. What a setup – I was finally sawdust free. I don't know why it took me so long to figure this one out. The guys could make all the jokes they wanted, but for me it was no more sitting outside the house cleaning my shoes and clothes before they would unlock the door.

If it was sunny, you would always find me wearing a pair of polarized sunglasses. I have never been able to take much sun in my eyes. My irises are very light blue so I have no pigment protection from the sun like other folks who are gifted with darker colored eyes. I can't see a darn thing when the sun is out since my eyes involuntary squint so as to cut down on the brilliance. My sunglasses serve double duty as safety glasses, and it is only when working on a very dark cloudy day outside or on something indoors that I might consider swapping them out for clear safety glasses.

One would be hard pressed to find more accommodating climates than Santa Barbara, CA, or the East San Francisco Bay Area and I was blessed to have spent many decades framing in both. In the winter, it might be cool in the early mornings and I would usually just throw on a sweatshirt until the fog burned off and the temperature had warmed up some. Surprising how fast your body warms up when you are driving nails and moving lumber.

3-26 Framing in colder parts of the country required a change from my standard shoes and shorts attire

Other guys might also throw on a pair of sweatpants for those chilly hours in the winter morning, but I hate long pants of any type, so I try to avoid them at all costs. Sweatpants permit a carpenter be very limber when he moves compared with jeans, which restrict movement. It is also my opinion that long pants present more risk when working up high since they could hang up on something and cause a stumble. It was only on chilly winter jobs in Oregon, Alaska, or Massachusetts that I was forced to don jeans, a light jacket, and a skull cap. **(fig 3-26)** On some of Dan Daley's big commercial jobs, I was forced to wear OSHA-designated construction attire including hardhats and work boots. **(fig 2-27)** This only motivated me to work even faster so I could get out of there and return to my normal framing attire.

I am also not a fan of a brimmed hat or head attire of any type when framing. I tried them a few times, especially after learning about skin cancer risks, but every time I used one it did not end well. A human being has a 135° vertical range of vision but approximately 60° of the upper portion is blocked by a brimmed hat. So when I did wear a baseball cap or hard hat, I would always smack my head on something ahead and higher simply because the obstacle was obscured by the brim. Besides this, a hat or helmet holds in heat, which was a big enemy in warmer climates. So other than being forced to wear a hard hat by some big commercial jobsite protocol (like when I worked for Dan Daley or National Lumber), I never wore anything at all. Up in the air, the only thing I ever had to worry about falling on my head was some drizzle from a seagull. Even when I had my own framing company, we would never wear hard hats, and this was not because I didn't care about the guys, but because we all flowed through the job together. We finished the bottom story walls and we moved up to frame the second floor together. Nobody stayed behind. We finished the top floor, and we all went up to frame the roof together. At no time did I have one group of guys working below another group of guys. If a guy wanted to wear a baseball cap on the crew who was I to stop him, but very few ever did. Most came to the same conclusion as I had, that it was safer to have that extra 60° range of vertical vision than to do without by wearing a brimmed hat. Besides, when you are bent over most of the day, sun in your eyes is a nonissue.

When I was younger, no one really had any clue that too much sun was dangerous. Sunburn was just something you endured until your skin darkened up a bit. A bronze color was regarded as the sign of a healthy outdoor lifestyle. If that was true, I was plenty healthy since my backside, arms, and legs were pretty brown. It was only in the late 1970s that medical professionals started to preach about covering up and using sun block creams. My sister was a student teacher at Cal Poly Pomona paralleling some of the time I was framing out in the East Los Angeles basin, and she started making up some skin protection concoction using para-aminobenzoic acid (PABA) in her chemistry laboratory classes that I could apply to my backside until the same thing became available commercially. Unfortunately, the damage had already been done and I would end up paying for it later on in life. All my life, I would prefer lathering on sunscreen versus putting on a shirt. If I did put one on, it was always soaked in sweat. I went shirtless for so many decades that the habit has carried over into old age. I still hate wearing a shirt. They are just too blooming hot.

When I went to the Tropics to help out as a volunteer I faced a whole new set of heat challenges. For me nothing is more miserable than hot humidity. Give me the dry 110° heat of Phoenix, AZ, over these hot steamy jungles any day. I can't believe people fight wars to get a piece of these wastelands. Just let them have it. The folks who live in these climates certainly possess a much more durable physical constitution than I could ever hope to have. They even wear jeans when it is 90° outside with 90% humidity. To me this is unfathomable. I suppose growing up along the California coast has spoiled me climatewise. Anyhow, in the Tropics I had to surrender to wearing thin long pants and a thin long-sleeve shirt just so my skin didn't die from the intensity of the sun and to help prevent being carried off by the hordes of insects that were pursuing me all day. I know they wanted nothing better than to give me some incurable disease or torment me with painful bites. They seemed to just laugh when I slapped on a little more U.S. Army issue 100% DEET (stay down at 30% for health reasons). Since the direct sun is too hot for them, that was the only place you could go to escape their attacks, all the while praying for a strong wind so they would be forced to go find a bush and hang on. In the Tropics, I even wore a full big-brim hat or a cap with a neck protection flap. It was a good thing no one knew who I was or it would have ruined

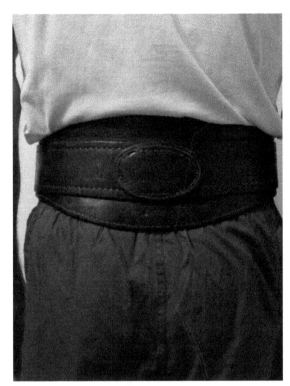

3-27 Use a weight lifters belt to protect your low back when lifting materials

my reputation. I have no clue how the indigenous peoples of many Central America countries, like the Embera Indians of Panama's Darien province or the Tarahumara Indians of Mexico, can run around with nothing on but a loin cloth, considering the bugs and intense sunlight. Truly amazing people.

One last item that I suppose one might consider a clothing item is a weightlifter's back support belt. Having developed low back issues, I started using one of these if I would be lifting anything of substantial weight. Normally, I would remove my nail bags and use it solo, but if I had to I could wear them both together for brief moments but it was not real comfortable. It would have been cool if I could have threaded my weightlifter's belt through the nail bags belt loops but it was way too wide for that. **(fig 3-27)**

Simplicity is the ultimate sophistication. – Leonardo da Vinci

4

A Man and his Truck

The great pleasure in life is doing what people say you cannot do.
– Walter Bagehot

Could it be that carpenters and cars are somehow inherently linked? It occurred to me that a very high percentage of the carpenters I know have some type of mechanical interest in motors, hot rods, 4×4s, etc. I most certainly do. My favorite car has always been the early 1970s Ford Pantera. With its mid-mounted 351 Cleveland motor and low clean lines, it was pure speed. Hard to believe they sold for a mere $10,000 brand new. Being a poor boy, I never had the money to buy one, but even if I had, I wouldn't have fit since I am too long-waisted. My head would have been through the roof. In the early 1970s, my younger brother was a street racer in the style of Ron Howard's *American Graffiti*. He raced either his 1962 Nova with a built-up 350 motor and shift kit modified turbo 400 tranny, or his 1967 Nova with a souped up 327 motor and 2-speed Powerglide. Living in Los Angeles, at the time, I wasn't around to see him smoke folks out on a lonely stretch of Hollister Avenue west of Santa Barbara, CA, but it must have been fun. I wonder if he inherited his racing blood from my mother's side of the family, since our uncle had been a professional stock car racer.

When I started working in the Los Angeles housing tracts I bought my first 4-wheeled vehicle, a 1965 Ford 100 truck, from a friend for $500. Before that truck, I either got around by pedal power or on my old Yamaha 125 Enduro. With the Ford, I was forced to become an amateur mechanic just to keep her rolling down the highway, since I certainly couldn't afford to pay a professional mechanic every time something went awry. Since I grew up on a little farm, I had had some exposure to repairing things, so it didn't take long to pick up the skills required to take care of the motor and drive train. Back before they added all this modern day smog and electronic crap, vehicle maintenance was a lot simpler. Anyhow, the Ford sure liked to test my patience and ingenuity until I had all the gremlins worked out. I remember one time having to swap out a U-joint on the side of a busy Los Angeles freeway after the drive-shaft separated. Another time the "3 on a tree" manual transmission linkage messed up and wouldn't shift gears, so I pulled all that factory junk off and installed an aftermarket conversion kit to change it to a "through the floor" stick shift style. Never failed again.

My only modification to this truck was to fabricate a plywood camper shell to keep my growing collection of tools safe from theft and provide me with a place to sleep if needed. There were many times I just simply stayed on the jobsite to save time since I was working from 6 a.m. to 6 p.m. I learned to take a sponge bath with a 5-gallon bucket and a gallon or two of water. The camper shell came in real handy when I drove out to the East Coast and back in 1977. Since it was hot as hell all across the lower 48 that summer, I created a little makeshift air conditioner by redirecting the incoming air ducting that normally went to the heater core across a 12-lbs block of ice sitting in a pan on the floor. Worked great, and I was traveling in luxury.

That same year I decided to upgrade to a 1966 Ford 250 truck with a 4-speed tranny in order to have more carrying capacity. Like a turtle, I carried all my personal belongings in the back of the truck and, very slowly, the gross vehicle weight was creeping up. This faithful, hard-working Ford truck would stay with me for the next 35 years and together we racked up over 400,000 miles, including trips not only for work up/down the California coast, but to jobs in Oregon, Washington, and Alaska. I had bought the truck in Arizona and came to learn that, in order to license her in California, she would need to be weighed empty so she could be placed in the correct license fee category. They would not accept the manufacturer's data. Even back then the state of California was a tax-sucking leech. They knew that most trucks gained weight over their lives and saw a reweigh as an excellent opportunity to collect higher fees. The lowest fee category was for trucks under 4000 lbs, so the Ford went on a crash diet because she was going to make that weight one way or another. When I took her in to a certified scale she had less than a gallon of gas in the fuel tank, no front seat, no spare tire, no battery, and minus anything else that could easily be removed. She tipped the scale at 3998 lbs. Pretty good for a truck that years later would max out at over 9000 lbs loaded up.

My first modification to the 1966 truck was to mount a utility bed. I called around to all the junkyards and found one reasonably priced that would fit my frame. It happened to be a 1-ton Harbor Fabricating model that was probably used on a Southern California Edison power company work truck. Being a bit wider than the standard 3/4-ton pickup versions was a bonus. This utility bed allowed me to really organize my tools, and now I could find

4-1 Long locked pipes down the sides of my utility bed barred the doors closed

anything in seconds. I was able to fit all my tools, except for the dado and beam saws, in the shelves and various compartments. I was even able to stash my 2-ton floor jack in a lower-level compartment. Using a scarp piece of 4-inch well casing pipe, I welded up a 78-inch bumper to store both my long and short levels. They stayed well protected inside this pipe bumper for as long as I was a framer. Having a utility bed on your truck is a sure sign that you have valuable tools stored inside, so years later I would run a steel pipe down each side like a door bar to provide double protection against any of the doors being forced open by a crow bar. **(fig 4-1)**

Next, I went about upgrading the chassis's springs and shocks. On the rear axle, I fitted several extra leafs from a truck boneyard into the spring packages to stiffen them up. This included a full-length HD leaf just below the top leaf and a super thick aftermarket "Add a Leaf" under the whole set. When I was done, she sported an 11-leaf spring package on each side and didn't squat down much no matter how much weight she was forced to carry. **(fig 4-2)** On the front, I replaced the stock coil springs with aftermarket HD units and swapped out the standard Ford dropped I beam axles for Off Road Distributors straight-arm versions. These two items raised the front end of the truck up 3 to 4 inches so she sat more level and didn't look like a stink bug anymore. I found a place that made custom sway bars and had them fabricate a super HD model for the front end. I wanted a "real" sway bar not one of these wimpy units offered in the aftermarket or by the Ford dealer. My bar was 1¼ inches in diameter, and it worked so well that the loaded

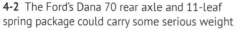

4-2 The Ford's Dana 70 rear axle and 11-leaf spring package could carry some serious weight

4-3 My modified front end and heavy duty custom sway bar

truck handled curves better than most regular cars. **(fig 4-3)**

To beef up the braking system, I ran a remote Hydrovac off an old school bus for a while before mounting a firewall power brake unit and the disc brake setup off a 1978 Ford Camper Special truck. That was a terrific upgrade, and I now had decent braking. For tires, I installed a set of mud/snow 33×12.5 R16.5 tires, and, with a Detroit Locker differential in the rear axle, I could get in/out of muddy jobsites with no problem. The front tires were street tread 235/85 R16s. Well, not exactly a Baja 1000 Trophy Truck, but she got the job done.

I bought a used Hickey Sidewinder 8000-lbs electrical winch and installed it on a custom skid-plate mount that I welded up. **(fig 4-4)** I replaced the stock alternator with a 125-amp version and stuck a second 12v battery under the hood. I wired the winch to the number two battery with an isolator, so it was impossible for the winch to draw down the truck's number one battery. I fabbed up a HD front push bumper out of the same 4-inch pipe that I had used on the rear. Inside this front bumper I stored snow chains for the big rear tires. The winch came in very handy, and we used it many times for anything from raising big walls to yanking somebody's stuck truck out of the jobsite mud.

The truck remained with an open rear bed for a few years early in the

4-4 The Ford's vertical drum style Hickey sidewinder winch raised many large rake walls

1980s because I had stashed all my odds and ends at a storage place. I was taking some welding classes at Santa Barbara City College in the evenings, and, after spying a good used Onan powered 200-amp Miller welder/generator, I purchased it for the jobsite. Not wanting to mount it in the truck bed, I welded up a small trailer and towed it to the job as needed. I built the trailer as a project for my welding class along with a 10-foot crane that mounted on the rear pipe bumper of the truck. While we didn't use the crane much on the jobsite, it came in real handy when I was doing engine swaps to move the motor blocks in and out of the truck bed. I held on to the welder/generator through the 1980s while I had my Santa Barbara–based custom home framing business, but ended up selling it when I began traveling around the Western United States to work as a freelance roof cutter. I did miss the welder/generator and eventually replaced it with a small under-the-hood, engine alternator-powered unit called the Hehr Power Arc 2. Powered by a 200-amp alternator, it would stick weld OK with a $1/8$-inch rod, and the 2400-watt generator output would run all my power tools including the high amp Skil barrel saws. Having the ability to use electricity and weld at a roadside repair was invaluable, especially now that I was traveling great distances between jobs. (fig 4-5)

Another truck-mounted tool that has been super important all my life is a 360° swivel, Cole Mfg., 4-inch bench vice/anvil. On the Ford, I used the hitch receiver as the mount for a vice. Years later I found that mounting the vice on the end of a tube bumper worked better if the truck had a drop-down tailgate. (fig 4-6)

4-5 Electrical power when and where needed with my under hood 2400 watt DC generator/arc welder

4-6 I mounted my detachable Cole Mfg. Swiveling 4-inch bench vice/anvil on the rear well-casing bumper

My next big project for the Ford was to mount a cab-over 8-foot camper. I had spied a used one for sale out along Highway 99 near Bakersfield and it fit the utility bed perfectly. **(fig 4-7)** The utility and the camper added some serious weight to the truck and it only made sense to rejuvenate the tired motor with a rebuild. The Ford's motor was a 300 cid straight 6 cylinder. I ordered a short block from the parts house, and somehow things got screwed up so I received a 240 cid version not a 300 cid. I didn't catch this error until after the engine was installed and I took the truck out for a test drive. The 300 cid motor is a stroked version of a 240 cid motor so it is identical from

4-7 The cab over camper helped make my "traveling roof consultant" business a reality

the outside. The 300 put out a ton more torque than the 240, and, of course, torque is what is needed to move a heavy work truck. Somehow the 240 got mislabeled, or something like that as Murphy's law would have it. That poor little motor was working itself to death and the mpg dropped to 7 mpg. I yanked the motor and decided that instead of installing the correct 300 cid I would upgrade to the venerable 390 cid V8. At a Ventura boneyard, I spotted a 4-barrel 390 cid V8 in a Mercury Cougar and shortly thereafter I delivered it to a local Santa Barbara machine shop to rebuild. The 390 cid was a big improvement and I absolutely loved it. Unfortunately, Murphy's law just wouldn't leave me be, and a wrist pin clip let go, causing the wrist pin to scarf out a groove in the cylinder wall and I had a major blow-by problem. So out came the motor. I had the machine shop resleeve the cylinder but this time upon reassembly I had them drop in a 428 cid crankshaft that a guy had traded me in exchange for some work. That upped the total cid to 410. The engine now had tons of torque, but it didn't rev nearly as well as the 390 cid. Since my Ford truck came from the factory with a 6 cylinder it had a lower geared rear differential (4.56) than a normal V8 powered version did (4.10, 3.73). While this gearing caused no problem for the 390 cid, it must have been too much for the stroked crank and she bent a rod. Out came the motor again. Looks like Murphy was still after me. I was living up in the Bay Area at the time, helping rebuild some of the big custom homes that had been burnt down in the Oakland Hills firestorm of 1991, so I went over to Diablo Engine, purchased an off-the-shelf balanced "390 Beast" with all the HP extras, and dropped it in. This time Murphy left me alone. The motor ran

4-8 I got some more juice and mileage out of the Ford 390 V-8 by installing a Paxton Supercharger

like a dream the rest of the years we shared together. In time, I added Tri-Y headers, a 4-barrel Edelbrock carburetor, and a Ford 406 "Sidewinder" aluminum racing intake. I really liked the Ford 406 engine, which was a bored out race version of the 390, and had plans to convert my 390 into one of these, so I always had my eyes open for parts. In time, I did find a set of the highly prized Ford 406 racing heads (same as 427 low-riser), but they never made it on the engine block, although I carried them around for many years while waiting for the motor to reach the point where she needed a top overhaul.

The 1966 Ford came with a Warner T-18 transmission that had a nonsynchronized super low granny first gear that was great for off-road driving (6.32/1 ratio). The truck could climb a tree if a bear was chasing her. When the tranny started making funny noises, I contacted a shop in Los Angeles about getting it rebuilt. Since I hardly ever used the granny first gear in the street because it wasn't synchronized, I decided to swap in a T-19 (the T-18 younger brother) instead, which did sport a synchronized first gear. This made it much easier to get the heavy truck rolling from a dead stop and made a huge improvement in everyday driving.

One day, turning onto a freeway on ramp, I snapped a rear axle shaft. While I love the Detroit Locker differential for messy jobsites, they can be very hard on axles in a street application, especially when you get into the position where one wheel slips for some reason and the locker brusquely engages the opposite leg. If the vehicle is heavy and the tires have lots of traction like mine did, something has to give when the coasting leg is instantaneously connected to the driven torque and that something is usually the axle. I replaced the broken axle with one from a junkyard, but it snapped again a few months later, so I bought a pair of Dutchman high-strength Dana/Spicer 60 racing axle shafts. That ended the axle shaft snapping problem, but, after pondering the situation, I decided that if I could find a 1-ton Dana 70 rear axle I would yank out the Dana 60 unit. Having to resort to racing axle shafts was a clear sign that maybe I was pushing the old Dana 60 too hard and she was getting old. Although I had maintained the truck as if it were an aircraft, even down to maintenance logbook entries, annual/mileage inspections, and setting time limits on parts, the rear axle had constantly been loaded at near its maximum weight-carrying capacity for several decades, so it probably wouldn't be long before some other part would also fail because of metal fatigue. It is exceedingly easier to change out a questionable part in a controlled environment than out in the boondocks somewhere, so an upgrade seemed like the right thing to do. A Dana 70 would give me a much tougher axle with near a ton more carrying capacity than the old Dana 60. While working on a job in Oregon, I spotted a used 1978 Dana 70 that would fit my frame perfectly, so I snagged it. I chained it up to my rear pipe bumper and hauled it back down to Southern California where I installed it at a friend's ranch. It had 4.10 gears which lost me a bit of power, but with the larger wheel bearings, larger ring and pinon, larger axle shafts, and 2½ inch × 12 inch drum brakes, it was a good trade-off. Hooper's Rear End in Sun Valley, CA, dropped in a new Detroit Locker and I was back in business. The axle was for dually wheels, but I ran it with my big fat single tires so as not to spend any more funds. **(fig 4-2)**

I also decided that, because of higher gas prices, it was time to pull the 1200-lbs cab-over camper and exchange it for something lighter in hopes of upping my gas mileage. I ran across a camper shell that fit the utility bed well and, with great sadness in my heart, said goodbye to the cab-over camper that had served as my occasional jobsite home for several decades. **(fig 4-1)** The lighter load did help increase the mpg a bit, but gas prices kept going up and, at 8 mpg, I was beginning to fork out some serious dough at each fill-up. I was forced to add a second gas tank back where the spare tire normally lived just to get some decent range. I know the 390 cid motor was working hard to haul the beast around and began contemplating swapping in a 460 cid V8 to lessen the fuel burn. Since the 460 was so powerful, it required very little throttle and, even though it is a bigger motor, the fuel burn would be less than a straining 390 cid motor. In the end, the expense couldn't justify the gain so I decided instead to mount a Paxton supercharger on the 390 cid in order to up the produced horsepower (hp) and hopefully net some better fuel economy. The Paxton supercharger option on the Ford Shelby GT-350 Mustang boosted the power from 271 hp to 395 hp on the small block 289, so just think what it might do for the FE big block. I found a company in San Diego who sold rebuilt Paxton blowers so I fabbed up a mounting bracket and an inlet bonnet, installed a Holley 650 double-pumper carburetor, found a spot to mount a semitruck air cleaner cannister, swapped on a special fuel pump, and then gave it a whirl. I did see a big boost in power, and gas mileage went up to about 9.5 mpg. Anything at this point was a help. **(fig 4-8)** As gas blew past $4 per gallon I was forced to sell the

4-9 The Toyota Hilux 4×4 was one sturdy little rig after I got done upgrading her

old Ford. It is hard to believe that when I first purchased the 1966 Ford, the price of gas was around 50¢ per gallon. It was a very difficult day when a gentleman from Houston, TX, bought her and I had to say my final goodbye. She and I had gone through a lot together and much of my success in framing must be credited to her faithfulness.

Needing an economically gas-minded truck after the 1966 Ford I chose a used 1997 Toyota Hilux diesel crew-cab 4×4 truck. **(fig 4-9)** She would be equivalent to a US 1985 gas version with a solid front drive axle. I have now had this rig for a decade and a half, and she has served me well. I did have to go through the same upgrading procedure as I had done on the Ford, only this time around it was faster since I knew what I needed. She had been driven by a "drive until it breaks" type of guy so I spent the first year that I owned her just swapping out parts that should have been replaced years before. After this, I went to work on the motor. The 2.8-liter diesel was atrociously underpowered, but I had the fix for that. Having seen what a supercharger could do on the Ford, I figured a little boost would pep her up. Looking through various junkyards I found a 2.4-liter turbo diesel motor and pulled its intake and exhaust systems. These I remounted on the 2.8 in place of the original normally aspirated system. The 2.4 and the 2.8 use the same block, so everything bolted up with ease. I had talked to a few guys in

4-10 The diesel motor was a tiger after I adapted on a turbo and intercooler

Australia who knew the Toyota diesel well and they assured me that the 2.8 could handle the increased pressure from a turbo installation. The turbo made all the difference in the world and now I was able to keep up with the traffic flow. The way I figured it, she went from an 80 hp dog to a 125 hp tiger. I eventually adapted the intercooler off a Mitsubishi Montero into the system for better efficiency and installed a free-flowing 2½-inch exhaust system. **(fig 4-10)**

I did have some *déjà vu* with the 1966 Ford when I rebuilt the diesel on account of excessive blow-by. After remounting the resleeved engine, I found it had the same amount of blow-by as before, when there should have been none, so out came the engine again. This time the machine shop pressure tested all the cylinders and, sure enough, we came to find out that an internal sleeve support was cracked, allowing the sleeve on one cylinder to flex on the power stroke. The only way to resolve this was to replace the block. When one was found and rebuilt, I had no further blow-by issues. It had been a while since I had last seen Murphy (Murphy's Law), but it appears he was still lurking about just looking for the right opportunity to strike.

The next project I jumped on was to change the differential ring and pinion ratios from the standard 4.56 gearing to a slightly lower 5.29 gearing in order to pick up more low-end torque and run taller tires. And, while the third members were out of the axle, we installed a Detroit Locker in the rear and a True Trac in front. I found the Toyota to be a pretty tough little truck and I was impressed by her durability but, harboring memories of broken axles on the old Ford, I installed super strong Longfield axles and Birfields in the front axle and Front Range Off Road's full floater kit to the rear axle.

4-11 Fear of snapping drive axles led me to convert the rear axle to a full floating design

(fig 4-11) In addition to making the rear axle a full-floating axle design like the Dana 60, it gave me rear disc brakes. These drive train modifications were followed by installation of aftermarket front and rear leaf spring sets in order to lift the truck 2½ inches and increase the useful load-carrying capacity some 500 lbs. I also changed the Toyota tie rod assembly and steering box to a Marlin Crawler design, which eliminated the notoriously feeble "J arm" setup. The installed 5-speed G52 tranny, while perfectly functional, seemed a little lightweight for the motor's increase in power, so I set out to find a suitable upgrade. After a year of Craigslist hunting, I located an old used Toyota R151 tranny and the appropriate bell housing. We did a quick dissection to replace bearings and syncros and into the truck it went. The 5-speed R151 can handle up to 500 hp in rough duty, so it was a huge improvement from the standpoint of strength and durability.

On the front of the truck, I mounted a Mile Marker 9000-lbs hydraulic winch since my Hickey Sidewinder winch had been sold with the Ford. I decided to go with a hydraulic unit this time, because there wasn't enough room under the hood for a second battery like on the Ford, plus a hydraulic winch has a 100% duty cycle versus a 10% to 20% duty cycle for an electric equivalent. Both winches have their good and bad points, but since I was planning to use the winch more for jobsite assistance and not four-wheeling through rivers and mud holes, the hydraulic seemed like a better choice. The truck's upgraded leaf springs easily handled the extra +100 lbs hanging off the front end. **(fig 4-9)**

I had pulled my Hehr welder/generator from the Ford before I sold her, and it was quite the adventure to install the kit's high-output Ford style alternator on the 2.8 diesel. On the 1966 Ford it had been a breeze to install since the unit was physically identical to the one that was already mounted. On the Toyota, the stock alternator was dinky and it sat tightly nestled below the A/C pump. On top of that, the alternator drove a vacuum pump to power the brake booster. Everyone thought I was plumb crazy to try and mount the alternator, since they were positive it would never fit and I would just be wasting my time. Never tell me something can't be done – it only motivates me more. Well, I had to make all kinds of modifications, but a week later I had the Hehr unit mounted and running like a top. I did have to mount an electric vacuum pump for the brakes, but that was a small sacrifice compared to having a welder/generator onboard.

I welded up a rear pipe bumper like the one I had made for the Ford, but since the Toyota was much narrower of a truck, it was not long enough to store my 78-inch level. I mounted my 4-inch Cole Mfg 360° swiveling vice on the end of the pipe bumper instead of using the hitch receiver like I did on the Ford since the Toyota had a normal truck bed with a drop-down tailgate. The tailgate made an excellent work bench, and mine has seen heavy usage in that capacity. With the vice mounted on the end of the pipe bumper, it was adjacent to the tailgate work bench. **(fig 4-6)**

Instead of installing a utility bed on my work truck this time around, I wanted to try something different, something lighter. I decided I would cover the rear bed with a top that was level with the side rails and then install some drawer units inside. I copped the truck bed cover idea from the rig of an old roof cutter whom I had worked with in the Los Angeles housing tracts and the tool drawer idea came from a McWelco unit that Shone Freeman had in his truck during the late 1990s. The elderly roof cutter's truck was an early 1960s Dodge Power Wagon with a step-side rear bed. He stored all his roof cutting tools in the bed and they were securely protected by a $1^1/_8$-inch plywood cover that sat on the side rails. It was a long time ago, so I can't remember the details, but it was "cool" enough that it has stayed in my memory ever since. With the super strong plywood top, the truck did double duty as a mobile jobsite scaffold and I remember using it once to move a big hip beam to its final location after it had been cut. I covered my Toyota's rear bed in a similar manner but fashioned my top out of metal instead of using $1^1/_8$-inch plywood to save some weight and better survive wet weather. To build the top, we welded together a rectangular frame using thin gauge $1^1/_4 \times 1^1/_4$-inch angle iron and covered this with $1/_{16}$-inch thick sheets of galvanized steel. **(fig 4-12)** For the installation, we hinged it to the factory lumber rack at the cab end of the truck bed so it would swing open like a clam shell. To help lift the top and keep it up in the open position, I installed a pair of gas-charged rear door struts from a Ford Aerostar. **(fig 4-13)** While the metal cover wasn't strong enough to use as a mobile scaffold like the old

4-12 The truck's rear bed cover helped protect its contents from both weather and thieves

roof cutter's cover was, it only took a few 2×12 planks tossed on top of the cover spanning from side-to-side, for it to fill this role.

The next part of my Toyota truck bed project was to fabricate some slide-out truck drawers. For this I began by installing a sheet of ¼-inch plywood on the floor of the bed as an abrasion protector, then I built (8) +/–10-inch-wide × 12-inch-high × 26-inch-long tool boxes out of ¾-inch plywood. Five of these boxes fit snugly side-by-side across the width of the truck and were directly accessible from the open tailgate end of the truck bed. They could be pulled out easily onto the tailgate. **(fig 4-14)** A small stop the width of the truck bed was fixed to the plywood floor in front of them so they could not slide forward, and a loose spacer board set against the closed tailgate kept them from moving aft. They were locked in pretty solid. In each of the boxes I placed either tools, supplies, or car parts. I could fit a second row of 5 boxes directly inboard behind the 5 boxes at the tailgate, but they were more difficult to access, so I rarely put in any more than a single row of 5 boxes at the tailgate. Having a swappable sliding box arrangement allowed me to carry only what was needed for a specific task or that day's project and kept the truck light on her feet for the best diesel mileage. In one box, I kept all my mechanics tools and they never left the truck. In a second box were fasteners and car supplies that also never left the truck. In a third box, I had my Homelite XL chainsaw with its supporting gear. A fourth box housed all my 4-wheeler type gear. The fifth box was home to my Skil 77 and its supporting gear. In a sixth box lived my pistol grip drill and hand grinder

4-13 A pair of gas-charged lift struts helps open the clam shell style rear bed cover

4-14 Pull-out drawer-style tool boxes were easily accessible with the tailgate down

together with their myriad of drill bits and disks. A seventh box held all my carpentry hand tools. The eighth and final box housed my router, right-angle drill, and sawzall together with their accessories. In my older phase of life, this truck bed setup ended up as a reasonable compromise and, looking like a normal truck, it was less conspicuous to a tool thief than a utility bed.

I have always been big proponent of high-performance vehicle lighting and usually ran with 55/100 H4 halogen bulbs in my headlamps in addition to some auxiliary lights (eventually I will upgrade the halogens to LED). I know 100-watt high beams are illegal in some places, but they really lit things up if I needed. I wired them up so that, when I hit the high beam, the low beam stayed on. I also like to mount rear-facing flood lamps for backup lighting. They have come in handy endless times. Personally, I have never understood why the manufacturer doesn't install more functional backup lighting on trucks. **(fig 4-12)**

Aside from using a 1978 Dodge Power Wagon briefly when I was going through engine swaps in the Ford, the 1966 Ford and the 1997 Toyota are pretty much all I have ever owned in the vehicle department. If I had to do it over again, I doubt I would have set either of them up any differently. If you are a busy contractor, you need a utility bed. If you are lead on a framing crew, you can probably get away with a truck drawer unit. I am not a big fan of these across-the-bed-truck-mounted tool boxes. With a rear opening version, you must jump up into the truck bed to gain access. And no matter whether it is a side-opening or rear-opening tool box, every single one I have ever seen ends up a big mess, since it is nearly impossible to keep them organized with the limited amount of space they contain. Everyone eventually just ends up dumping their tools inside the tool box in a haphazard fashion so that, when they actually need something, they must dig around and waste a ton of time looking. Sometimes it takes so long, they even forget what they are looking for. Two of the most successful custom-framing contractors I know (Dan Daley and Shone Freeman) have work trucks that are impeccably organized. Dan has used a 1970s Ford utility all his life, while Shone, when he wore his nail bags, spared no funds to keep the most efficient tool drawer assembly in his truck. When either of these guys sent a worker to grab something out of their work truck, they were back within a minute. Dan and Shone both intrinsically operated on Benjamin Franklin's theorem – "For every minute spent organizing an hour is earned."

I am no psychologist, but having observed things over my lifetime I have come to see some correlation between a man, his truck, his character – and his performance as a carpenter. If his truck is clean and organized with all his tools in a specific place, this guy will make you money because that is how his brain works. Does he drive a flashy rig while his tools look forsaken? It may give you a good idea of his priorities. Is it because money and image are more important than quality of work? Does he stick with and take care of his rig for many years or does he turn it over for a newer model when something goes wrong? This may show whether or not he has good problem-solving skills and is patient. Does he like to modify and add things to his rig that make it more useful in his work? Sounds like he could make a good leader. Things to ponder in any case – what we do in life reflects back on who we are.

If you think adventure is dangerous, try routine, it is lethal.

– Paulo Coelho

5

The Making of a Framing Crew

A great leader never sets himself above his followers except in carrying responsibilities. – Jules Ormont

To see a good framing crew in action is an awesome sight. There are no wasted movements and no dilly dallying around. Everybody is purposefully involved in their tasks. There is very little talking as the team moves from one phase to the next. They follow the well-worn sequence of a tried-and-true production system. In a good crew, I find it difficult to spot the quarterback because he appears to be just one of the team. In truth, on a good framing crew, there is little need of direction as they have all been down this road many times before together. They know what comes next and how it will be done. It may be a different house on a different lot on a different day but the puzzle goes together in the same consistent manner. It is only at night that you might be able to spot their fearless leader by peering through the window of his study to observe him reviewing the plans and mentally prepping for the next stage. Efficiency in action on the jobsite arises from the solid preparation done beforehand.

During my days as a piecemeal roof stacker in the Los Angeles housing tracks, I worked solo. Each day I would arrive at the house whose roof I was to stack that day and begin by taking all the cut rafters situated on the cutting rack and standing them up around the house where they would be installed. If there where hip or valley jacks, I would preset toenails at the head cuts and hang them on the CJs or top plate near where they would be installed. Next, I would disassemble the cutting racks to use as my ridges, mark them with rafter layout, and lean them up off the ends of the building. I then set a toenail in one corner of all the precut frieze blocks and hung them around the building's perimeter inside the top plate. I also preset toenails on all my gable studs and hung them where they were to be installed. I nailed up sway sticks at all the gable ends. I tossed some 2×4 studs up on top of the CJs to use for bracing materials. I then grabbed my Skilsaw and set it in a central location and hung its power cord from a CJ so I could pull it up to the roof area. After filling my left nail bag a third full, I grabbed the keg of 16d nails and set it up on the wall plate in a location that could be easily accessed, yet wasn't in the way. I did the same with my hand cooler that was full of cold Gatorade and frozen water bottles.

After all these steps, I climbed up top and started pulling up all the rafters to begin the stacking process. When they were all up on top of the CJs in an organized fashion, I would set up the two gable end common rafters at each of the sway stick locations and followed that up with a pair of floating commons situated just short of the end of each ridge section. These floaters had to be nailed well to a CJ so they could stay up on their own. We stackers got used to raising these setup commons into position by stepping with one foot on the tail and then nailing off the birdsmouth and driving a few nails into the adjacent CJ. Next, I would raise the ridge between the common rafter pair at the sway stick, followed by raising the end of the ridge at the floating commons. If the ridge was composed of several sections set end-to-end, I would extend each section with an additional pair of floating commons as I show in *A Roof Cutter's Secrets* Figure 6-9, pg. 116. I would then erect additional pairs of common rafters every 8 feet as needed to both stiffen and straighten the ridge. This was followed by installing the required vertical and sway braces along the ridges. And last, to finish off the roof skeleton, I installed any hips or valleys. I then ran all the gable studs including boxing out for the vent while I still had lots of room to work. Next came any valley fill. With all that done, I would work down one side of the ridge and pull up each successive common rafter to nail it to the ridge. The bottoms ends were left to float until the frieze blocks were run. With all the commons nailed at the ridge I would work around the house counterclockwise (because I am right handed) to install the frieze blocks and nail off the birdsmouths. Since the frieze blocks were all hung from a nail set in the top plate, it was easy to reach down and grab them with the claw of my hammer. When the last frieze block was installed, I was finished and I would make my way back down to ground level. Of course a hip roof would be set up slightly differently than described, but you get the idea. It was a flowing, easy sequence that never boxed me in.

Now imagine how much quicker and easier all that work could have been accomplished if it had been done as a team. I would have been able to maximize my time in the task of assembly while other guys did all the prep and support work. While I was darn efficient as a solo stacker, I still had to go back and forth from the birdsmouth to the ridge-cut to get my setup rafters in position, etc. These wasted movements would have been eliminated if I had a helper.

5-1 I am third from the left as part of OCC's 1976 record-setting heavyweight crew (photo 1975 – courtesty OCC Crew archives)

When I moved into the custom home framing market, I came to realize that two men working together can damn near accomplish anything. There is some unexplainable mathematical equation that occurs when guys "click" and somehow become a team that is greater than the sum of their individual parts. I first experienced this anomaly in my crew rowing days at Orange Coast College. **(fig 5-1)** Eight of us lanky troublemakers were thrown together in a long thin racing shell. While we may have come from varying backgrounds, we shared one common goal, and that was to put that boat across the finish line first. To do well, we had to mold eight individuals into one entity. In practice, we strove to do everything exactly the same. It would be like in a perfectly balanced V8 motor where each piston is moving in the exact same manner. This precise harmony is what gives the motor its smooth unhindered rhythm. There can be no variation whatsoever in cylinder performance if that motor is to achieve its maximum power. This same harmony is what is striven for in crew, and, if it is achieved, something magical happens and the boat seems to just levitate from the water and sprout wings. This phenomenon is what oarsmen call "swing." This graceful united movement causes the boat to suddenly lunge forward as if it was gliding on ice. I believe the famous crew boat builder George Pocock put it best when he said, "It's a great art, is rowing. It's the finest art there is. It's a symphony of motion. And when you're rowing well, why it's nearing perfection. And when you near perfection, you're touching the Divine. It touches the you of you. Which is your soul."

5-2 Davido Biesinger was my first partner when I started framing custom homes after leaving the LA tracts (photo 1979 – courtesy Davido Biesinger)

5-3 Sharper than a tack, Chuck Cline always had my back through the 1980s (photo 1980 – courtesy Chuck Cline)

My first opportunity to actually run a framing crew came when I was 18 years old. While I had worked as a laborer and apprentice carpenter on framing crews as a young man, I did not have the knowledge to move up the career ladder much. It was for this reason that I chose to attend the Orange Coast College construction program. During the summer break fitted in the middle of the two-year program, one of the instructors recommended three of us students to a gal who needed a big custom home built near Lake Elsinore, CA. I was lucky to be one of those three. The house had open beam ceilings throughout with 6×8 rough sawn rafters, 6×12 rough sawn ridges and purlins, and 2×6 T&G decking. While I was the youngest of the crew (the other two being recently returned Vietnam veterans), I quickly morphed into the leader because of my previous framing experience, and also because I had the best handle of how to calculate, cut, and assemble roofs. We knocked the job out in record time, and it was a great learning experience for each one of us. It was the first roof that I actually cut on my own. I remember having to use a chisel to help make all the seat-cuts because I didn't yet own a dado or swing-table saw. That experience not only fortified my goal to be a roof framer, but it clearly demonstrated that I had been blessed with innate lead carpenter skills. I suppose I should not have been that surprised since I had been selected as team captain for my high school varsity water polo team and then again captain for the Orange Coast College crew team. I would go on to lead men in the "hands-on" assembly of houses throughout my entire +40-year framing

5-4 Dave Sylvester and I worked together in Santa Barbara in the 1980s and in San Francisco East Bay in the 1990s–2000s (photo 1993 – courtesy Dave Sylvester)

career. I loved nothing better than to be out working together with a group of guys to make something special out of a pile of wood.

The famous bike racer Lance Armstrong once said "...no one ascends alone." How true. Without his US Postal Service teammates to "cut the wind" it would have been impossible for Lance to have accomplished what he did. The same has been true in my life. It was with the help of my framing partners that I did so well in the custom home framing market. Without those guys it is hard to say what might have happened to me. I have been blessed to have had some amazing partners – some on individual jobs as I traveled around the United States working on complicated roofs and others who stood by my side for years or even decades. When I was project foreman for Hal Benhardt Construction in the late 1970s, it was Davido Biesinger who had the task of keeping me out of trouble. **(fig 5-2)** Then throughout most of my time as a framing contractor in Santa Barbara, CA, during the 1980s, it was Chuck Cline who had my back. **(fig 5-3)** Chuck and I were like brothers and he never missed the opportunity to double check all my rafter LL calculations and my gang-cut layout before I cut. I strove to teach Chuck everything I knew, so he was sharp. My habit during the roof phase of any house was to always layout the rafters for the roof cut on a Saturday or Sunday when nobody was on the job, since I needed total concentration and focus for this task. During the normal work day, I was busy running the job so time alone was not possible. If the timing for the roof cut couldn't wait for the weekend, I either stayed late after a normal workday or sent the guys home early so I had the jobsite all to myself. Knowing this, Chuck would come in early the next morning and go over everything I had done. Then I would pull out the roof saws and we would have the roof cut in no time. Chuck's diligence saved my bacon more than once.

Dave Sylvester is another terrific guy with whom I have had the privilege to work. **(fig 5-4)** Shortly after I started my own framing company, I met

5-5 Ken Nichols and I framed so fast that the jobsite had a perpetual breeze because of our movement (photo 1995 – courtesy Ken Nichols)

Dave and we worked together for several years until he moved up to the East San Francisco Bay Area. It was after Dave left that I teamed up with Chuck Cline who stayed with me until I shut down my framing company due to injuries in the late 1980s and decided to hit the road as a freelance cutter. Funny how life can sometimes do a full circle, for little did I know that I would reunite with Dave in Northern California to help rebuild fancy homes in the Oakland Hills after the firestorm of 1991. There we would remain as partners for more than a decade but, only this time, the roles were reversed and he was the framing contractor or more accurately the general contractor since he did it all. I would run his framing jobs whenever I wasn't in Alaska.

It was while working for Dave that I met Ken Nichols. **(fig 5-5)** Ken was a bright young man just out of the Pittsburg High School construction program (Pittsburg, CA). Dave snapped him up and put the two of us together on all his projects. Ken was thoroughly amazing, not only did he pick up everything easily, but he had the same speed gene that I had, so we were soon competing to see how fast we could whip up any project. We became the best of friends and he helped me at several *JLC* Live roof framing clinics in the late 1990s. I believe we were together some 4 to 5 years before Ken went off and joined the dark side (building inspector). Ken eventually became dissatisfied with that government welfare job and headed off into other endeavors choosing to stay away from construction so as not to end up a physical wreck like I was.

So how does one form a good framing team? It is an interesting question that is a bit difficult for me to answer at this stage of my life, since leadership and team formation are intuitive and I do them at an unconscious level. Before today, I had never sat down to analyze or quantify it. There are many things written on teamwork in general, but nothing I could find was specific to forming a top-notch framing crew, so what follows are a few thoughts that I dredged up from the recesses of my subconscious.

I believe that first and foremost to forming a good crew is having a solid production system of assembly to follow. Without this you can put the best rough carpenters in the world together and they will only embarrass themselves. Everybody has to be on the same page. They have to understand and agree with the process. Without that, you are just spinning your wheels. Unfortunately, I see this all too often in real life. Great personal skill levels but dismal jobsite performance. There are many folks who never had the opportunity to learn an efficient assembly system or what they were taught was dismally inefficient. Of all that I was exposed to in the Los Angeles housing tracts, learning an efficient production framing system has been by far the most useful and important thing for my framing career. The system that I did learn had been refined by trial and error during the 1950s, 1960s, and 1970s as Los Angeles developed into the premiere home construction center of the world. I benefited greatly by the struggles of countless ingenious men who had toiled over several decades to develop a simple and efficient system. Unfortunately, a good system is something that one can only learn by doing. I can try to describe the correct flow through a framing project but, like learning a second language, it doesn't stick unless you are immersed in it on a day-to-day basis. The small ultra-important nuances are only caught as you work side-by-side with someone who knows them.

As a youngster I had to take 2 years of a foreign language to graduate from high school. Languages are very difficult for me. I guess my brain just isn't wired correctly for them. I took Spanish for my first year and was getting a "D" so I switched over to French for the second year in hopes that somehow I might do better in that language. Unfortunately I achieved the same poor results, but at least after the second year I had fulfilled the requirement and my suffering was over. In the 1990s, as more Latino workers entered the California construction market, I learned a few job-related Spanish terms in order to get by, but it wasn't until I went to Central America as a humanitarian aid volunteer in the 2000s and spent years immersed in the Spanish language and culture that I finally really did learn a bit of Spanish. Now, I may still struggle at times with the finer intricacies of Spanish, but at least I can communicate in most everyday situations. The Spanish phraseology that I learned incorrectly from the start has been the worst to erase and refit with the correct form. There are two lessons that I wish to share with you through this story. The first is that, to really learn a system, you must become a part of it – it cannot be learned from a book or video, although both of these can be an aid. And second, it is a bitch to unlearn something, so put the right stuff in your brain from the start. Individuals will absorb whatever they are taught, whether it is good or bad, so be very careful to only expose yourself to the best. If you learn a bad system, it will linger with you throughout your life since very few people are truly open minded enough to throw it off in order to relearn a better system. Your first exposure creates a lasting impression. So, if you are a young man thinking of starting a framing career, be very finicky about who you choose as your first employer. Watch various crews in action to see if you can find a fluid efficient team to join. Unfortunately, these crews are usually the same ones that rarely need anybody since they stay together for decades.

All through my time as a framing contractor in Santa Barbara, CA, we had guys coming by the jobsite hoping to join the crew. We had a good reputation for production and they wanted to learn our system. Not that I didn't want to teach them, but I rarely had space for a new guy since most of the time I ran with only four guys including myself and it was seldom that anyone left. Internally, I did sympathize with these guys knowing full well that, except for the Grace of God, I could very well be in their shoes and out looking to hook up with a good framing crew so I too could learn. I would always write down folk's names and contact information just in case a spot came up. In Santa Barbara, Paul Franz loved to hire me independently now and then to run his crew on some specific job just so his guys would have the opportunity to learn production techniques and methodology. Paul has always been a pretty savvy builder and he has done a lot of trick stuff. I always had fun working with his guys, and I am sure I spiced up their lives a bit.

You can always tell a crew that has a poor production system since they have a ton of lumber cutoffs left over at the end of the job and they spend weeks on "pickup" projects. Lots of cutoff scraps show that they do not know how to order material wisely or use it efficiently. Many days or weeks of pickup show they do not follow things through step-by-step to completion but instead move ahead in an unorganized fashion, leaving much undone to be finished up later. The habit of backtracking is a huge waste of time and much slower than if one would have spent a few more minutes on it when you were there initially. For example, it is much faster to frame in for a medicine closet before the wall is stood because you are right there with the wood and tools rather than save it to do later after the house has been sheathed. If it is done as "pickup," not only must a carpenter drag his tools and some wood back to that spot again, but framing in a stood wall is more time consuming. So, the two things to identify an inefficient crew are the size of their jobsite dumpster and how much time they spend doing pickup after the walls and roof are sheathed. In the Los Angeles housing tracts, we rarely had more than a block or two left over at the end of a phase – they were that tight on their lumber orders. The lumber drops were never unbanded until they were to be used and that material went up fast so as not to allow it to sit around and twist up in the hot sun. The tract developers only moved wood used for a specific phase to the house site. For example, they did not drop the rafters, fascia, roof sheathing, etc. together but rather brought each one of these to the site the evening before it was to be used. Of course, on a custom home this may not always be possible, but I did try to use this methodology as much as I could when I was a framing contractor. I preferred smaller more frequent drops as opposed to a big drop that had to be broken down. This also gave me a better chance to look over the wood they were delivering to make sure they hadn't buried some junk in it. I had no problem rejecting a load if I found bad boards, and I did this as often as needed until the lumberyard realized I only wanted the best quality. Good wood allows you to frame much faster. If I did have to have a combo drop, I told the lumber yard the order I wanted the material loaded on the truck. They might have complained some, but they always came through, even though at times they may have had to throw a few extra-long boards on the bottom of the stack as a sacrifice when they rolled the load off the truck. I had them drop lifts of plywood at various locations around the jobsite to facilitate our team's performance. A good driver had no problems with any of this. Of course a telehandler can make easy work of moving lumber around the jobsite, but back then they weren't all that common, only having been invented in the late 1970s. It would take several decades before they found their way into usage on small individual custom home jobs, and, then again, for steep jobsites like we faced in the Oakland Hills, they served little purpose.

The second most important facet of a good framing crew is choosing the correct team members. Think of the selection process the US Navy has in place to identify the guys for its SEAL teams. They test the living daylights out of these volunteers, not only to see who can survive the hell of war, but also to find the guys who are team players, who are unselfish, who are flexible and teachable, who remain positive, who never give up, who maintain attention to detail, and who finish what they start. Aside from the ability to survive the hell of war, I believe those same characteristics make a good list of the qualities one would hope that each member of his framing crew might possess.

The responsibility of identifying the right carpenter to fit into the crew lies squarely on the shoulders of the team leader. Every leader probably does this differently, but I subconsciously size up a guy by the way he approaches me. Does he come with an ego pushing how good a framer he is, or is he a humble type of guy who prefers to let his hammer do his talking? I ask him if he was ever a tract framer. If he tells me he was, I ask him what he did and give me a quick rundown on his chore. I ask him what was the piece price per square foot for his task. If he stumbles there, he is gone. It's amazing how many say they were tract framers to puff up their employment appeal, but really weren't or tried it once. I could care less if they were or weren't, but what I do want is honesty and integrity. Someone with character. I can help anyone get the skills they need to be a hotshot, but these two traits they have to throw in the bucket. Has he ever been injured? Anybody who has ever spent any time "hands-on" as a framer has been injured at one point or another in their career. It's just the facts of life. The longer one is involved in framing, the more injuries to expect. How did the injury happen? Was he careless? Does he admit it? It shows character to take responsibility for one's actions. Has he been a part of a custom framing crew before? You can call his former boss to check out how that worked out. If he hasn't been on a framing crew before, did he play team sports? You need a team player not a ball hog. Who are his friends? Who they are will show you a good deal about who he is. How is he dressed? Not that he has to be all fancied up or anything but is he wearing clothes that show he is used to working outside in a hot, sweaty, production environment (shorts, T-shirt, as compared with jeans, long-sleeve shirt)? Not that you can't be a great framer wearing jeans, but jeans do restrict movement jumping around the rafters and I really don't want to be pulling your ass off the roof because you are having heat exhaustion issues. Maybe he comes from a union environment where these are part of the required dress code. Ask him about it. Are his shoes good for walking rafters or does he show up with big, heavy, steel-toed work boots that are better suited for a commercial union job than a residential custom home? As I discussed in the chapter "A Man and His Truck," one can glean a great deal about a potential crew member's character by the truck he drives. Is it flashy or is it utilitarian? Is it well maintained or does it look disheveled? How about the condition of his tools – are they clean and well taken care of? Is his pickup organized? These kinds of things will tell you about the way he thinks and the kind of work you can expect from him. People don't act one way in life and then change into a different kind of person on the job. If they show attention to detail in other areas of their life, it's a good bet they will also do the same on the job. Are his nail bags what you would expect to see a decent framer wearing? Do they look worn to fit with the number of years he claims to have worked in the trade. What kind of hammer does he swing – a smooth or corrugated head? What kinds of framing reference books does he own? If he is serious about his trade he will have some resources that he keeps on hand. How much did he earn on his last job? What does he want to earn working on my crew? Does the wage he request seem appropriate for his experience level? If it is ridiculous, it all ends right there. If a guy can show me he is good, I have no problem paying him what he is worth. What is his primary motivation for the job – to earn money or to do a good job? That reminds me of a story I once heard about a gentleman who was walking down the sidewalk and happened to pass three block masons working on a job. As he passed each one he asked them what they were doing. The first responded that he was laying block, the second responded that he was earning money, but the third responded that he was "building a cathedral." You want your guys to be like the third mason. "One person with passion is better than forty people merely interested." – E. M. Forster

All the things I noted help provide little clues that will help you identify the right person. Of course, there is nothing like observing him work a little bit to see what his skill level is. I typically like to give a new guy a simple task like running some frieze blocks. That gives me the chance to see his hammer-and-saw skills and whether he is good up in the air. I do this out of the corner of my eye so he won't know I am watching hm. To him, I look like I am just going about my business. My very first concern with a new guy is whether or not he is a safe worker. I will know almost immediately if he was fibbing or not about his framing experience. If he has trouble with that task when he shouldn't – he goes home. If he does OK, then I pair him up with one of my long-time guys like Chuck Cline on something and wait for Chuck to give me feedback later in the day. New guys can feel a lot of pressure to perform, and I want to lessen that stress so they can relax and do well. I find it best if I am somewhat out of the picture for a new guy's first day so he has the chance to get used to everybody. Many times, a new carpenter comes on the recommendation of someone who is already on the crew. I find this works fairly well since the crew member already knows him well enough to know if he will be a good fit. Every crew member realizes that their own reputation is on the line when they recommend someone so they are darn careful who they send my way. Likewise, occasionally, another contractor I knew would send a guy my way knowing he might be a good fit.

Sorry to all the gals out there that I never say "he/she." I am not trying to leave you out. It is just that in my lifetime I have never had a woman on my crew (with the exception of my wife helping out a time or two), nor has a gal ever even come by the jobsite looking for a job. I am sure there are many gals out there who are superb and would be a great addition to any team. Framing is hard, physically demanding work that requires a good amount of upper body strength and outstanding balance. One must not be afraid to work up high in very exposed conditions. Could it be that gals just prefer other aspects of construction? I don't know. Although I have known gals who have worked as masons, iron workers, and trim carpenters, I have never yet met a female framer.

To choose a laborer I always chose the biggest, strongest, fittest guys who came by the jobsite. Guys who have a passion for lifting weights and doing exercise. Guys that enjoy hauling stuff around the jobsite and see it as a strength-building opportunity. Guys who would almost pay me to be out there on a real-life "CrossFit" gym all day long. I had that same mentality when I was younger and worked as a laborer, so I can spot a compatriot from a mile away. I have had many memorable laborers. For example, one was a former middle linebacker for the University of Oklahoma Sooners – some 245 lbs of solid muscle. He could move wood like no one I have ever seen. He would run (not walk) with a big stack of 2×12s FJs on his shoulder to get them to where they were needed. He was also the Santa Barbara wrist wrestling champ. I wrestled him for fun one time and there is certainly no need to tell you how that ended up. He helped us out for a few years and then got a job climbing trees for a tree trimming company. I always liked to slide laborers into carpentry work when they weren't needed to move materials around. If they had the aptitude for carpentry I would move them up in the team. This is what had happened in my life and, being eternally grateful for that opportunity when younger, I wanted to offer the same to as many young men as were interested.

The third most important facet of a framing crew at all levels is humility. A competitive spirit is a good thing to have on the job, and since most carpenters were some type of athlete when younger, it is just part of our makeup. We need competition to get the blood flowing, but when someone starts pushing that they are better than others on the crew or that the success of the crew is because of them – team spirit will be destroyed faster than anything else I know of. While carpenter skill levels and framing knowledge will always vary within any crew , each and every person is important and is essential to the overall success of the team no matter what position they hold. This brings to mind a Scripture:

"As it is, there are many parts, but one body. The eye cannot say to the hand, ' "I don't need you!" ' And the head cannot say to the feet, ' "I don't need you!" ' On the contrary, those parts of the body that seem to be weaker are indispensable, and the parts that we think are less honorable, we treat with special honor. And the parts that are unpresentable are treated with special modesty, while our presentable parts need no special treatment. But God has put the body together, giving greater honor to the parts that lacked it so that there should be no division in the body, but that its parts should have equal concern for each other. If one part suffers, every part suffers with it; if one part is honored, every part rejoices with it." (*1 Corinthians* 12:20–26)

It is the responsibility of the leader to mesh the crew and assign tasks in such a manner as to make each individual know that he is vital to the success of the project. There is nothing like a few positive comments to let folks know how good a job they are doing and how much you appreciate their efforts. I believe a good leader will have a real willingness to teach each crew member as much as they have an interest or yearning to learn. This has always been my personal standard operating procedure (SOP). If you ask me about something we will look at it together when we can. I have always wanted everyone that I come in contact with whether on my crew or otherwise to end up as a better carpenter, roof framer, or man than I ever was. I do not fear that I might be training up a competitor who will go head-to-head with me for a job down the road. Let the cards fall as they may but I do not hold anything back so that I can have an edge. In *A Roof Cutter's Secrets* I shared all that I know technically, and now in this book I share all that I know practically. So, if you master everything in *A Roof Cutter's Secrets* you will be as good or better roof cutter and stacker than I ever was, and if you learn from the mistakes I share in this book, you certainly will be wiser.

Back in the mid-1990s, Dan Daley of Bend, OR, contacted me asking if I was available to do some roof-framing tutoring. He had tracked me down using the contact information found in the 1988 edition of *A Roof Cutter's Secrets*. I told him that I would be happy to help him out. So after finishing the summer flying season in Alaska and on my way back to the Bay Area to work, I stopped in and spent the afternoon with Dan. When we met I came to find out that he had spent the first part of his framing career working for various high-end builders in Beverly Hills, CA. Now, he was a framing contractor in Bend, OR. We worked together on determining ridge beam and tall wall heights, and calculating various rafter lengths. Dan easily absorbed it all. To this day, I still believe he had most of it already wired but just lacked a bit of self-confidence. It is a lonely place when there is no one else around of the same caliber to verify that what you are doing is correct. Dan just needed that little confidence booster before he started taking on these big complicated jobs where he might be cutting up $20,000 to $30,000 worth of roof-framing material. My time with Dan underscored just how important and reassuring it is to have a guy of your same caliber on the crew to back you up. Dan told me about his struggle to find someone to teach him roof framing in the early 1990s. Already an accomplished framer, he wanted to better his roof-framing skills, so he found a well-known builder in Los Angeles who just happened to be a very talented roof cutter and offered to work for him cheap on the premise that the gentleman would teach him to cut roofs. Dan told me that he busted his butt working for the guy but, in the end, got very little out of it. The guy didn't teach him much. I guess, after seeing how hard Dan worked, the guy was scared that Dan might end up

5-6 Dan Daley was a framer in Beverly Hills, CA before relocating his business to Central Oregon (photo 2002)

being his competition so he decided to hold back. Anyway, Dan and I became good friends and as a result I had the opportunity to work with him on many fun challenging jobs in Central Oregon. **(fig 5-6)** Moral of the story – share what God has blessed you with. It is a gift to everybody – it is not yours to keep – you are just the vehicle the Man above chose to deliver it through. This was laid on my heart as a young man, and I have always felt a responsibility to pass it along. I am only a runner in a relay race. Someone handed the baton to me and I have done what I could with it, but there is a guy right ahead of me to whom I must pass it on.

The fourth and final thought on what makes a good crew is that a good crew will always have a great leader. "If you build an army of a 100 lions and their leader is a dog, in any fight, the lions will die like a dog. But if you build an army of a 100 dogs and their leader is a lion, all dogs will fight like a lion." – Napoleon Bonaparte. A framing crew is nothing more than a direct reflection of their leader. If you have a disorganized, undisciplined, close-minded, or lazy leader you will find his crew to be the same. If you have a strong, honest, goal-oriented, disciplined, hard-working, and productive leader, his crew will be the same. This can be seen in framing companies like SR Freeman (San Jose, CA), or Daley Construction (Bend, OR), plus many others. Amazing crews reflect an amazing man at the top. They do not exist in isolation. Not only does this principle apply to framing companies but also to any individually directed labor or production oriented business where the boss came up through the ranks just like everyone else and built a company by the sweat of his brow. If a company has the reputation for doing great work on time with a fair pricing system, you can bet this comes from the stellar character of the leader. Likewise, poor crew performance reflects a leader that is struggling in his position. Not all guys have the makeup to be a leader. This is not to say anything against them but just to speak the truth. Some guys are better suited as followers. Success depends on both parts – leaders and followers. I find it sad when a guy thinks he has great leadership qualities when all the evidence around him suggests otherwise. He blames everyone and everything else for the failures of his crew rather than being introspective.

It is my belief that a good leader always leads from the front and he should always outperform everyone else on his crew. He is the example to follow. My vision of a good leader has him moving along so purposefully that everyone else is nearly running just to keep up. Throughout my framing career, I have pushed myself in hopes of fulfilling this vision. There are lots of guys stronger and more talented than I am, but after doing everything I could to better myself in both of those areas, what I counted on to pull me over the top was working harder than anyone else. I have never allowed anyone to outwork me. That same philosophy I have used as an athlete and in most other aspects of my life. "When you can't beat 'em – outwork 'em." Even as an old man I would challenge the young bucks to try to outdo me. It was a good way to motivate them. They certainly didn't want the stigma of being outdone by an old man. I remember leading a three-man crew on a project to frame up four small Dutch Hip roofed houses when I was in my mid-50s. My two teammates were young guys in their 20s. They had little carpentry experience, but they worked hard and always gave their best effort. That is all I have ever asked of anybody. My focus on this job was to teach them Western style production framing. They picked it up pretty well. In the end, it only took the three of us 31 days to frame the 4 houses and that included moving all the lumber from more than 1/4 mile away to the building site by a 4×4 truck. Now, if you take into account that we had no nail-gun or compressor and these houses were raised floor dwellings with both the floor and the roof sheathed using exposed 1×4 T&G – we were moving. An experienced Canadian framer arrived to give us a hand by installing the siding and build the decks. After watching us for a day, he commented to the contractor that the lead carpenter (me) was worth about four journeymen. I heard about the comment later on and thanked the gentleman for his kind words. It is doubtful I was worth four journeymen, but the point was that he was very impressed with the speed and efficiency with which we moved as a team and got our tasks done. That was probably the last job I was really able to go full speed because, within a few years, my long list of accumulated injuries forced me out of the trades.

A good leader sets the tone for the job. If you set a cheerful happy tone, morale is high and everybody looks forward to putting in a good day's work. (fig 5-7) Attitude is a choice. Work should be fun and the camaraderie of the

5-7 A happy crew. Donald Murphy (standing, wh sitting) started as a laborer and ended up a contractor. (photo 1995)

job was a big reason I stayed in framing so very long after my prime. My crew simply loved what they did. I never had to deal with anyone showing up late. They usually beat me to the job and had the cords strung out before I even arrived. It was a daily challenge on my jobs to see who could come up with the wittiest comment or the brightest idea to speed up some framing process. Whoever did so got the imaginary gold star for the day. Break time was for goofing around and most took advantage of it. **(fig 5-8)** Some of the crew liked to throw the football around while others like me tried to get in a quick cat nap after scarfing down a sandwich. I have no idea where they found all the energy. One of the few guys I ever fired had a bit of trouble turning off the goofing around when it was time to get back to work. Goofing around on the job is not only counterproductive, but it is also a good way for someone to get hurt. After a few days of being unemployed, the fired carpenter asked for a second chance, which I gave him, and the situation never happened again. In fact, he turned into one hell of a good contractor in the San Diego area some 7 to 8 years later.

A crew leader has to be understanding, because guys bring their private problems to the jobsite. They don't intend to do so, but when you spend more time on the job than at home, it is bound to find its way to the surface eventually. Trouble at home definitely affects one's jobsite performance and it is easy to spot. One day a guy is superman and bounding around the jobsite, while another day he has no spirit and is just going through the motions. Sometimes it is a temper flare-up by someone who is usually cool as a cucumber. I remember one time a carpenter yelling and throwing his hammer when I asked him to do something. Totally unlike him and the kind of behavior I would never allow on the crew. I let him be for a while and within 10 minutes he came by to apologize and say it would never happen again. He explained that he had just had a huge problem with his son the previous night

5-8 Break time vertical-jump competition in the Oakland Hills 1995 (left to right: Ken, Dave, Will)

and his head was all messed up. He asked for some time off to deal with it, which of course I gave him. I ended up gaining even more respect for him as a result of that incident, for he showed a lot of character to recognize an error and seek a pardon. A weaker man would prefer to just pretend it didn't happen. Sometimes I would end up being a counselor to try and help someone deal with a stressful situation. I can sympathize with guys facing many problems, because I myself have faced a boatload of personal issues that have brought me to my knees. The support of the guys on the crew is what pulled me through, especially Chuck who could always read me like a book anyhow. He and his wife Jennifer would go out of their way to help drag me through a rough spot. That is one couple that I have no doubts cares a great deal about me. Many times a guy just needs a little encouragement. I recently saw the skilled manager of a paving company reaffirm one of his supervisors who was struggling with self-doubt as a result of an error he had made on a job. It reminded me of how Our Lord in *John* 21:15–19 had reinstated Peter after he had screwed up big time by denying Him three times before the crucifixion. I learned a lot from just watching how the manager handled the situation.

Rest breaks are not only a time to get some nourishment and rest but also a time for developing crew camaraderie. In the Los Angeles housing tracts, breaks and lunch were your own thing, and I rarely stopped until I finished the roof I was working on. I preferred to just work right on through and get it done. But as a contractor or lead for a contractor, California labor law dictated that a worker must receive one paid 10-minute rest break for every 4 hours worked and a nonpaid 1/2-hour lunch break in a normal 8-hour work day. This time arrangement made little sense to me since, if you were up high on the roof, it might take you 5 minutes just to get down to the break area for your 10-minute rest break. So I did a little modifying to this absurd routine. What I did was combine the two 10-minute breaks together with the half-hour lunch period and then divided that 50-minute amount in half to create two 25-minute lunch breaks. A 25-minute rest/lunch period actually provides enough time to recoup a bit from heavy physical exertion. The other thing I did was to set the first of these two break periods at 10:00 a.m. while the second break period is set at 1:00 p.m. These break times are set for a work day that starts at 7:00 a.m. and ends at 3:30 p.m. By setting the lunch breaks on this schedule the time between breaks is progressively shortened to better match the growing exhaustion a worker is experiencing. When you first arrive on the job at 7:00 a.m., you are fresh from a long night's rest (I always got 9 hours of shut eye), so the first work period is 3 hours in length. The second work period shortens up a bit to 2.5 hours in length, while the last work period when you are the most exhausted is only 2 hours long. I have found this lunch break schedule to be unmatched in enhancing performance in the afternoon when guys normally start to drag. Of course, you better have eaten breakfast before you show up on the job or you will run out of steam long before the first break at 10:00 a.m. Just about everyone that has tried this break schedule ended up loving it once they got accustomed to it. I have noticed many other framing crews over the years have gone with the same or a similar schedule.

I am a guy who hates to be bothered by outside distractions so the big billboard sign on the work gates leading into the Los Angles housing tracts that said "No Drugs, No Dogs, No Radios" fit me to a tee. In those days the "No Drugs" referred to marijuana or speed. While I don't believe marijuana was ever smoked on the job because you would get silly headed and probably kill yourself, speed was probably used frequently by many of the guys just back from Vietnam where it was often used as a staple to keep oneself alive. Being an athlete, I had nothing to do with either. Of course, it was universally accepted that alcohol was prohibited while working, but it was not specifically restricted in the same sense as the other three, seeing how construction workers often had a tailgate party at the end of the day to share a "cold one." On all my jobs as a framing contractor I followed this same Los Angeles housing tract doctrine. There is nothing I hate worse than trying to compete with a radio while trying to communicate with someone. When I ran jobs for other contractors I often had to mellow up a bit on my "No Radio" restriction just to keep the peace, but I held on to the power to nix the channel if it was giving me a headache or shut it off completely if it was detrimental to the

5-9 Gusty Shone Freeman directs one of the San Francisco Bay Area's largest custom home framing companies (photo 1995 – courtesy Shone Freeman)

advancement of the project. I came to realize that many guys are simply addicted to having a radio going all the time and can't function well if they couldn't have their fix. I, on the other hand, love peace and quiet.

How does one decide how much to pay each crew member? For me it has been fairly easy: I typically just pay them what they ask. You might think I am crazy, but by choosing a crew member with true character from the start he will not cite some unreasonable amount. The wage for a journeyman carpenter or laborer in any area is pretty much common knowledge so most guys will typically just ask for this. I found that many guys of character undervalue themselves. If he doesn't want to offer up an ideal wage, I give him a middle-of-the-road wage and tell him that we will revisit it after we have had the chance to see how he works out. I have always tried to be more than fair with folks' pay. I personally believe that a rough carpenter's wages are way too low for the danger he faces, A carpenter will never get compensated for the joints and body parts he wears out or damages. Plumbers and electricians make a ton more money and face much less bodily damage or jobsite risk. Is their work any more valuable than a framer's?

While I always ran a small hand-picked crew and never took on more than one custom home framing job at a time, Shone Freeman's or Dave Saunder's framing companies operate/ed on another level entirely. **(figs 5-9, 5-10)** They typically have/had a bunch of jobs going on at the same time and a hierarchy of administration. Dave ran about 176 framers from his Hyannis, MA, based company and focused on prefabbing huge shopping centers, while Shone runs a similar amount from his San Jose, CA, base and focuses on difficult high-end custom homes. Shone generally starts any newly employed

5-10 Prefab genius Dave Saunders ran a huge framing company in Massachusetts and was my boss at National Lumber (photo 1990 – courtesy Dave Saunders)

journeyman at a middle-of-the-road locally accepted wage, but provides a stair-step structure for all his employees to achieve higher pay based on a combination of seniority, jobsite performance evaluations, and participation in free training classes that he offers on pertinent jobsite framing subjects. While I am sure there are other companies that operate similar training gigs for their framers, Shone's company is the only private enterprise that I know of personally who does this. Shone wants his framers to learn more so they can take on greater responsibility. He needs lead carpenters. It is pretty cut and dry with Shone – the more you know and get done, the more you get paid. I like that philosophy since, as a piecemeal framer, I have always preferred "pay for performance" over an hourly arrangement. Several years back I had the opportunity to teach a roof-framing course for Shone's crew. Talk about a motivated group. About 35 guys showed up on their own time for three Saturdays in a row. Everyone had a great time as we combined classroom discussion with hands-on practice.

I arrived at an unusual place in the Santa Barbara framing environment. When I initially got my contractor's license in California in 1979, I did what most framing contractors normally do and started bidding labor on jobs. As anyone who has ever worked in construction knows, labor is the most difficult thing to estimate since it is so personnel dependent. While I had run crews for many years at that point, I had little knowledge of actual costs. I just got my check every Friday and that was the extent of it. Money wasn't an issue with me. Anyhow, I won my first job bid and the job went well, but I was stressed out the whole time. I had just put together a crew and was unsure how we would perform. As a poor boy, my fear was that if I underestimated the cost of framing the project, I would earn zip and might even owe money. Some guys thrive on it, but not me. I am just a carpenter and my motivation is to do the best job possible in the least amount of time. I didn't like coming up with some numeric guess and then living with the stress and insomnia until the job was done. Probably pretty bad for my health.

I typically spent 40 hours (4 days) calculating a framing labor bid and assembling the lumber list for a big complicated 6000-square-foot custom home. It takes me a long time, because I am the type of guy who actually prebuilds the whole house in my head before I even snap a line. When I show up on the jobsite I just walk through everything physically that I have already gone through by mental visualization. Now the general contractor (GC) would take my lumber list and bid it out, then add that material bid plus my labor bid together with the bids from his other subcontractors, then tack on his percentage and toss that final number into the ring with a bunch of other GCs who had just done the same thing. Only if my GC wins the bid would I get the framing job. If my GC doesn't win the job, I would have just wasted four days mentally building the house. I didn't like this system, so I very simply stopped bidding. Since I had a fairly good reputation in town, I just told everybody that I would do the job for the actual wage costs of my crew and left it at that. They could throw in their own number and live with the stress but mine was gone. If I was smart I would have said "cost plus" but I wasn't and I didn't. But believe me, for the next decade that I operated my framing company (Will Holladay & Co.) we were never out of work more than a week between jobs. The GCs got the best work for the lowest cost, so they certainly had no complaints. I even stopped doing employee wage-related paperwork and put that and the required Workman's Compensation insurance on the GC as well. I simply had him put each of us on his payroll. I just gave him the weekly hours and wage for each employee when it was time to get paid. Before this, I was having to pull off the jobsite midday on Friday just to get all that crap done. I much preferred being on the job with the guys all day Friday and have the weekends open to head up to the Sierras to work as a Whitewater guide rather than be buried in administration and bidding. I realized that I was not a business man and never would be in spite of taking classes at Santa Barbara City College on the subject. Like I said earlier, some guys will never be good leaders and it follows that some guys like me will never be good businessmen. It's just not in their genes. Wise is the man who focuses on his strengths rather than dwells on his weaknesses. My father died of a heart attack at a young age, and only God knows if work-related stress would have done the same to me.

If you always hire people who are smaller than you are, we shall become a company of dwarfs. If on the other hand you hire people who are bigger than you are, we shall become a company of giants.

– David Ogilvy (Chairman Ogilvy & Mather)

6

Roof Cutters – a flash in time

Every man loves what he is good at. – Thomas Shadwell

Production roof framing is a fun subject that tickles the fancy of most rough framers. Sadly, it is only ancient history now, but I was blessed to have caught the tail end of it as a young carpenter. Just about everyone from that time period is either in the ground or soon will be. Roof trusses, which had first been introduced into home construction in the late 1950s, became the universal roof-framing methodology by the late 1970s and, like the magician waving his wand in a disappearing act, production roof cutting was no more. It had spanned only a brief 25- to 30-year period, but the procedures we learned from that time period will live on and on. Nowadays, I do occasionally hear young fellas self-proclaim themselves "roof cutters," and I must admit that I do get a kick out of it because I have a totally different concept of the title. To me a "roof cutter" is like one of the twelve apostles – they were here during a special time that has since come and gone – there will be no more. This is not to discount modern-day carpenters who cut roof rafters, it is just to say that when the job title "roof cutter" was first coined, it had a much different connotation. A journeyman carpenter cutting the roof rafters on an individual building project could in no way be compared to an individual whose specialized daily task was only gang-cutting rafters. While the named journeyman carpenter may be exceptionally skilled with complex roof construction, he could never equal the speed and efficiency of the mass production techniques used by the tract "roof cutters" who typically cut 3 to 4 house roofs per day.

The history of production roof cutting and thus "roof cutters" is inevitably tied to the events of the mid-20th century. During World War II the federal government was the driving force in the housing market. It required over 2 million new housing units for factory employees, shipyards workers, military personnel, etc. The vast majority of these units were out in California as dozens of new military installations were added in both Northern and Southern California. Building materials were restricted from being used in private projects and redirected to the wartime effort. Because of the "need for speed," the centuries-old method of having a team of carpenters build one house from start to finish went by the wayside and an industrialized methodology was adopted. Up until World War II, the standard builder did a maximum of 4 houses per year with only a few of the largest developers finishing more than 10 per year. By applying lessons learned in the factory production of wartime ships and aircraft, the wartime builders were able to swell their completion numbers to 400 homes a year. Since one couldn't very well put a house on a factory assembly line and move it from one work station to the next, these tract developers had their "work stations" move from one house to the next in timed precision.

The huge migration of folks to California for war-related work changed Los Angeles into the nation's second largest industrial production center behind Detroit by 1945. My family was one of those who relocated from Virginia to Los Angeles in order to work in the aerospace industry. Originally mostly an agriculture-based economy, California became the largest producer of ships and aircraft during the war years. This population influx combined with both stark private housing construction stretching from the Great Depression to the end of World War II (16 years: 1929–1945) and all the baby boomer births (such as mine), created the perfect storm for the colossal California housing crisis after the war. Those same building developers who had been called on to handle the government's housing shortfall during the war now found themselves in a perfect situation to do the same for the private sector. It would take 30 years from the mid-1940s to the mid-1970s to overcome the housing deficit, and, during this period, some 6 million housing units (including 3.5 million single-family homes) were built in California as its population tripled to become the nation's most populous state, with the Los Angeles basin receiving the brunt of this increase. While the East Coast would see some population growth after World War II, it saw no boom like California, and, for this reason, the development of the same type of mass production mentality lagged behind the West Coast. It should also be noted that the 33,954 square miles of the greater Los Angeles metropolitan area was especially conducive to massive tract style development since it was generally a flat landscape consisting of huge parcels of open or agricultural land that could easily be converted to residential use. Throughout this 30-year boom-build period, the typical housing tract development size in Los Angeles ranged between 250 and 400 homes, but there were many that contained from 500 to 1000 homes. The first stage of **Dave Bohannon's**

San Lorenzo Village tract development (San Francisco East Bay Area) was 3000 homes. It is reported that some developers refined the production system so well they were able to finish one house every 45 minutes (*Tract Housing in California: 1945–1973*. California Department of Transportation; 2011).

Through the simplification of labor tasks, the contractors were able to assemble the needed manpower for these large projects. Whereas it took many years of apprenticeship to train up a journeyman tradesman, it was relatively easy to teach an individual some singular assembly task that he would repeat over and over thousands of times on near-identical buildings. This near-instantaneous expansion of available labor permitted the experienced craftsmen to be assigned to the more complex tasks. As a result of this specialization, tract workers became absolute masters in one assembly or production task. Tract carpenters like all other tract construction tradesmen were paid by the piece – a price per square foot to do a certain task. For example: $0.05 a square foot to snap, plate, and detail; $.08 cents to stand walls; $.04 cents a square foot to cut rafters, etc. (mid-1970s prices). With pay for performance as the incentive, tract workers could make some big bucks if they were fast. To save time, tract carpenters thought up new techniques, found short-cuts, modified existing tools to do something more efficiently, and invented new tools. While many recognize Dave Bohannon of the San Francisco Bay Area as the father of tract style production building, the Los Angeles basin, by its sheer volume of projects, became the center of tradesman ingenuity. From within the Los Angeles housing tracts arose almost all the specialty framing tools we use today: bolt markers, layout sticks, wall intersection markers, framing hammers, saw hangers, dado saws, beam saws, etc.

I have shared much on the tools and techniques of production roof cutting over the years, but no book of mine would be complete if I didn't at least touch on the subject a bit – so just for "kicks and grins," let's take another stroll down memory lane. Although I personally can only speak about production roof cutting beginning with my first involvement in it during the mid-1970s, the information I share about the preceding several decades was gleamed from the old-time "roof cutters" with whom I worked, plus from my long-time friend Nate Fletcher of Nate's Saw Shop (Anaheim, CA). Nate, who retired in the 1980s, was responsible for modifying many of the saws used for gang-cutting rafters during the Los Angeles building boom years, so he had as good a handle on the subject and timing of it all as anyone.

During and immediately following World War II, the typical method that was used to manufacture rafters in the large tract home developments was to set up a cut station with several Delta 18-inch or 20-inch radial arm saws and gang-cut several handfuls of vertically stacked 2×4 or 2×6 rafters at a time. **(fig 6-1)** While a single blade with the bevel set to the roof pitch was used

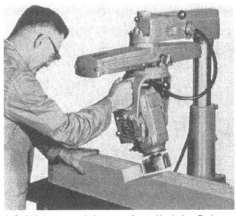

6-1 In early production days a Delta radial arm saw was used to gang-cut rafter head-cuts (photo 1952 Operators guide)

6-2 With a special cutter installed the Delta radial arm saw also gang-cut birdsmouth notches (photo 1952 Operators guide)

to make the ridge-cut, a special rafter notch-cutting head (4-inch diameter wood shaper carrying 4 cutter blades) was installed on the big saw to make the birdsmouth notch. This cutting head spun vertically like a router blade. **(fig 6-2)** It was reported that Dave Bohannon's rafter-cutting yard in the previously mentioned San Lorenzo Village tract was able to put out 700 rafters per hour in the late 1940s. The only downside to this speedy method was that the lengthy lumber had to be moved twice, once to deliver it to the cutting station and then from there moved to each individual home building site after it had been fitted with a birdsmouth notch and ridge-cut.

Since tract builders are all about efficiency, they desired to make the production cutting of rafters a moving "work station" type chore eliminating the extra material-moving step. But, to do this, specialized hand portable saws would need to be devised to substitute for the work done by the esteemed Delta radial arm saws. It made no sense to move them from house to house. Since nothing suitable could be found in the market place, the genius of American industry soon had what was needed. As far as I can tell, it was around the early to mid-1950s when production roof cutting took a big step forward with the adaptation of the Skil 117 Groover to be used for the home site gang-cutting of rafter birdsmouths. The Groover was a portable 18-amp worm drive electric saw that sported a 2-inch-wide by 7-inch-diameter dado set. **(figs 6-3, 6-4)** It appears to have been based on the Skil 114 (an early version of the 107), which was a 10-inch worm drive circular saw. The 117 had been designed specifically for electricians so that they could cut square notches in beams or joists to run knob-and-tube style wiring. While the 117 had retained the same saw-foot with bevel adjustment system of the 10-inch worm drive, its purpose only required a vertical depth

6-3 A modified Skil 117 Groover allowed gang-cutting rafters to become a homesite task in the 1950s

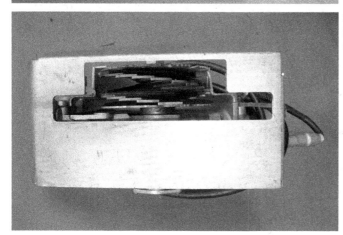

6-4 The Groover sported a 2-inch-wide by 7-inch-diameter dado blade set

adjustment, so its side-tilting movement was restricted by an enveloping top blade guard design. It only took some minor modifications to the top blade guard (it had no lower guard) for the bevel adjustment to be brought into service, and the 117 was converted into a terrific skewed notch cutter. With space on the 117's blade shaft to add another ¼-inch-thick dado blade, the resulting 2¼-inch birdsmouth notch became the housing tract standard size for many years. If you are prone to decry the small seat-cut size, I must point out that most 2× joist hangers have the same 2¼-inch bearing surface, so if it's sufficient for a heavier floor load, it certainly will work for a roof (the minimum bearing distance required by the UBC to transfer a load when using 2× material is 1½ inches).

The Groover saw only very limited production since rapid advancements

6-5 My Skil 127 has a series B s/n with a 20-amp motor that spins at 2500 rpm

6-6 My Skil 117 has a series F s/n with an 18-amp motor that spins at 2900 rpm

in the method of home electrical wiring (ie, armored sheathed cable [BX] and nonmetallic sheathed cable [NM]) made the saw obsolete for its purpose soon after it was first produced. All the 117s that were aimlessly floating around were slowly snatched up to be used by tract "roof cutters." Not being a tool historian, I have no idea how long the 117 was actually produced but if I compare the appearance of the data plate from my late-model 117 (s/n F) to that of my late-model 127 (s/n B) they appear to be of the same vintage, so I suspect the Skil model 117 may have been produced into the late 1960s, at least, or possibly the dawn of the 1970s. The data plate off my mid-1970s Skil 107 (s/n H) does have a different layout, so it is unlikely the 117 production ran much into the 1970s if at all. I don't have a clue if the serial number sequencing has anything to do with the age progression, but my guess is that it logically would have. If that hypothesis is correct, then my 127 may very

6-7 My Skil 107 has a series H s/n with a 15-amp motor that spins at 3400 rpm

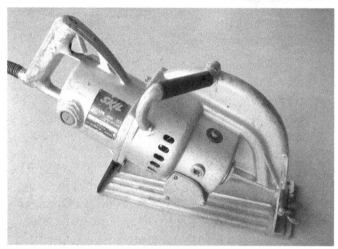

6-8 The Skil 127 was a 12-inch-diameter worm drive circular saw that was available through the late 1960s

well be the oldest of my barrel saw family with the 117 in the middle, and the 107 the baby. **(figs 6-5, 6-6, 6-7)**

Now having a tool available to gang-cut the birdsmouth notch, some portable tool was needed to gang-cut the ridge-cuts as was done at the cutting stations by the big radial arm saw. For this operation, the 20-amp Skil 127 worm drive circular saw with its 12-inch-diameter blade was chosen, seeing as how it was the largest portable circular saw available at the time. **(figs 6-8, 6-9)** Having a blade projection depth of near 5 inches, it could easily gang-cut 2×4 rafter ridge-cuts, but fell short of reaching through anything larger. Since many of the earliest tract home developments used 2×4 rafters, this worked out well, but when 2×6s became more prevalent, a new approach was needed. The obvious answer was to modify the 127 to run the larger 18-inch- or 20-inch-diameter blades found on the big Delta radial

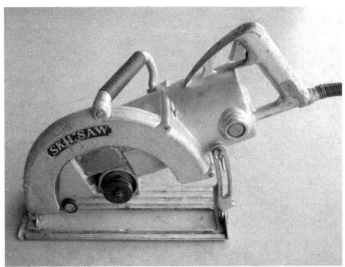

6-9 Many Skil 127s were modifies into 18-inch to 20-inch cross-cut saws and used to gang-cut 2×6 ridge-cuts

arm saws, and, to this end, various saw shops around Los Angeles offered this adaptation starting in the 1960s through the 1970s. The 20-inch converted 127 could cut through 2×8s racked on edge up to a maximum pitch of about 5/12, if I recall correctly, while the 18-inch converted 127 worked well for racked 2×6s. Since an adapted 127 was expensive (think $1000), a less expensive method to gang the ridge-cuts became popular with many folks including myself. In this method, the roof cutter would use the 127 (or even a standard Skil 77 worm drive) to make a starter ridge-cut pass as deep as possible and then finish off the unreached part of the cut with a sidewinder blade mounted on a Skil 77 worm drive. While inherently dangerous because the blade sat outside the guard and was fully exposed, the sidewinder in the right hands proved to be a very efficient tool for finishing off plumb-cuts. **(fig 2-1)**

By the mid- to late-1960s, the supply of Groovers was drying up, so several saw shops in the Los Angeles area began modifying the Skil 107 to carry a 3½-inch dado set. This was done by copying what Skilsaw had done originally to convert the Skil 10-inch worm drive circular saw into a 117. The saw-foot and upper blade guard were enlarged; a new extended blade shaft was machined and installed; and, finally, a massive 3½-inch-wide dado set was mounted to satisfy the demands of contractors who wanted full-plate-width seat-cuts. Sticking on a wider dado set than what was designed into the original 117 applied a greater cantilever force to the blade shaft, but it didn't seem to have any ill effects. Since the 107 spun at a higher rpm than the 117 (3400 rpm versus 2900 rpm) many thought it wise to use a dado stack of a slightly smaller diameter than came mounted on the 117 so that the torque would remain in the same range. My converted 107 sported a

6-inch-diameter dado set, and I had no problems with it during the 40 years she was on active duty. Nate told me that he modified close to two hundred of the old barrel saws (nicknamed "barrel saws" because the motor body was round and canister shaped) into dado saws or monster beam saws during the Los Angeles building boom days. This would include converting many 117s over to handle the wider 3½-inch dado set. There were other saw shops that did the same modifications, but Nate's shop had the lion's share of the market due to his highly visible location along the side of a busy Los Angeles freeway and word of mouth.

The history of my personal converted 107 dado saw is interesting. **(fig 6-10)** The model Skil 107 was a fairly long-running saw model. I don't know exactly when it first went into production and neither does Skilsaw, since it seems no records of this type were kept, but an educated guess puts its earliest production in the late 1930s or early 1940s. The 107 seemed to have gone through a couple of versions, but they appear to be only amp output variations or something esthetically minor with its last production date sometime in the early 1970s. The 107 definitely outlived the Skil 127 which appears to have been manufactured only up until the late 1960s. With the advent of the new lighter second-generation worm drive saws (6½ inch, 7¼ inch, and 8¼ inch) carpenters were overjoyed to get away from the big heavy barrel saw designs of the early years like the 107 which weighed in at near 30 lbs. These old saws certainly weren't a "one-handed" saw for most of us. Because of the precipitous fall in demand, the 107 and 127 were slow to disappear from the distributor's shelves, but by the mid-1970s it was becoming more difficult to find either of these two models new. So, being in the market for one, I was pleasantly surprised to find the 107 suddenly listed for sale in an ABCO Hardware and Builders Supply flyer in 1978, and without a second thought ordered one up to convert into a dado saw. I believe it cost around $495, which was real pricey back then, but if you wanted to cut roofs efficiently, a dado saw was an essential. It would sure be infinitely better

6-11 My converted Skil 107 dado saw weighed nearly 38 lbs

6-12 The 107's blade drive shaft was removed and replaced by a new extended shaft similar to the 117

than the swing-table saw I had been using when I couldn't borrow a dado saw. I asked the ABCO sales representative how they had come by a bunch of new 107s, and he informed me that they were selling off a crate load of 107s that had been returned from Australia. When these few were gone there would be no more, since the inventory system was dry. I will never know if his story was true, but it seemed like a reasonable explanation if one considers that Australia uses 230v and these were 110v versions, so somehow the order had gotten screwed up. The saws probably sat in limbo "down under" for a year or so before being returned to the United States and sold. However it happened, I was happy to get one new, and she would serve me well all my life. Without a doubt, my 107 is one of the very last of this model to come off the assembly line. After she spent a week at the saw shop getting modified into a 4-inch dado saw, I handed over $500 and drove off with my first and

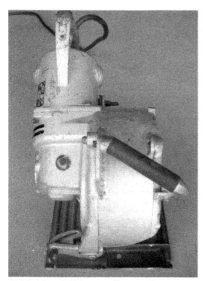

6-14 I ran a 4-inch-wide by 6-inch-diameter dado set consisting of (15) ¼-inch cutters and (2) blades on the 107

6-13 The 107's saw-foot and top blade guard were widened to compensate for the dado set

only (in the jobsite work sense) dado saw. After spending another roll of hundred dollar bills on a 4-inch-wide by 6-inch-diameter carbide-tipped dado set, she was ready to go. **(figs 6-11, 6-12, 6-13, 6-14)** Aside from normal maintenance functions like an occasional $200 dado set sharpening and changing the brushes, the trigger switch, and the oil seals, she has been totally faithful. I am quite sure she could do another of my lifetimes with little trouble. American-made products from the old days beat all. Parts for the 107 would stay around for many years, and even Sears showed parts availability in their tool catalog at least through the late 1970s.

It would be a decade later that Nate Fletcher would find me an unused "cherry" 117 as the old Los Angeles tract cutters sold off their gear. **(fig 6-3)** They all recognized that a special epoch had ended when the truckloads of roof trusses began arriving. I would reserve this untouched 117 specifically for roof-cutting demonstrations throughout the 1990s and into the 2000s so all could catch a glimpse of history. The only thing I did to her was swap off the original upper guard for a modified version so the original could remain unmarred.

I haven't written anything about gang-marking simply because this procedure probably dates back to Adam and Eve, but this methodology was sure put to good use in the tracts by "roof cutters." With the 117 and 127 serving as the basis of production roof cutting, it was possible to gang-cut infinitely more than the dozen or so rafters previously done with the big radial arm saw arrangement. The only limitations to the amount of rafters one could gang-cut now was the length of the rafter-cutting racks themselves and whether you had enough extension cords to reach it all. One had to be particularly careful with the extension cord's wire size and length or you could easily smoke your pricey specialty saws. Since my 127 pulled 20 amps, I would only use it on a 50-foot-long #10 cord and therefore always positioned the rafter-cutting racks fairly close to the jobsite's electrical subpanel. With my converted 107 dado saw that pulled 15 amps I would go out to 100 feet using a #10 cord, but at that length I limited its use to a 20% duty cycle. This generally wasn't an issue since her work was done in minutes. When I bought a used Miller 200LE welder/generator and mounted it on a trailer (then later a HEHR power plant under the hood of my truck), I was no longer limited by cord length. Now, wherever I could get my truck to within 50 feet, I could build rafter-cutting racks. To rewire the saws for 220v would have allowed me to use longer extension cords, but I never saw the need.

Because the dado saw required quite an investment ($1000+), an optional method to gang-cut birdsmouth notches arrived on scene in the early 1960s in the form of the swing-table saw base for the Skil 77 worm drive. It was inexpensive, simple, and favored by anyone other than the dedicated tract roof cutter. A swing-table saw base installed on a standard 7¼-inch or 8¼-inch worm drive circular saw allowed it to swing well past 45° and get the shallow angle required for the seat-cut. I still remember my first swing-table saw base. It was handmade by a guy in his Los Angeles garage and sold through a local framing supply outlet. It, together with a sidewinder blade and two Skil 77s, made up my earliest production roof-cutting tools. Once I could afford my own dado saw, the swing-table saw became a backup. Under-stand that in the common low-pitched tract style roof-cutting situations of the Los Angeles basin area, a dado saw was far superior to a swing-table. My swing-table, not to be condemned to total obscurity, would again see her day when I was framing custom homes with steep pitches. 7/12 pitch was kind of like my personal cutoff point for dado saw use. While the dado saw could easily tilt to 45° (12/12 pitch), for pitches over 7/12 (30°) it was slow going and hard on the motor (remember we use hard Douglas Fir on the West Coast). One could make successively deeper saw passes with the dado saw to lighten the load on the motor, but, by that time, it would have been faster just using a swing-table saw to make the seat-cut from the start. Dado saws are unequaled at lower pitches where the Skil 77 sized swing-table is absolutely miserable, but the two different saw types swap efficiencies in the steeper pitch ranges. A swing-table saw can be real bindy at shallow pitches if there is any variation in the dimensional height of the racked lumber, but this difficulty improves progressively the closer the blade angle gets to verti-cal. While making a 45° bevel-cut is hard enough for any saw motor, imagine how hard the motor is working when the angle is laid way over to make the seat-cut on a shallow pitch roof. I mounted my first swing-table saw base on

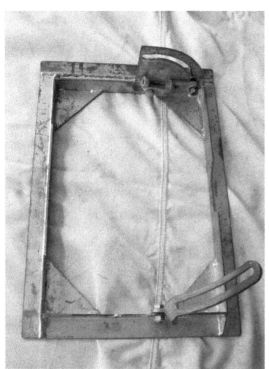

6-15 Mounted on a swing-table, the Skil 127 can make 5-inch seat-cuts

a Skil 77 worm drive but, after frying the armature a few times, I mounted it on the more powerful Milwaukee 7¼-inch worm drive which lasted 3 to 4 times longer. Few carpenters used the Milwaukee worm drive for everyday framing due to its heavier weight, but, for a dedicated swing-table saw that only went from the truck to the racked rafter pile, it was great. I always mounted an 8¼-inch blade on my 7¼-inch worm drive swing-table saws to get a 2¾-inch seat-cut. These blades fit easily when the lower blade guard was removed. Since I never was really happy with how the commercial angle iron swing-table version worked, I eventually designed my own swing-table saw base. I used a flat sheet of aircraft aluminum with a rectangular hole cut in the middle for the saw blade. With its wider borders and slicker material, she slid much easier over racked rafters. **(fig 2-5)** After rubbing the bottom surface of the saw base with some paraffin wax and spraying the blade with silicone, she moved along like she was skating on ice. I would eventually mount my 12-inch Skil 127 on a fabricated swing-table base. **(fig 6-15)** It made one heck of a versatile birdsmouth saw. If we disallow a chainsaw, and I was only limited to one birdsmouth cutting saw, this would be it. It could easily make seat-cuts up to near 5 inches wide and, with the 127's sheer bulk weight and raw power, binding was a nonissue even at the shallowest of pitches. When 5-inch birds-mouth seat-cuts were required for our newly formed precut roof division at

National Lumber in Massachusetts, the Skil 127 swing-table was our mainstay. In the 1990s, Big Foot Tools started modifying the second-generation Skil 77 and 78 with larger blades to fill the big hole in the market that up to the 1970s had been previously owned by the Skil 127. As time went on, Big Foot offered an optional swing-table saw base for their saws.

Portable roof-cutting tool use in Northern California always lagged slightly behind Southern California, because it took time for the new methods and tools to migrate north. Although the Bay Area did see fairly brisk population growth through the boom years, it was nothing on the scale of what happened in the sunny southern regions of the state. I have heard of many exceptional framers in Northern California, but all were known for their achievement in the exclusive custom home markets. Since my personal exposure to framing in the Bay Area didn't begin until the early 1990s, I have had to rely on the memory of Frank at Furber Saw in Martinez, CA, to recreate a bit of the history of production roof cutting for this area. Frank recalls that their biggest bump-up in the blade-resharpening business happened during the 1980s, when tract home development on both ends of the San Francisco Bay had a short-lived building wave. Since Northern California appeared to be some 6 to 7 years behind Southern California in converting all their tract home roof designs over to trusses, some cut-and-stack tracts could still be found until the mid- to late-1980s. This matched with what roof cutter Eric Karlonovich told me about the South Bay regions when I worked for him in the late 1990s. Since few of the big barrel dado saws or 20-inch converted Skil 127 circular saws ever found their way to Northern California, there was a definite need for this type of specialized roof-cutting equipment. Starting in the early 1980s, Pairis Products of Phelan, CA, began supplying a bolt-on 3½-inch dado kit for the Skil 77, while Furber Saw began producing their own line of 3½-inch dado saws based on the Skil 78. Frank believes they produced between 50 and 75 of these saws to meet local roof-cutting needs. The Furber dado saw was popular due to their rugged design and integral one-piece blade shaft. Both of these options were available up until the early 1990s.

These second-generation dado saw versions worked well, but there was no comparison to the big barrel saw versions of the earlier decades when it came to heavy-duty use. You cannot compare the amp output of today's circular saws (Skil 70/10-inch/15 amp) against the ones of yesteryear (Skil 107/10-inch/15 amp). Skilsaw states some electronic gibberish that their "four stator windings reduce the amount of turns per coil and thus the amount of resistive losses caused by parasitic electrical currents circulating within the motor and therefore they are able to get an increased power out of the small sized motor." The techs at Eurton Electric told me that the real test of performance is under load where the old and new saw versions are in different galaxies. Skil's second-generation circular saws must spin at some 1200 rpm above the old versions just to get their purported power. The new-generation Skil 10¼-inch Sawsquatch spins at 4600 rpm, while the old 107 lopes along at 3400 rpm and only barely falls off in rpm when loaded. That can't be said of the Sawsquatch, which, if loaded in the same manner, will nearly choke and die. An older Caterpillar (Cat) diesel motor in a tractor trailer truck spits out about 300 hp at 1900 rpm. There are various cars on the road today that put out double that amount of horse power at 3 times the rpm, but not one can equal the work output of that diesel. It's not so much about horse power as it is about torque output. In this arena, the Cat diesel dominates. I am no engineer, but there has to be something like that going on between these two generations of saws for I know from personal "hands on" usage that a 15-amp saw motor from the old barrel saws will smoke one of these supposedly 15-amp saw motors of today by at least twice over. Just the difference between the size of the two motors' armatures and drive trains would be like comparing Arnold Schwarzenegger to Olga Korbut. Mafell AG came out with a 4½-inch skew notch cutter for its old-time timber-framing customers in the late 1980s. I had the opportunity to try one of these saws for gang-cutting rafter birdsmouths while at National Lumber in Massachusetts (2001). I found it severely lacking in power, and the straight planer style blades cut very poorly. I cannot comment on their more recent upgrades. If the tool was worm drive driven instead of direct drive and had a spiraling multitooth-type dado head, I believe it would work much better. In any case, the $5000 price makes it a bit steep for most framers to consider as an addition to their tool collection.

The gang-cutting of the ridge-cuts was a real problem for many who lacked access to a big 18-inch or 20-inch modified Skil 127 circular saw. This was especially true in Northern California where hardly a soul knew anything about the method of using the simple sidewinder blade instead of those giant saws. Certainly no tool manufacturer saw any financial benefit in producing a monster worm drive circular saw for a tiny niche market composed of only a few hundred roof cutters. Skilsaw had been down this road before with the Skil 117 Groover that had been specially designed for electricians. That project would have been an abject failure if it hadn't been rescued by the tract roof cutters who found an alternative use for it. It would not be until near 50 years later (late 2000s) that Skil would again even entertain the idea of producing a second-generation 10-inch worm drive saw (model 70) to replace the venerable 107. In the late 1970s, Makita came out with a direct-drive 16-inch circular saw (model 5402) for 6× beam cutting. Some folks used it to gang-cut ridge-cuts on 2×6s (5/12 maximum) but unfortunately it lacked the power to make this long milling cut with any speed. As 2×8 rafter stock become more and more common, frustration in a lack of options to gang-cut the ridge-cuts only increased. It was during the 1980s that San Jose, CA, roof cutter Eric Kralonovich began to free-hand gang-cut horizontally stacked rafters with a chainsaw while Furber Saw up at the north end of the Bay made some gas chainsaw–powered cutting machines modeled after Mafell AG's 1960s vertical cutting chainsaw.

In the late 1980s, the Linear Link saw (Muskegon Tools, North Muskegon, MI) was introduced. It was a self-oiling 14-inch chainsaw bar attached to a Skil 77 motor body and could swing angles just like a normal 77, so some carpenters used it to gang-cut the ridge-cuts on racked rafter material. Sadly, it was severely underpowered for this type of cutting and could not hold to the precision needed for quality ridge-cuts due to the narrow saw base width. Another similar device, the Prazi Beam Cutter (Prazi USA, Plymouth, MA) came along in the mid-1990s. It had the same drawbacks as the Linear Link, but, even worse, it had no self-oiling provision for the chain. While I used both of these products during roof-cutting demos at *JLC* Live conferences in the 1990s, they fell well short of filling the industry's need for a serious gang-style ridge-cutting saw. I had only used them out of desperation because the convention's rules restricted me from firing up a gas-powered chainsaw indoors or demonstrating an illegal tool like the sidewinder blade. In 1997, Big Foot Tools began producing an angle-adjustable saw-foot for gas-powered chainsaws under the model name "Headcutter." **(fig 6-16)** Simply clamping this saw-foot to a chainsaw's chainbar instantly converts it into an amazing vertical milling machine. Its large saw-foot provided the stability for super accurate cuts. Installed on a decent-sized chainsaw (+5 hp) it handles the gang-cutting of ridge-cuts on any size rafters with total ease. This tool instantly became the best option available for gang-cutting the plumb-cuts on common rafters. Besides that, since the saw-foot will adjust from vertical to 15° of horizontal it can serve as a swing-table saw for seat-cuts when a shorter chainbar length is installed on the chainsaw. **(fig 2-41)** When the chainbar is fitted with a chisel-tooth ripping chain, it is hard to distinguish the cuts made using a "Headcutter" from those made with a circular saw. The "Headcutter" also became popular for precutting bundled I-joists to length or sizing structural insulated panels. In the end, this tool has been a roof-cutting game changer since it can easily do the job of both the dado saw and monster circular saw combined. With a "Headcutter" saw-foot, a Stihl 044 chainsaw with various length bars, and a Skil 77, a carpenter is all set up to production cut rafters.

To complete the circle, let's now return to take another look at the old Los Angeles housing tract cut-and-stack days when I was involved. I suppose it is obvious that one certainly didn't just walk onto the jobsite proclaiming oneself to be a "roof cutter" and immediately start cutting roofs, even if they had the equipment, the knowledge, and training. The job of the "roof cutter" was probably one of the most highly prized carpenter positions so the slot was rarely ever vacated by attrition. A housing tract typically only required one cutter since just one could normally keep pace with the number

of house foundations that were laid each day. If a "roof cutter" slot did become available, it would quickly be snapped up by an older journeyman who had been with the company for a long time. Even though a roof cutter had to rack up all his 2×6 rafters, it certainly was less strenuous than most other framing tasks. And, if you had a young buck like me around to do the grunt work of racking and crowning the rafters, the job was an absolute cake walk. After cutting the first few roofs in any new tract, the cutter had all the LL measurements memorized for the next 250+ houses. From then on it was only racking lumber, snapping some cut-lines, plowing the 117 and the big blade-modified 127 through the pile, cutting a few sets of California valley fill and gable studs, and on to the next house to do it all again. The roof designs were very simplistic in order to keep the building costs to a minimum.

While many know me from the "roof cutter" aspect, few realize that I spent most of my time in the Los Angeles housing tracts during the mid- to late-1970s as a stacker by choice. After helping a few "roof cutters" and absorbing all their tricks, I did some cutting but soon found that it was more to my liking to be running around the top plates throwing rafters up than spending all day down in the dirt endlessly loading rafter racks and milling rafters. Aside from being a person who gets bored very easily cutting the same thing over and over again (monkey on a saw), stacking was a better fit for my athletic ability. I liked to move around and erect things. With most of the cutters being old timers in their 40s or more and I still being several years away from legal drinking age, it felt like I was running around with grandpa when I was down in the dirt. My instructor at Orange Coast College, Hank Resse, had been a hellacious tract stacker so I could cut or stack on par with most guys after he got done with me. At first I paired up with another stacker on a house or two in order to learn the ropes and then I was on my own. In the tracts, I would always stack solo like most of the other guys. Stacking was like a game to me, and I thrived on the challenge. As I got better I started pushing myself to go faster and faster. I preferred stacking single-story houses and usually left the two-story houses for someone else who was better up there than I. I suppose I had little fear of jumping down from 8-foot walls if I lost my balance, but jumping to avert a fall from two stories up probably would not have ended very well. I don't ever remember specifically falling from the wall plates while roof framing, but I do remember acting like an idiot and jumping down from the 8-foot wall plates a few times. I was young and cocky.

Getting work as a stacker was fairly easy, since few possessed the understanding or skill to do it well. Since a tract roof cutter put out 3 to 4 new roof packages every day, stackers were in high demand. I don't ever recall be turned away from any tract job if I told them I was a stacker. Most of the tract jobs were supposed to be union jobs, but normally the framing contractor didn't give a flying rat's ass if you were or weren't, as long as you did a good fast job. When the union representative came onto the jobsite to check everyone's journeyman card, we nonunion types simply took an extended "coffee break." Everybody was paid in cash back in those days and hell if I was going to share some with the union. Besides, it really eked me that a portion of the dues they collect go to support the campaigns of leftist political hacks with whom I have nothing in common. Only a few years later when I was stacking roofs on a housing tract up in Lompoc, CA, did the contractor beg me to get a journeyman's card or else he would suffer the wrath of the local carpenters' union. I suppose it was easier for the union to exert pressure in these little towns as opposed to the never ending metropolis of the Los Angeles basin. Only a week prior to landing the Lompoc job I had left Los Angeles in search of the last few scattered cut-and-stack housing tracts since all of Los Angeles had been swallowed up by roof trusses. I had no interest in sticking around for that. Needless to say, while the Lompoc framing contractor probably would have paid for my journeyman's card just so I would stick around and finish stacking out the tract, I decided not to break with principle and headed down to Santa Barbara, CA, to try my hand at framing custom homes again after a five-year hiatus. Although I do hate to walk away from any stacking job, especially piece work, in the long run it was the right decision, for my return to Santa Barbara would challenge me in a new dimension that tract framing never could. Although I would continue to piece cut roofs on many cathedral-style condominium developments in the Santa Barbara, CA, area during the 1980s, that job in Lompoc, CA, would be the last time I would ever work as a piecemeal tract roof stacker. Within a year or two after it there would be no more large-scale cut-and-stack tracts left anywhere in Southern California. "Light duty" tract roof cutting did grind on another year or two after roof trusses took over the Los Angeles basin because the California valley intersections and hip roof ends were stick framed until the truss companies figured out how to truss these areas.

Before I bring this chapter to a close, I want to share some thoughts on roof framing from both the "roof cutter" and the roof stacker points of view. Both of these skills have been an integral and inseparable part of my life and define who I am. Carpenters most certainly will always respect those who cut roofs knowing that they have mastered the roof trigonometry and principles involved in joining sloping surfaces. This is not an easy task, and those who end up extremely proficient in it have had to invest a great deal of time, concentration, and study. But at some point when you have the roof math down pat, to simply mill rafters becomes quite tedious except when cutting rafters for the most complicated of custom roofs. A "roof cutter" develops a routine – studying the building prints to create a plan of attack, calculating rafter lengths, racking and crowning the rafter material, snapping cut-lines on this material, and finally gang-cutting the racked lumber into "ready to install" rafters. His job is to produce "perfect" rafters for a "perfect world." The stacker, on the other hand, is the individual who must take those "perfect world" rafters and make them work on an imperfectly framed house. He is the one who ends up solving all the "real-world" problems. He must deal with dimensional errors, rafter walls not being parallel, the building being out of square, walls angling up or down, bearing walls that don't plane with one another, walls bowing in or out, walls with crowns or dips, etc. Every little error from a bad foundation through sloppy wall framing comes to rest at the top plates from where he works. And this does not include all the issues he will face with the rafter material itself, like crowned or bowed rafters, etc. Not only must a stacker have all the head knowledge and rafter-cutting ability of a "roof cutter" but he must be able to visualize how the flawed wall frame on which he is balancing will affect the roof's assembly and what to do about it. Through my life I have met many guys who know how to cut roof rafters well yet are totally dismayed and dumbfounded the minute things don't fit like they are supposed to up in the air. Likewise, I know of many stackers and contractors who immediately blame the cutter for a "bad cut" if all the rafters don't nail together smoothly. I have always stressed that to be a capable roof framer one must be able to cut and stack equally well. These pair of skills are like the two sides of a coin – you need both sides for the coin to be of any value. While the "roof cutter" solves mathematical problems, the roof stacker solves practical problems. One can learn roof cutting math and gang-cutting techniques rather quickly, but the ability to visualize and solve problems in the air takes time.

So to summarize, my time and experience in the Los Angeles tracts had a lasting effect on my life as a framer. It gave me an unbelievable foundation from which I would grow. I would take the production methodology and skills learned there and apply them directly to the following four decades of my life in custom home framing as a foreman, a contractor, and a consultant. I shared as much of this as I could with all those who are interested in *A Roof Cutter's Secrets, The Complicated Roof,* and by presenting seminars, workshops, and clinics at the *JLC* Live trade conferences. While cutting rafters or stacking a roof was "the job," perhaps the biggest take away from it all was learning how to organize your thought process so as to approach and complete a job in an organized and efficient manner. It wasn't so much about cutting rafters as it was about how to arrange those rafters on the racks so you could cut them all in one nonstop, flowing sequence without moving anything. It wasn't so much about stacking a roof, but how to do it in a fast, easy, and fluid manner. These things I learned.

> To look is one thing. To see what you look at is another.
> To understand what you see is a third. To learn from
> what you understand is still something else. But to act
> on what you learn is all that really matters.
>
> – Malcom McNair

7

Smiles and Frowns –
successes and failures

*My greatest concern is not whether you have failed
but are you content to live with that failure.* – Abraham Lincoln

When I sit down to think about the jobs that I have worked on over the past 40+ years, lots of little memory flashbacks shoot through my head. It's kind of like a wall collage. Sometimes I visualize the crew of guys who were with me; sometimes I remember the time of year and whether it was hot, cold, or rainy; sometimes I see the building lot and its physical features (steep, muddy, etc.); and sometimes I visualize my performance. Inside the performance flashbacks there are pleasant memories where things turned out well along with sobering memories where I screwed up somehow. I have had a bunch on both sides of the hill as does everybody. Many people believe that I, being a roof cutter, am some kind of infallible wizard and therefore set the bar so high that it can only be seen from the space station. I hate to bust their bubble, but I don't walk on water. I used to jokingly run a "3 strike and you're out" error policy on the jobsite. If you made more than 3 errors in one day you went home. I don't remember if I ever sent myself home for having reached that milestone, but I certainly came close on many a day. We all hate screw-ups, but they are a part of life. The man who says he never makes any is either a terrible liar or doesn't do anything.

I wrote this chapter to share a few chuckles. It contains my most memorable framing assembly screw-ups (or at least the ones that time has yet to erase from my mind) together with some of my most thrilling framing assembly successes. Since I always like to end on a positive note, let's do the errors first.

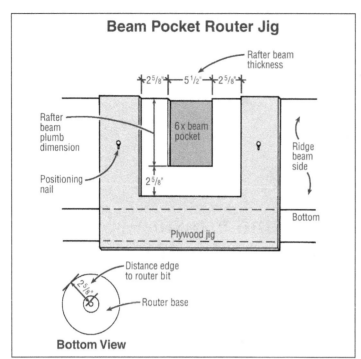

7-1 A beam pocket router jig is easily made from a scrap piece of ¾-inch plywood

FROWNS

The first in the time-line of commemorative screw-ups happened while I was working as a framing foreman for Hal Benhardt in Santa Barbara, CA. I was in my early 20s at the time. We were framing a large custom home whose primary architectural feature was a long gable roof running the length of the building, with several smaller gable roof wings darting off at 90°. The highlight of this house was an exposed rafter beam ceiling in the gigantic living room. This room stretched full-width across the main span gable (+30 feet) and was some 22 feet long. It sported a 6×14 ridge beam with 6×8 rafter beams pocketed in across the room at approximately 4 feet OC and 2×6 Spruce T&G above. We had done several of the same style houses just prior so this one, so it was really no big deal. I had a crane scheduled to show up the next morning to set the ridge and rafter beams so I was staying late to do my last minute preparation. The rafter beams were all cut and only the ridge was lacking the dadoed beam pockets, so I got busy with that. I did my calculations to find the OC spacing, then laid out each side of the ridge beam accordingly, and using a fabricated jig scarfed out the beam pockets with a router. **(fig 7-1)** When that was done, I headed home.

The next morning when we set the ridge, I instantly saw that I had screwed up the beam pocket layout since the last rafter beam spacing was very obviously larger than all the others. My heart was in my throat as, not only had I destroyed a beautiful 26-foot-long "select exposed" 6×14 beam, but I would also need to get the crane back another day with its added cost, and my fast efficient framing flow through the job was in ruins. What was worse than making the error was that the boss had showed up to watch the beam setting spectacle and he too saw the screw-up. I went over to Hal to apologize for the mess I had made. I have never seen Hal upset and he wasn't then, but he was quiet and I could see he was playing out various solutions in his head. Not only was Hal the builder, but he was also the designer and had some incredible visualization skills. A few minutes later he told me what he wanted me to do. I had the crane yank the beam down and very quickly, while the crane was on standby, re-laid out the ridge beam pockets correctly and dadoed in new additional beam pockets. The side faces of the beam looked like a disaster with both the old and new beam pockets in plain sight but up the ridge went again this time for good. In no time we had all the rafter beams set and the crane was sent home. Hal had taken off but showed up the next morning with two absolutely perfect 22-foot-long 2×12s. He worked on the job that day and from those two 2×12s he cut a face board for each side of the ridge having slots for the rafter beams. When these two trim pieces were fitted in place the incorrect beam pockets were well hidden. Hal was a superb finish carpenter, so it looked like art when he was done. I suppose we could have also just pressure blocked between the rafter beams at the ridge, but it was a style thing for Hal. Of course I had made a simple math error that had bit me hard in the butt. While I often worked late, I had failed to consider that I may have lost some of my mental edge just from simple fatigue. By the end of each day, one certainly isn't at his best when it comes to concentration. My error might have been caught if someone other than I had double checked my work before I fired up the router. This error taught me a good lesson and I tried to never again put myself in the same situation. If I did happen to stay late to layout out beams or rafters I would wait until the following morning to cut them after both I and someone else had had the chance to double check everything. The old axiom of "measure twice cut once" works super well if the second measurement is done by someone other than he who did the first. "Two heads are better than one, not because either is infallible, but because they are unlikely to go wrong in the same direction." – C.S. Lewis

When one calculates beam spacing across a room, the correct procedure is to measure the inside room dimension following the direction of the ridge or perpendicular to the rafter or ceiling beams, then you subtract off the thickness of the wall covering on each end wall, together with the sum total of all the rafter beam thicknesses, to arrive at the net exposed ceiling surface length. This net dimension is then divided by the number of beam spacings to get the spacing measurement between the beams. If you plan to mark layout as an OC spacing as I had done, you must add to that measurement

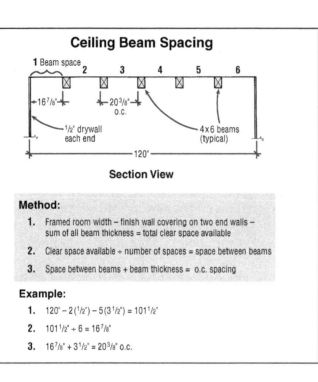

7-2 The mathematical method to calculate equal rafter or ceiling beam spacing across any size room

Ceiling Beam Spacing

1 Beam space 2   3   4   5   6

←16⁷/₈"→   ←20³/₈"→
                o.c.

¹/₂" drywall   4x6 beams
each end   (typical)

←————————— 120" —————————→

Section View

Method:

1. Framed room width – finish wall covering on two end walls – sum of all beam thickness = total clear space available

2. Clear space available ÷ number of spaces = space between beams

3. Space between beams + beam thickness = o.c. spacing

Example:

1. $120" - 2(¹/₂") - 5(3¹/₂") = 101¹/₂"$

2. $101¹/₂" ÷ 6 = 16⁷/₈"$

3. $16⁷/₈" + 3¹/₂" = 20³/₈"$ o.c.

the thickness of one rafter or ceiling beam. This step is what I had forgotten to do, so I wound up using an OC spacing measurement that was short 5½ inches of what it should have been. Why in the world I hadn't checked the last rafter bay measurement remaining at the far end of the ridge beam to see if it matched the others remains a mystery but after this error I would always check everything from right-to-left and also from left-to-right. I detailed the correct procedure in *A Roof Cutter's Secrets* (RCS) so that other folks might avoid making the same mistake that I had made (RCS pgs. 257–258). **(fig 7-2)**

It wasn't long after the ugly beam pocket spacing incident that we were framing a large beautiful Tutor style home in a luxurious part of Santa Barbara, CA, called Hope Ranch. I still remember it well for it was on this house that I had the good luck to cut and stack various roof situations that are not seen all that often. It was a chopped up 12/12 pitched hip roof with 9 different ridge heights, a couple of dormers, a Bay Roof extension, and two towers at 14/12 pitch. One of the towers was conically shaped and was framed using (24) 2×8s converging to a peak. The other tower was an open beam octagon and was framed using 6×8s that butted to a shaped 10×10 king-pin with 2×6 T&G above. This job provided me with the opportunity to develop many procedures that I would pass along 9 years later in the 1988 *A Roof Cutter's Secrets.* They included: setting up broken hips (RCS pgs. 79–81); layout and cutting of hip or valley beam rafters that bear on a ridge beam (RCS pgs. 75–79); conical tower wall construction (RCS pgs. 216–227);

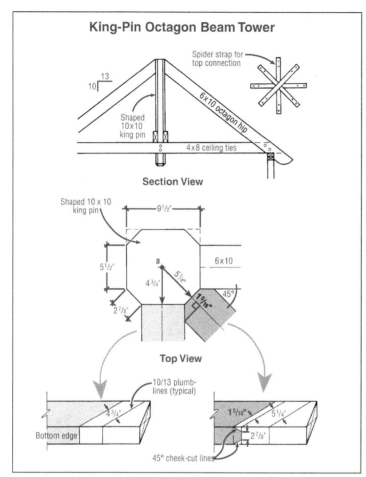

King-Pin Octagon Beam Tower

Spider strap for top connection

6x10 octagon hip

Shaped 10x10 king pin

4x8 ceiling ties

Section View

Shaped 10 x 10 king pin

9¹/₂"

5¹/₂"

a

6x10

4³/₄"

5¹/₄"

1⁵/₁₆"

45°

2⁷/₈"

Top View

10/13 plumb-lines (typical)

4³/₄"

1⁵/₁₆"

5¹/₄"

2⁷/₈"

Bottom edge

45° cheek-cut lines

7-3 Each of the four intercardinal rafter beams had partial 45° cheek-cuts at the head

framing king-pin octagon beam tower roofs (RCS pgs. 211–214); converting an octagon tower to a conical shape (RCS pgs. 221–222); and connecting a flat plane roof to a conical tower roof overlay style (RCS pgs. 227–229).

It was during the late 1970s that I was developing my "snap it out on the floor full-size" methodology to get run measurements, cut angles, shortening, etc. for complicated roof connections, and, on this house, I had done it for the Bay Roof, and both the conical and the octagon towers. While I do figure all the shortening and cut angles by math, verifying everything on a full-scale drawing provides an extra level of security, especially considering that these two towers were my very first ones. The rafter beam head-cuts for the octagon all converged around the upper end of a 14-foot-long shaped 10×10 king-pin. The architect had designed it so that four cardinal positioned rafter beams (N, S, E, W) would butt the king-pin with a full-sized square-cut head, while a second round of four intercardinal rafter beams (NE,

7-4 If possible, prebuild complicated roof elements on the ground and lift them into place with a crane (photo courtesy Reta Benhardt)

SE, SW, NW) would fit between these beams and sported partial cheek-cuts at the head. **(fig 7-3)** After cutting both sets of rafter beams to length with a square-cut head, I went about cutting the partial cheek-cuts on the four second-round beams. I had the brainstorm idea to bypass the cheek-cut layout and simply make the 45° cheek-cuts by running the saw up and down on the square-cut head after laying out the correct 2⅞-inch width in the center. So I set my Skilsaw to 45° and in no time had all my roof-framing members cut and ready to be stained, so that the following morning we could set them with a crane. Just so you know, these two towers are the only ones I have ever stick framed in the air. After this house, I would always prebuild any tower on the ground and set it as a finished unit. Anyhow, when we set the four rafter beams having the partial cheek-cuts, I found the joints open near 1/4 inch on the end of the cheek-cut farthest from the king-pin. I knew right away that the saw's bevel adjust must not have been set correctly or the degree gauge was not accurate. Being a speed freak I had not even checked its accuracy by making some trial passes and verifying that the saw was indeed cutting at a true 45° angle. The beams and king-pin had a dark stain and looking up from the ground the tiny gaps were hardly perceptible so in the end we just filled the gaps with a small bead of black silicone and called it good. **(fig 7-4)** The engineer did verify that the 2⅞-inch head-cut against the king-pin was the structural component and the cheek-cuts not being tight was no big deal. Whew! While I had slid out of this error OK, my pride in doing only the

7-5 I make a handsaw pass down exposed beam joints to tighten up the gaps

highest quality work had taken a hit. Believe me, it would never happen again. In fact, from that day forward, my level of beam work would be unequaled – it had just taken a good stiff kick in the butt to get me there. **(fig 7-5)**

So what had I learned? First off, recognize that all too often it is the simplest, most avoidable things that do us in, so give even the most mundane activities that "attention to detail" they deserve. Second, don't take shortcuts. I should have laid out the cut-lines on all four sides of the beam and paid attention to them as I cut. If I had done that, it would have been obvious within a microsecond that something was awry. Third, on special connections where there can be no error, always cut a practice piece and trial fit it in a mockup to verify everything is good to go. I could have very easily avoided that embarrassing "oops" situation if I would have only taken a few extra minutes to cut a trial piece. And last, when doing fancy exposed beam work or things along that line be as meticulous as a finish carpenter or a cabinet maker. Save that "speed is paramount" nature for other tasks.

Frankly, after those bad cheek-cuts, I cannot remember another major fabrication type screw-up until some 20 years later while working for Dan Daley in the late 1990s. I am sure there were others, but they have long since evaporated from my memory. Anyhow, on this spring day, I was up helping frame the roof on a big two-story Tutor style house somewhere close to the Deschutes River in La Pine, OR. Not only was this job memorable because of a cutting error that I made, but also because of a screw-up in jobsite oversight that almost had fatal results. I will never forget the day that John Zarr saved my life.

This house was so large that I had divided the chore of cutting rafters into two phases, something I rarely ever do. I think it had something to do with space issues and leaving access for the crane to get where he needed to go, etc. Anyhow, I cut the main house first and then planned to cut the detached guest house/garage as a second phase. All the big glulam ridges and hip/valley beams that formed the roof skeleton would go up with the crane, and Dan would move all the fill rafters around the site with his Gradall telescopic forklift. We had just set all the ridges with the crane and were moving on to place all the various hip and valley beams. Normally, I am the one who slings the beams and works with the crane while directing the stacking crew as to where each member goes. But for one particular bastard valley glulam, I decided that it was best if I jumped up top

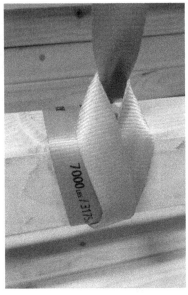

7-6 A double-wrap choker hitch is used to single sling roof beams into position

to position the birdsmouth, so I asked someone else to sling it and headed up to the second floor. John Zarr was up high at the ridge to receive the head-cut and I was just getting ready to scale the outside wall when the beam being overhead slipped out of the sling headed right toward my head. John saw it unfold and somehow had the wherewithal to smack the beam enough so that it was diverted from its lethal course and burrowed through the floor to my side instead. Surely Our Lord played a part in guiding John's reflexes. Since I was focused on getting ready to climb the wall I had no idea anything was going on until the beam dove right through the floor right at my side. Evidently, whoever I had asked to install the sling on this beam had never done a single sling lift before, so he was unfamiliar with the correct type of choker hitch to apply. I should have verified his knowledge – an oversight that nearly cost me my life. Normally, a level beam like a ridge or purlin is set with two slings, but beams that sit at a distinct angle, like a hip or valley, I always set with a single sling since this makes it much easier to move them into position. When you do a single sling it must be a double wrap so that the beam cannot slip out. This wrap is called a "double wrap choker hitch." **(fig 7-6)** This wrap is then positioned along the beam so that when it is lifted it will hang more or less at an angle that matches the plane of the roof. This usually takes a couple trial lifts from the cutting racks to position the choker hitch along its length so the beam hangs at the correct incline. Many times on single-slung beams I even add a block of wood to the top edge of the beam at the uphill side of the choker

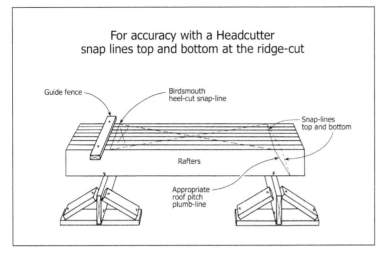

For accuracy with a Headcutter
snap lines top and bottom at the ridge-cut

Guide fence

Birdsmouth
heel-cut snap-line

Snap-lines
top and bottom

Rafters

Appropriate
roof pitch
plumb-line

7-7 Place snap-lines top and bottom of racked rafter material to clearly identify the plumb-cut angle

hitch as a safety back up. I double wrap choker hitch everything, even beams that are set level with two slings.

My failure to double check another carpenter's work in a critical situation can be considered a major screw-up. Having just arrived to help Dan's crew with the roof portion of this house, I was unaware of everyone's knowledge level and evidently whoever I placed in charge of installing the sling on this one beam knew less about the task than he had indicated.

No need to detail my error in this incident – it's pretty obvious. The phrase "Never ASSUME, because when you ASSUME, you make an ASS of U and ME" comes to mind.

Back to the main story. After we had cleared the racks of the main house's rafters, I racked up to cut the roof for the guest house. Some (80) special ordered 22-foot-long 2×12s rafters were to be used as common rafters. It was a big steep Gable roof with a four large dormers, two out each side. The rafter cut was uneventful, and the heavy awkward common rafters were spread down each side of the building. We jumped up top to stack and, as we pulled the first rafters up to butt the preset glulam ridge beam, I noted in quiet dismay that the rafter ridge-cuts were open by 5/8 inch at the peak. The seat-cut looked good, so I was puzzled as to what was going on. I quickly rechecked the ridge height and verified the rafter line-length. Both where dead on, so I sampled the head-cut angle with my Quick Square and found it to be the culprit – off by just under 3°.

So somehow I had set up the Headcutter with the wrong bevel angle. Bummer. I always run a trial milling pass to confirm that the Headcutter's bevel matches a marked ridge-cut line and then, when gang-cutting the ridge-cuts, I follow a pair of snap-lines that define the plumb-cut angle through the pile. **(fig 7-7)** By watching how the chainbar tip follows the

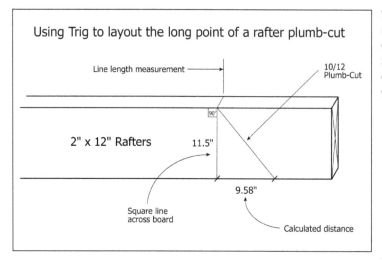

Using Trig to layout the long point of a rafter plumb-cut

Line length measurement

10/12
Plumb-Cut

90°

2" x 12" Rafters   11.5"

9.58"

Square line
across board

Calculated distance

7-8 I erred by not reading the tape correctly – marking 8⁵/₈ inches instead of the calculated 9⁵/₈ inches

snap-line on the bottom of the pile, you can verify that all the head-cuts stay "dead on." This methodology assures that you are not putting some weird pressure on the chainsaw motor body and causing the chainbar to flex in/out. Evidently, I must have laid out the head-cut's plumb-line incorrectly, since while cutting, the chainbar had followed both snap-lines perfectly. While on smaller rafters like 2×8s at shallow pitches, I use my Quick Square to layout the head-cut angle on the side of the rafter pile, on large rafters especially when it incorporates a steep pitch I use trigonometry. I find the distance that the LP of the plumb-line extends beyond a square "across the board" line and then draw a line connecting that measurement back up to the LL snap-line. With this job's 10/12 pitch and 2×12 rafter size (11.5 inches), the plumb-cut LP would be placed at 9.58 inches past a square across line on the bottom of the racked lumber. (CM calculator: 10 Inch Pitch, 11.5 Run, Rise **9.58**). In retrospect, I had marked 8.58 inches instead of 9.58 inches, so that explained why the plumb-cut was about ⁵/₈ inch open at the LP tip. It appears I simply hadn't read my tape measure correctly. Oh well, it was done now and "no sense crying over spilt milk". **(fig 7-8)**

Because these rafters were special order due to their length, I had a big problem on my hands. Dan was pretty upset with me. I certainly couldn't blame him, since most folks somehow believed that when it came to roofs I just never made mistakes. In boxing matches when I was younger it wasn't until after I got tagged a time or two that I got serious. It was like a wake-up call to get after it. Same happened here. I went to work to find a solution to fix my screw-up. That's really what framing is all about – finding solutions to problems. The better you are at finding good fast solutions, the better a framer you are. Rarely does anything on the job (or in life) go exactly as planned. You best be ready to bob and weave. Roof framing problem solving is a visualization game, and I actually thrive on these types of challenges.

OK, so we could enlarge the seat-cut by ⅝ inch allowing the head-cuts to be recut correctly but with the new smaller heel-stand I would have to either lower the ridge beam a taste or chamfer-cut it on both sides at the top. It is a royal "pain in the ass" to re-gang-cut birdsmouths to a larger size after they have been done, so one usually just ends up recutting them all by hand. Just imagine hand cutting all those monster rafters one at a time – not a pleasant thought. Then again, even if it was easy to re-gang-cut the birdsmouths I would have to recut all the head-cuts by hand because the Headcutter needs more than ⅝ inch of wood on the cutoff side of the LL snap-line for the saw-foot to have any hope of gliding along stably. I thought back to Hal's calm handling of my erroneously placed beam pockets some 2+ decades prior and used his idea to devise a fix. The framing plan had little collar ties installed under the ridge beam from side-to-side, creating a small flat ceiling at the ridge peak, so anything I did at the ridge would be hidden. I decided to furr-out each side of the ridge beam enough to easily re-gang-cut the ridge-cuts shorter using the Headcutter and not touch the birdsmouths. Installation of a pair of 2×6s full-length along each side of the ridge beam like a double high ledger took no time at all and having 1½ inches on the cutoff side of the reracked rafters provided enough support for the Headcutter to glide along well. Having the chainbar buried in new wood for the whole cut would be more accurate than trying to do a ⅝ inch to nothing sliver cut even if it was possible. So we pulled down all the common rafters, reracked them, and then recut them for the now 3 inch thicker Ridge beam. Might have lost 3 hours or so, but soon Dan was back smiling.

Lessons learned: double check your math calculations and any measurements. Seems like we have seen this lesson somewhere before. A failure of this type brought to mind a concern that I had had of my 12-inch Quick Square slipping out of adjustment and creating a similar mess. To combat it, I started the personal policy of tightening the thumb adjuster on my 12-inch Quick Square with a pair of Channellock pliers. In 2001, when I went to work for Dave Saunders out at National Lumber, Mansfield, MA, one of the guys helping me with the precut roof division, Henry Viveros, bought me a cool miniature pair of Channellock pliers to carry in my nail bags for just that reason. **(fig 3-6)** Another observation about this milling angle incident was that it would have never happened if I had just kept my roof cutting tools set up after cutting the main house. Both the guest and main house roofs were the same pitch and the main house head-cuts were tits.

Speaking of using a Quick Square for layout: one error that I had made a couple times was adjusting the Quick Square to be used on hip/valley head-cuts and then forgetting to switch it back to the common rafter setting when it was needed for that task. After making this mistake a time or two, I quickly added a color-coded second 12-inch Quick Square that was designat-

7-9 The Safeway shopping center in Bend, OR was a sculpture of glulam beams (photo 2002)

ed exclusively for hip/valley layout. On any roof cut job I would set up both squares at the start of the roof-framing process and never adjust them again until that roof was done.

By the way, I highly recommend the trigonometric method of calculating and layout for square-cut lines in addition to finding the LP extension as previously described. It is a method that I started using in my youth because of its absolute precision. No type of marking square can compete with its accuracy. It comes in super handy on any large square or angled cut. The methodology can be found in *A Roof Cutter's Secrets* Figure 5-9, pg. 98, where it is shown being used to find the long overlay cut on California valley jacks. While it is shown there using the appropriate RR ratio, a CM calculator makes the procedure even easier. While working for Dan Daley in Bend, OR, we did the framing on a big Safeway store off SW Century Drive that had all kinds of extreme-sized exposed glulam beams in the roof sections over the store entrances. **(figs 2-27, 7-9)** By using trigonometry to layout a precise square line across the beam, I was able to cut all the pieces with pin-point accuracy. For an example of how it's done, let's walk through placing a square line down the side of a 48-inch-tall glulam beam using nothing more than your calculator and a tape measure. Call the place you want to locate the square line "A." Find the actual beam height dimension (i.e., 47.5 inches) and then mark that height dimension along the beam's top edge to the inside of point A (A-B). Next, use your CM calculator to find the length of a 45° diagonal that corresponds to that height measurement and measure this distance off diagonally from point B toward the bottom corner edge of the

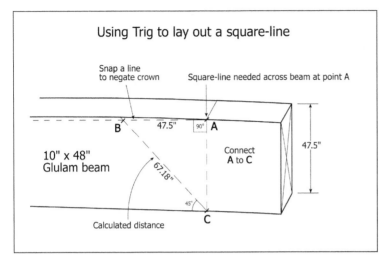

7-10 Using trigonometry to get an accurate square-cut line on large-sized material

beam (CM calculator: 45 pitch, 47.5 Run, Diag **67.18**). The spot where this diagonal measurement meets up with the bottom corner edge of the beam (C) is the lower point of the square across the board line from "A." If a beam has a built-in camber that is unlikely to be loaded out, snap a line from the top corner edge on one end of the beam to the top corner edge at the point where you will place the square line (A) and use this snap-line as the straight top edge for this procedure. **(fig 7-10)**

SMILES

OK, enough on screw-ups. Let's turn now to those more pleasant job memories of things well done. Thank goodness these memories far outweigh the bad ones, otherwise few would want to hire me. I have already written some about the Tutor house in Hope Ranch, CA that we framed while working for Hal Benhardt Construction, so I will skip that one except to say it was a very special job since it was my first real opportunity to apply the complicated roof-framing methodology that would become my forte throughout the 1980s and beyond. You could say that it was on that job that I more or less "cut my teeth" on the more advanced aspects of roof framing.

In the mid-1980s I had the chance to frame a huge Tutor home for Paul Franz in Carpinteria, CA, which is just south of Santa Barbara. This ocean front lot was a beauty and I actually yanked my camper off the truck and lived on the jobsite for 6 months. I did double duty as night security. This saved me from paying rent and all the driving back and forth from town. It took me a few weeks to get used to the crashing wave sound before I could finally sleep soundly, but it was well worth that initial inconvenience. This was the only time I can actually say that I lived in a wealthy neighborhood – even if it was only in a camper parked on the jobsite. If you know anything

7-11 We framed this fancy Tutor home on the beach in Carpinteria, CA in the mid-1980s

about me at all – it is that I hate driving to and from a jobsite and sacrificing all that time. During my framing career I always tried to live within 30 minutes of any job. That is all I was willing to give any employer or job. I consider travel time to be part of my work day. I certainly don't do it for fun. If I spend a total of 1 hour traveling to/from the jobsite and then I physically work 10 hours at the jobsite, I would have actually devoted 11 hours of my life to that job. So if I earned $22 an hour while on the jobsite I was paid $220 ($22 × 10) in actual wages but my real wage was $20 per hour since I had to dedicate 11 hours of my day to gain that wage ($220 ÷ 11 = $20). The shorter my travel time, the higher was my real wage, so on this Carpinteria job where I had zero travel time, my actual wage was my real wage. I know guys who travel over an hour each direction to/from a jobsite where they can earn a higher wage but when you sit down and calculate their real wage it is less than if they had worked a lesser paying job closer to home. During the extra time that they had spent traveling to/from the far-off job they could have simply worked "hands on" at a lower wage and come out spades ahead, not to mention anything of the car maintenance and gas cost.

Anyhow, this project was designed by the Santa Barbara architects Ketzel and Goodman. It sat on a five-acre estate and included a gate house plus a large guest house over a six-car garage in addition to the elaborate main house. I did many projects during the 1980s where Ray Ketzel and Jerry Goodman were the architects since they seemed to have cornered the market for the Tutor design along the Central California Coast. I found their plans

7-12 Lots of dormers, intersecting ridge lines, snub nose hips, etc. will keep any roof framer happy

very well thought out. That is not something I can say for modern-day architects who use CAD. These CAD guys leave much to be solved on the jobsite by the framer. In the old days architects had to think everything through as they drew by hand. They also had to have at least a few years of "hands on" construction jobsite experience before they could even test for the architect's license, unlike modern-day architects who might never have set foot on a jobsite before their first set of plans leaves the building department. This house on Padaro Lane had all the trappings that made any job loads of fun: lots of different level ridges to be connected, open beam ceilings throughout, dormers out the wazoo, arched hallways, and a tower or two. This house would go on to have a stellar future since a later owner was friends with the Clinton family and several times during Bill Clinton's presidency the property served as the West Coast White House during vacations. **(figs 7-11, 7-12)**

After I shut down my framing company in the late 1980s, I worked for a variety of folks, including one custom home framer from Ventura, CA, by the name of Jim Martin. He did a lot of framing in the wealthy Montecito, CA, area, and I would cut his complicated roofs and sometimes snap/plate/ scratch for wall framing. Jim was quite the character and had an excellent crew. All his guys were hard workers and they just blew through projects. Jim was Mr. Practical and one of the best I have seen at solving assembly problems. I have no idea where he learned to frame but he was a natural. As hard as his crew worked during the day, they went and lifted weights at night. That was their standard MO unless of course the surf was up, which meant you wouldn't see a soul for days. Jim always took on more jobs than he could handle, so he and his crew were constantly flipping back and forth among the various jobs to keep the myriad of contractors happy. He was cheaper than most other Santa Barbara, CA, framers, so he always had folks pounding down his door with projects. I doubt he ever turned down a job. I had operated my business in the exact opposite manner and never took on more than I could frame one at a time. I did enjoy working for Jim and picked up some good framing tricks from him.

Since I only cut roofs for Jim, I missed out on the stacking, which I always felt was the best part of any framing job. I remember after cutting the roof on singer/songwriter Kenny Loggins's Santa Barbara, CA, house (no, I never saw Kenny), I dropped back by the jobsite a week later to look over Jim's stacking job. There was a huge plate beam that was supposed to carry the bottom ends of a bunch of rafter beams on the rear patio deck area, but the concrete piers for the twin vertical support posts weren't in yet, so I had figured they would have to hold off stacking that section. Low and behold when I looked out back at the patio area the roof was all framed up and that huge 6×12 plate beam was just dangling there all by itself some 12 feet up in the air. Not a single stick of wood was holding it up. Blew me away. I asked Jim how he had done that stint of magic and he told me that they sent a few lag screws down into the plate beam from a couple rafter beams to hold it up in place. That allowed him to finish the roof and be done with the job. That was just the kind of guy he was – always thinking outside the box. Somehow he must have counterbalanced those rafter beams to support that load.

You also didn't mess around with Jim, kind of like Jim Croce's song except in this real-life version Slim doesn't whoop Jim. I remember the time an owner of a house Jim was framing arrived on the job just as he and his crew were finishing up the project and getting ready to shove off. I suppose Jim had arranged for him to drop by so he could get his pay. For some reason, the owner told Jim he wasn't going to pay. I wasn't there at the time, but I heard about it afterward from his guys. They said Jim all quiet-like walked over to his truck, grabbed a chainsaw and started walking back toward the newly framed house while he fired it up. The owner ran over to him and asked what he was going to do. Jim answered that it was "he who put the house up and since he hadn't got paid for doing so he was simply going to take back his labor by knocking the building down." The owner cut Jim a check right then and there.

Another famous house I worked on in the 1980s was reportedly built for a sister of the Shah of Iran and sat atop a hill just west of downtown Santa Barbara, CA. The house itself had been framed up for the singer Frank Sinatra but was never finished for what I suspect was financial reasons and sat naked for several years until resold. The mysterious new owner had hired the local contractor Parton & Edwards to finish up the house on a super short time contract. At one point, we had nearly 80 guys from every trade tripping over one another to get the job done. There wasn't much new framing on the project, but I remember doing all types of pickup items from installing ¾-inch sheathing over the concrete slab for wood floor installation, to sheathing a living room ceiling some 20 feet in the air for a fancy wood sunburst mural, to capping the double block 8-foot concrete wall that ran around the whole 10-acre plot with wood so it could be stuccoed with a crown molding type detail. A lot of money was thrown at that house in a short time, and it was fun to have been a part of it. The best thing about the job was that we were paid at "time and a half" for anything over 40 hours a week, and since I was doing 12-hour days, my paychecks were fat. It didn't last long, of course, but it was good incentive to work long and hard. This would be the only time in my life where I would be paid more than straight wages for the extra time I worked as a framer. "Time and a half" was unheard of in the construction industry back in those days. I heard that another one of the Shah's relatives built a fancy home in Montecito, CA, which had an outside swimming pool that stretched inside the house under a glass wall. You could enter the pool inside and swim out if you so desired. The house was some 20,000 square feet. I would have liked to have worked on that house, as well as the huge mansion built for talk show host Oprah Winfrey in the same neighborhood, but, by then, I was on my way out of the Central Coast of California and headed for other pastures. Besides, it was high time to let the young bucks move up and take my slot. Santa Barbara, CA, would always be one of those classic hotspots for building high-end custom homes, and, when I look at it from Google Earth nowadays, it is hard to believe that it used to be a sleepy little town. After leaving Santa Barbara, I would spend the next 15 years working in the San Francisco Bay area when I wasn't in Alaska. First, I would help rebuild custom homes in the Oakland foothills after the firestorm of 1991, and then I would cut and stack homes for many different contractors in the more luxurious areas outside San Jose, CA, during the dot-com boom.

Next in time-line of fond memories jumps forward all the way to the late 1990s. Funny how life works – one might go for several years just framing mundane homes until the chance to frame something special pops up. In was in 1997 that I began to work on an updated version of *A Roof Cutter's Secrets*. Looking back now, it seemed that it was just after I decided to do this that the Lord tossed a whole string of new and different complicated roof-framing projects into my life for the specific reason of having them included in the RCS rewrite. Who was I to argue with the Big Guy. It all started when I was asked to help cut/stack the roof on a monster house in Medford, OR. It was built by Jack Resner for the owner of *Guitar* magazine, and the roof plan outline was featured as the new cover of RCS 2002+. On this job, I had the opportunity to get some good photos of the supporting/supported style of running hips and valleys since there was a full sampling

(RCS pgs. 100–107). The job also contained a handful of other useful topics like Bay Roofs (RCS pgs. 231–237), off-angle California valleys (RCS pgs. 182–183), etc. I was also on this job that I dealt with my first moment frame. The new age of embedded steel was on its way, and I had my first twinge that I was indeed becoming a Neanderthal. After that job I, headed over to La Pine, OR, to help Dan Daley on a classic Tutor log style home along the Deschutes River. Aside from cutting the regular roof rafters, which were all TJIs due to the size of the spans, my main project was to frame up a +20-foot open eyebrow dormer. I had never done one of these before, since eyebrows aren't all that common in West Coast architecture. I hit the library to try and get some ideas and then called my buddy Dave Saunders back East to see if he could send me some sketches on how he used to build them in New England. In the end, nothing worked so I had to invent a new methodology that I fashioned after how I believed a boat builder might handle the challenge. It was a great new subject matter to add to *A Roof Cutter's Secrets* (RCS pgs. 194–203). I had been asked about eyebrow dormers a time or two but really couldn't comment because I had never done one. Dan's roof cutting specialist, John Burrell, and I had a great time jigging it up; it is always reassuring to have another sharp mind backing you up.

After the eyebrow job, it was down to the San Jose area to work for Shone Freeman on the most complicated roof that I have ever had the pleasure to cut and stack. It is featured near the front of the updated *A Roof Cutter's Secrets* and also one of the roofs I included in the roof-framing workbook entitled *The Complicated Roof.* Its complexity made it a great learning example and, by writing the methodology down, I made sure that I would never forget how it was calculated and cut. This roof had a mix of everything one could imagine plus several things I have never encountered before. As a result of this roof, I added another new section to RCS entitled "Dog-Leg Bastard Broken Hips" (RCS pgs. 154–158). The house was a real test of stacking skills and, luckily, when you put Shone Freeman, Rodger Allen, and myself together back in the old days, there wasn't much we couldn't do. As complicated as it was, everything fit together flawlessly. That goes to show you how good a framer Shone is since the wall heights, diagonals, spans, etc. were all tits. In the tougher sections of the house, we used a snapped out roof skeleton view on the top floor decking to help us stay on track. I would have to say this roof was the masterpiece of my life. There had never been before or will there likely ever be again, in what remains of my limited lifetime, a chance to do something on that scale of difficulty. I praise the Lord often for that unique opportunity and pray each one of you may also share such an experience in your career. **(fig 7-13)**

After cut/stacking a few more complicated roofs for various framing contractors in the San Jose area, one which had some dovetail hips (RCS pgs 158–162), it was back over to the East Bay to work for Dave Sylvester on a

7-13 S.R. Freeman specializes in framing complicated homes in the West San Francisco Bay area (photo courtesy Hawkeye Aerial Photography)

real chopped up addition. The "addition" was twice the size of most folk's entire homes. It is featured as a photo in *A Roof Cutter's Secrets* 2002+, pg. 149. The photo caption said there was (6) dog-leg bastard hips, (7) dog-leg bastard valleys, (2) dog-leg bastard broken hips, (4) regular hips, (1) regular valley, (2) California valleys, (1) regular broken hip, and (1) hip-end California framed onto a conical tower. Do you think it was a pure coincidence that right after I had just done a bunch of these never-seen-before dog-leg bastard broken hips on Shone's job that I would so quickly have a second chance to do a few more on Dave's job? Naw, the Lord's signature was all over it. That job was a fond memory because I was able to work with one of my favorite framing partners, Ken Nichols. We were always competing against one another and blew the whole job out from ground up in record time. The owner of the house was an open heart surgeon, and while we were framing the roof he loved to study what we had done when he came home from work. He was quite impressed with our skill and one day, to our surprise, complemented us by saying so. Pretty awesome coming from a gentleman who's medical skill saves lives and I fired right back to him that this was kid's stuff compared to what he did. Sure made our day to be genuinely appreciated by a guy of his incredible caliber. To us it was kind of like the US president himself had stopped his limo parade to give us the "thumbs up" on our work.

It was 2001 when I headed East to work for Dave Saunders at National Lumber in Massachusetts. Islamic terrorists had just knocked down the twin towers in New York City, so the country's mood was somber. I loaded my roof cutting tools in the Cessna 206, stuck the truck in storage, and headed out to Mansfield. No long drive like the last time I went out East and worked in 1977. I was charged with setting up a precut roof division for National Lumber. Contractors could drop off their house plans and National Lumber would in short order deliver a complete roof rafter package to their jobsite all cut and ready to install. It was also my job to cut all the roofs for the 120-man framing division that National Lumber operated. Dave was the brainstorm behind all this and more. Well the precut part for the general public never took off probably because it always ended up cheaper to do the little roof jobs with trusses (National also had a truss division) so I stayed busy cutting big custom homes, etc., for National's framing crew. After the first job it also became part of my job to go out and stack the roof skeleton since the crews didn't seem to have the expertise needed for this task. I learned real quick that general framing skills on the East Coast had fallen into decline since the last time I was there, simply because so much was being prefabricated. The carpenters had really morphed into installers with little opportunity to develop true rough carpentry skills. The crews seemed to have little understanding of how sloppy wall assembly affected roof framing. It became a real challenge to put roofs on buildings that didn't hold consistent spans (off up to 2.5 inches) or had major out-of-square issues. Somehow we made it work. My team and I would also preframe complete dormers as units. Some being purely architectural were framed to sit on a finished roof surface while others were functional and we framed them attached to their associated doubled up common rafters supporting members. Both types were trucked to the jobsite and set with a crane. It was a blast. Weather didn't bother us since we had our own indoor work area. We prebuilt tower roofs or any other roof detail that Dave decided he wanted prebuilt and everything was sent out to the job on a flatbed. Towers

7-14 We prefabbed all kinds of roof structures when I worked for Dave Saunders at National Lumber (photo courtesy Dave Saunders)

that were wider than the maximum truckable load width we built in two parts cut vertically right down the middle to be joined on site. **(fig 7-14)**

One house National was framing in Boston proper had two towers that were too big to do at the shop so we had to assemble them on site. Jim Rouvalis was the job foreman, and I can't say enough good about him. Smartest roof guy I have ever seen. He has spent his whole life building high-end homes on Cape Cod, MA. Whereas I was a production framer who now and then had been blessed to have the opportunity to work on custom homes in the top 5% of difficulty and price range, Jim had spent his whole career in that top 5%. Anyhow, this house was being built for one of Fidelity Investments fund managers and tipped the scales at 20,000 square feet. I can't remember much of the ends and outs of the building's layout, but if I recall correctly it had an underground area that was to house either an indoor swimming pool or a basketball court. Could have been both for all I know. Anyway, when we arrived to frame up our two towers, Jim was working on joining two roof planes over the main house that intersected at a dog-leg angle. One roof plane was a monstrous shed roof and the other a convex arc or more technically a 90° segment of a horizontally set cylinder. The rafters for both were TJIs and, if I recall correctly, the shed roof's rafters ran top-to-bottom in the standard roof rafter format, while the arched roof's rafters ran horizontally side-to-side. Since the intersection between the two roofs was open, Jim was constructing a live valley between the two planes built out of a bunch of LVLs sandwiched together. He had plumbed up a

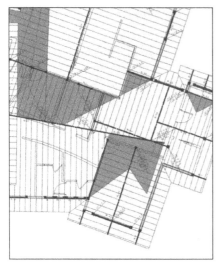

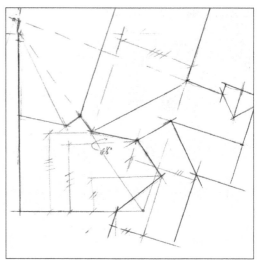

7-15 Many architects have trouble visualizing how to connect tricky roof sections

7-16 My sketched solutions to clean up the roof lines on one section of a Park City, UT roof

bunch of long 4×4 temporary posts every 6 to 8 feet that followed a curved line he had marked out on the floor denoting the exact union between these two dissimilar roof planes. On each post he had a height mark, and his crew was slowly bending each LVL around the 4×4 posts and it was attached just above the height marks. The 4×4 posts were to be removed after the valley was fabricated and all the rafters were tied in. Don't ask me how he figured the placement of that curved valley line on the ground, etc, because to this day I still don't know even after he tried his best to explain it to me when we had lunch one day. On difficult roof situations Jim always builds a scale model so he can work through his framing approach beforehand.

Dave Saunders hoped I would stay on at National forever and that would have been fine with me, but I started having medical issues and had to return to California for surgeries, which put me down for most of 2002. By the time I had healed up to be able to return to work, I had been replaced by a $500,000 programmable robotic wood cutting machine, and National no longer had its framing crew, so I began working for framer Nick Ridge in the Bay Area when I wasn't serving as a humanitarian aid volunteer overseas. With the start of 2007-09 US economic recession and the resulting multi-year building slowdown that followed, fancy jobs were few and far between.

The last really cool job that comes to mind was the chance to help out briefly on a Park City, UT, mansion for the Salt Lake City framing contractor Mark Monasmith. It would have been late summer 2014. Mark had sent me a set of plans for a house with a roof that had some parts he couldn't quite get his head around. I studied them for a while and soon I too had spotted the same strange elements. It appeared as if the design had exceeded the architect's roof knowledge. I visited the architect's website and, while they had done some very nice homes, there was nothing on the level of this job's complexity. For one thing, they could not visualize how to join a scattering of building wings converging at different angles in one corner of the building. It also looked like they hadn't considered all the ramifications involved in transitioning the main gable roof into a gently sloping two directional circular roof. Therefore, the structural pages and architectural pages were unclear and appeared to be in conflict. It would have been a difficult roof design for any architect since most really don't spend a lot of time studying the intricacies of roof framing. They focus their energies on the stuff that is of paramount importance to the client like interior layout and taking advantage of the views. For most architects the roof is there to keep the rain/snow out and give the exterior some aesthetic appeal. Over my lifetime I have had the pleasure to help many architects resolve roof design issues. The real good ones seek out your input, for they realize that someone who has dealt with roofs all their life may very well have some insight that they don't have. I for one like the challenge of difficult roof situations and, while I may not be a math wizard, the Lord has blessed me with some exceptional visualization skills – as long as it is flat plane roofs intersecting. If it gets harder than that I will be giving Jim Rouvalis a call. **(figs 7-15, 7-16)**

Mark Monasmith is as sharp a framer as they come. On his worse day, he is twice as sharp as I am on my best day so it only took us a few hours to snap out solutions before I was no longer needed. Wish I was young again, it would have been fun to work with Mark on a house or two. He was one of those guys like we had in the old Los Angeles tract days – fast and efficient. One of his very first tool purchases as a framer was an extended reach forklift (telehandler) just like Dan Daley. Wish I had been that savvy. But then again, when I was younger these trick machines weren't even around, so we destroyed our backs moving material. In those days, the Pettibone carry-lift machines were cutting edge.

Like ocean waves, life will always bring us smiles and frowns.

The value of experience is not in seeing much but in seeing wisely.

– Sir William Osler

8

Where was Adam when we needed him – names matter

Change is the law of life. And those who look only to the past or present are certain to miss the future. – John F. Kennedy

I speak Spanish, so those of you who do not *habla español* (speak Spanish) may not realize that there are some 20 variants of this language. If you are used to speaking Mexican Spanish and visit Chile, you will come to find out that many of the subject nouns you use in Mexico have different meanings in Chile or don't even exist and are replaced by some totally new words. Spanish is a very complicated language if you consider just a couple of its idiosyncrasies: it has 99 forms of each verb while English has 6; every noun is either male or female, while in English they are all neuter; simply changing the accent on a part of the word can change its meaning. Spanish is not very conducive to efficiency, whereas English is. Being simple and precise is the reason English does double duty as the official international pilot language and also the unofficial international business language. The English language has matured quite a bit since the old days, just read Shakespeare or the King James Bible to get a taste of how it was spoken in the 16th century. I for one am immensely happy that it has evolved for I certainly can't see myself talking with all these gibberish "thees" and "thous." Rough carpentry like any other specialized skill or trade has its own "language" that has developed over time and will continue to do so long after you and I are both gone. In order to understand rough carpentry and communicate with others in this field one must learn the "lingo." If you stay in the trade for an extended length of time, you will see new words or meanings arise and old words or meanings fall away.

I started teaching roof-framing seminars at *JLC* Live conferences in the early 1990s, about 4 to 5 years after the first edition of *A Roof Cutter's Secrets* was published. Words that were commonly used to describe a certain aspect of roof framing on the West Coast drew only blank stares when I used them at my East Coast presentations. It brought back memories of 1977 when I worked for a framing contractor in Framingham, MA. That adventure was an eye opener for me, as I experienced firsthand the stark difference between East and West Coast methods of framing. None of the carpenters on the job where I worked had ever seen production roof cutting performed much less eyed a wormdrive Skilsaw (they all had sidewinders). Rough framing on the West Coast has always been progressive and inventive in both methods and terminology, while the East Coast had held more to the "old school" true craftsmanship type of methods and terminology. How a person wants to do something is their own business, but, as for me, I am always looking for faster and simpler way to do things. I am not married to any system or method. If you show me a less complicated or quicker way to do something I will immediately absorb it into my bag of tricks. The same holds true with framing terminology. If some old term, or the usage of a term makes little sense in the current application, let's do something about it. Let's modernize it, let's clarify it. That is in essence what I tried to do in *A Roof Cutter's Secrets* and during my teaching opportunities at the *JLC* Live conferences, etc.

I am a man of few words. When I speak I like to say things in a concise, clear fashion. My goal is to get to the point quickly and be done with it. I like words that accurately describe a visual situation in as commonsensical way as possible. Maybe this is a hangover from being an aircraft pilot and the way we pilots communicate over the radio, but efficiency has always been high on my list. I hate it when someone talks to me for 5 minutes about something that could have been passed along easily in a single, well thought out sentence. I recognize that not all people are that way – my wife is a good example of spending a lot of time talking but saying little (Don't worry, she's laughing). I have learned that you never want to get directions from this type of person. Many times I will ask someone off the street where such and such a place is, and if they start rambling, I politely thank them for their time and move along to get directions from someone else.

Framing terminology has changed big time over my lifetime with the addition of many new words. Many have to do with the new fasteners and seismic type metal that invaded construction in the 1990s and onward. Things like: hold downs, post caps, SDS screws, moment frames, ad infinitum. There were also many words added to name new lumber products like: parallams, TJIs, LVLs, OSB, etc. Over my lifetime, rough framing has gone from simple S4S wood assembled with 16d hand-driven nails to high-tech materials assembled with specialized equipment. We have seen many framing words fall out of usage or reassigned new duties. Since I have spent

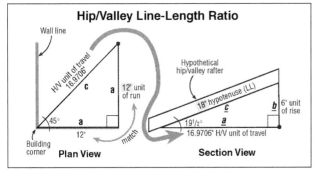

8-1 "Travel" was coined to describe the horizontal diagonal distance below any hip/valley

most of my framing career messing around from the top plates up, I thought it would only be fitting to tell my side of the story in how roof-framing terminology has evolved in the past 5 decades.

It was in the later 1970s that I first started looking at roof-framing terms from the point of sensibility and started noticing a real lack of congruity. It happened right after I came out of the Los Angeles housing tracts where I had worked solo and didn't talk to anybody and then went to work in Santa Barbara, CA, as a framing foreman. In my new position, communication with the crew was paramount since I had to teach them how to do certain things. For centuries the word "run" has been used to described half the building span or half the perpendicular cross-section dimension of the building with the unit of run as 12 inches. OK, I am fine with that, everybody gets it. But then to layout a hip or valley with the framing square, we find out that the "unit of run" had miraculously morphed into 17 inches in length. On an octagon it morphs again into 13 inches. Now I am a logical guy, so this bothered me. Run cannot mean different things in different situations without confusing people so I coined a new term "travel" to describe the horizontal diagonal distance under a hip or valley (RCS pg. 3). **(fig 8-1)** This allowed the word "run" to stay specific to just one situation which in reality is the foundation of all roof framing. Now when stepping off a hip or valley with a framing square, the "unit of **travel**" would be the previously noted 17 inches. Of course, we don't step off anything anymore but rather use calculated line lengths that are faster and more accurate, but I mention this just as a way to tie everything together. While one might on occasion use a framing square set up with the "unit of roof rise" and the "unit of travel" to layout the head-cut and birdsmouth on hips and valleys, more often than not a Quick Square or Speed square is used in modern day roof framing. Think of "travel" as the shadow line on the floor below a stacked hip or valley with the sun at high noon. "Travel" also applies to any bastard hip or valley in the same manner. This term has worked out well and gained universal acceptance over the years. "Run" stays confined to mean only half the cross section of the building with the unit of run always 12 inches.

Another new term that jumped into the carpenter's vocabulary list came from a simple change I made to the standard roof cutting methodology. As I learned production roof cutting from cutters in the tracts, I noticed how they all took the building span and found the associated common rafter length from Riechers' rafter table book. Then, with this dimension they laid out the rafters and physically shortened for half the thickness of the ridge by drawing it out on the side of the rafter with a Squangle. All fine and good. This method of shortening had been done since the ice age, and there is certainly nothing wrong with it. But being a young buck who wasn't yet set in his ways, I suggested that instead of going through the physical shortening step why not just subtract the thickness of the ridge from the span dimension and look that number up in the rafter table book. It worked out great and caught on all over.

I used the rafter table book to find rafter lengths for many years but, while working in Santa Barbara, CA, I exchanged that well-worn book for a simple solar-powered calculator and began calculating things mathematically. This all came about when I had to frame an unequal pitch gable roof that had 12/12 on one side and 5.625/12 on the other side. I can't remember why it had to be that odd-ball pitch but, it probably had to do with head room or something like that. Anyhow the blasted pitch wasn't in my *Riechers Full Length Roof Framer*, so I went to the builder and asked if I could adjust the roof pitch up or down slightly so I could use my rafter tables. Say up to 5¾ or down to 5½. My request was denied. Bummer! Now I was forced to figure out the rafter lengths by math. This is when I first began to develop my line length ratio methodology (LL ratios) that I would go on to use for the next 20 years. I used them up until I purchased my first Construction Master calculator in the late 1990s. In reality, I should thank that house for forcing me to advance. Now, you framing square guys are probably all smiling since this situation could have easily been handled by stepping the rafter off with that fabled tool. I knew that as well but I sure as hell couldn't do it, because I had a reputation to protect. It would have been terribly demoralizing to have to resort to the ancient methodology of playing patty cake with a framing square since everyone knows that a real live "roof cutter" only works with line lengths. What would the crew think! Remember, I had just spent a bunch of years in the housing tracts where a framing square was never seen, much less used. The 8-inch Try Square was used by the fascia, layout, and pickup guys, while the Squangle was used by the roof cutters and the stackers. No one else (wall framers, joisters, etc.) had any need of a square whatsoever since most everything from headers to crips to sills was precut by the radial arm saw guy. That which was required to be cut in assembly, like double plates, trimmers, CJs, were all done by eye. When the Triangular square came along years later, it replaced both the Try Square and the Squangle.

While I am no math whiz, I did make it out of high school with a decent understanding of mathematics up through basic geometry and trigonometry. I wasn't very good at algebra and had no desire whatsoever to try calculus. So it goes to say, I remembered how to apply Pythagoras theorem to solve for the sides of a right triangle and how to set up a relationship in order to solve for an unknown value using cross-multiplication. Those two processes were all I needed. So for this odd ball pitch I mentioned earlier (let's say 120 inches was run), I set up a relationship with the roof pitch 5.625/12 = X/120, then cross-multiplied 5.625 × 120 ÷ 12 = 56.25 to find total rise for the 120 run. Then I would install both the total rise and run in Pythagoras theorem $(a^2 + b^2 = c^2)$ to find the hypotenuse, and I was all set with the rafter length. In time I learned that I didn't have to go through this two-step process every time I had to find a new rafter length, but could shorten the procedure by using the proportion of the given roof pitch's "rise/run" or "hypotenuse/run" to solve things (RCS pgs. 3–5). Anyhow, I now needed some names for these ratios and decided to name them with words that best described their use in roof framing. So "Roof Rise ratio" (RR ratio), "Common Line Length ratio" Com LL ratio), and "Hip/Valley Line Length ratio" (H/V LL ratio) were born. It wasn't until a year or so later that I came to find out my ratios were nothing more than basic trigonometry functions. What I had named "RR ratio" was "tangent" of the angle in trigonometry and what I had named Com LL ratio and H/V LL ratio were "secants" of the angle. I decided I liked the names I had reassigned these age-old trigonometry functions since they fit the roof-framing situation better, so I kept them as part of my "lingo" and I shared them with others.

Certainly it is true that if I had spent some time studying the fancy charts on the blade and tongue of the framing square, I might have had an easier time with all this math stuff, but I didn't know they had anything to do with my dilemma. While I had played around with the framing square at Orange Coast College, we stuck to its elementary uses of rafter and stair layout, squaring up things, etc. We used a rafter table book to find all our rafter line lengths. I suspect in the end it was a good thing that I was ignorant of the framing square charts, since having to fight my way through the math aspect of roof framing caused me to develop the simple roof rafter calculating system that became immensely popular after I shared it in the original *A Roof Cutter's Secrets* (1988). With the advent of the hand-held calculator in 1967 and, even more so, with the advent of the Construction Master calculator in 1984, all those crazy charts on a framing square became totally irrelevant.

In my LL ratio methodology of solving rafter lengths, I would take the building span, subtract off the thickness of the ridge to find a "shortened span" dimension. Now instead of looking for the associated rafter length in a rafter table book, I would divide "the shortened span" in half to come up with a unique horizontal distance that is then multiplied by the appropriate

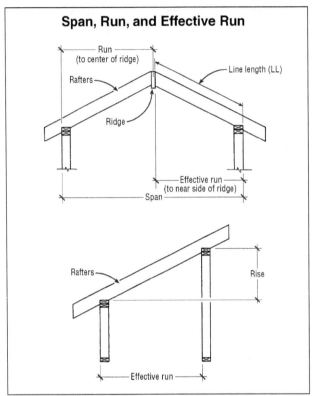

Span, Run, and Effective Run

Run (to center of ridge)

Rafters

Line length (LL)

Ridge

Effective run (to near side of ridge)

Span

Rafters

Rise

Effective run

8-2 "Effective Run" is the horizontal distance from outside wall to the ridge below a common rafter

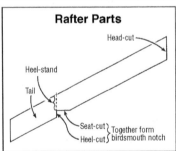

Rafter Parts

Head-cut

Heel-stand

Tail

Seat-cut ⎫ Together form
Heel-cut ⎬ birdsmouth notch

8-3 I worked to develop universal name conformity for the various parts of a rafter

LL ratio. My dilemma was what to call this new horizontal distance since it certainly wasn't "run" which was measured to the center of the ridge. I struck on the name "effective run" and that name has served it so well that it has now been universally used throughout the USA and abroad after some 40 years (RCS pg. 2). **(fig 8-2)**

During my younger years, I worked diligently to develop some kind of universal name conformity for the various parts of a rafter (RCS pg. 1). **(fig 8-3)** Many centuries ago the parts of the skewed birdsmouth notch had been given names corresponding to a man's shoe. The "heel" tucked up against the outside of a bearing wall, while the "toe" was the end of the notch closest to the building's interior. I haven't a clue why these terms were chosen, but I can easily envision a small-sized, upside down shoe fitted in the skewed birdsmouth notch. The horizontal and vertical cuts of the birdsmouth notch came to be known as the seat-cut and heel-cut, respectively. Many folks unknowingly have called them "level-cut" and "vertical-cut." While technically correct in general terms, these terms lack any specialization to the roof-framing application unless they are accompanied by the word "birdsmouth." It is would be like calling a "2×4 stud" a "2×4 board" instead. The word "stud" was developed to better describe where this "2×4 board" is actually used. Another example would be "plumb-cut" and "ridge-cut." The ridge-cut is a plumb-cut, of course, but by using the word "ridge" it further narrows down the particular use of that "plumb-cut." Therefore, "seat-cut" and "heel-cut" better define where those level and vertical cuts are located without the need to add in the limiter "birdsmouth." "Seat-cut" was aptly chosen for, just as you sit in a chair, a rafter sits on a plate.

The plumb distance of the rafter above the seat-cut set in line with the heel-cut I have always called the "heel-stand." I got the term from the Los Angeles housing tracts. All roof framers know how important this dimension is to set up hips, valleys and various ridge situations. Many folks use the designation "HAP" or "height above plate" to describe this dimension. Marshall Gross used it in his popular book entitled *Roof Framing* (1984) and this initiated its usage. Personally, I do not like the term HAP. To me it is once again like saying "2×4 board" when one should be saying "2×4 stud." HAP is ambiguous. I use "height above plate" to name the placement of many things like ridges, purlins, pony walls, etc., so for this reason "heel-stand" is a better use limiter. It is very simply the vertical extension of the heel-cut line. In my mind, I envision a tiny cartoon character "standing" at the heel of a birdsmouth notch with his height being recorded by a nurse. Some folks use the wording "heel-height" to describe this distance, but I believe this is a poor choice of wording as well, since someone could very easily think it is referring to the dimension of the heel-cut itself, since "height" is a general use term.

Few roof-framing words bring up more contention with the old timers than "roof pitch." They, like I, originally learned that roof pitch was the unit of rise placed over 24 inches (unit of span) and then the resulting fraction was reduced to its simplest numeric form. So a "1/4 pitch" roof (6/24) was what we now refer to as 6/12. I have no idea how far back in history this strange relation was concocted or for what purpose, but one thing is for certain, X/24 has no relevancy whatsoever nowadays. Roof pitch as used today is a good example of an older term evolving for the better. The term "pitch" by itself alludes to an angle in degrees and what better way to describe that angle in the roof-framing sense than with Pythagoras's right

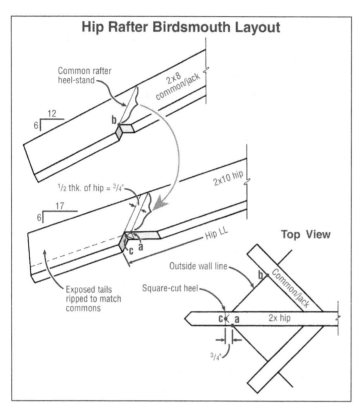

Hip Rafter Birdsmouth Layout

Common rafter heel-stand

2x8 common/jack

12
6

b

1/2 thk. of hip = 3/4"

2x10 hip

17
6

Hip LL

c a

Exposed tails ripped to match commons

Outside wall line

Square-cut heel

Top View

b

Common/jack

c a   2x hip

3/4"

8-4 No hip is ever "dropped"; rather, the common rafter heel-stand is positioned to plane it into the roof

triangle rise/run methodology. So if "roof pitch" is the roof's angle measured from a horizontal plane, then a roof angle of 26.57° would be much better described in the trigonometric sense by 6/12 with "unit of rise/ unit of run" than does "1/4 pitch." To reduce 6/12 down to its simplest numeric form also makes no sense since roof framing chose to use 12 inches as the horizontal component.

One term I have tried to erase from roof-framing usage is "dropping the hip." I was taught this term as a young carpenter on the jobsite and later its use was reinforced in the Orange Coast College construction technology program's roof-framing module. I personally think it is a bogus concept and rather confusing. No hip is ever "dropped" but rather the heel-stand of a common rafter is placed where the side of the hip rafter crosses the outside plate line if the top edge will remain unbacked. I will continue to fight for its demise. **(fig 8-4)**

Out of the Los Angeles housing tracts arose the ever popular "California valley" style of handling roof intersections (RCS pgs. 93–98). **(fig 8-5)** In the earliest days of tract framing, a lengthwise interior footing was placed under one interior hall wall for the specific purpose of providing support for vertical

8-5 The "California valley" or "layover valley" was originally designed to lower concrete slab foundation costs in tract homes

braces to the main ridge, purlin braces, and miscellaneous other braces that carried regular valleys, etc. Since mega-tract construction is always focused on lowering building costs and simplifying assembly processes, the tract architects in the mid-1970s began eliminating these long interior footings with the intent to place all the roof loads solely on the exterior wall footings. To accomplish this, they upsized the rafters and/or narrowed the OC spacing permitting the rafters to carry the roof loads without the need of purlins. They lapped the CJs with the rafters at least every 48 inches OC to create a triangular truss-type ridge support that replaced vertical ridge bracing. To do away with the requisite of vertically supporting the interior end of an intersecting secondary span ridge and her associated hung valleys, they devised a new system of framing roof intersections where a secondary span roof transferred its weight to the roof surface of the main span instead of to a pair of valley rafters. In this new system, the main span's common rafters were framed full-length right through that part of the roof that had previously been handled by conventional hung valley rafter framing. The main roof was sheathed and the secondary span's valley jack rafters and ridge were cut to rest on the main span's sheathed surface. This overframing roof intersection methodology also became attractive because it offered some valuable seismic benefits. Earthquake-proof durability had become an important design consideration in Southern California building following the 1971 Sylmar earthquake. "California valley" style intersections went on to become quite popular in custom homes because it allowed designers to place a raked ceiling on either the primary, or the secondary span, and die

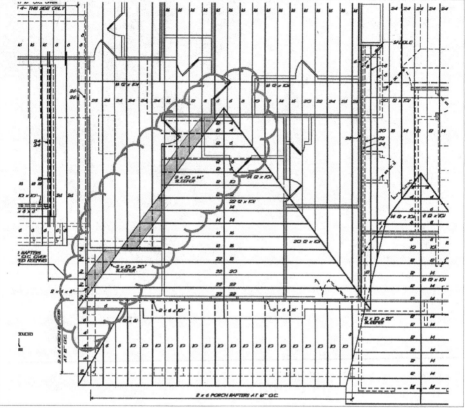

8-6 On this custom home, the "California valley" flips back and forth between the primary and secondary spans

the opposing roof on top. Sometimes, the overlap might even jump back and forth between the two roof planes, as required by the cathedral ceiling details below. **(fig 8-6)** When the technique first began in the tracts, the jack rafter's raked level-cut at the bottom was nailed directly to the sheathing. Since the roof pitch on tract homes in those days was low pitch (3.5/12 to 4/12), some part of the valley jack's long level-cut always bore directly on a primary span's common rafter and its load was directly transferred. When the standard rafter spacing jumped up to 24 inches OC as the function of improved strength in manufactured plywood, it was now possible that the bottom ends of CA valley jacks could theoretically sit on unsupported sheathing alone. To alleviate this condition, a bearing plate was placed on top of the main roof's sheathed surface following the valley line to carry the CA valley jack's lower ends. The addition of this "sleeper," as it came to be called, to CA valley framing was a big improvement since it allowed much better plywood nailing along the valley line. On the East Coast, the

8-7 "Broken hip" is the top section of a regular hip that has been cut or broken by an intersecting roof

"California valley" came to be known as a "layover" valley or "overlay" valley which in truth is a more use-specific term. Some folks use "blind valley" to describe this type of roof intersection, but I am "blind" to understand how this term applies.

As time went on, I faced many new challenges while building custom homes in Santa Barbara, CA, and as a result my roof-framing knowledge increased 10-fold. In the Los Angeles housing tracts, the roofs were not very complicated, being mostly simple Gables or Hips with one or two intersections. Some tracts had Dutch Hip ends and common rafters lapping over an exposed ridge beam, but rarely anything fancier than these. The houses were also relatively small, somewhere in the 1700- to 2000-square-foot size range. In a tract of several hundred homes, it was typical to have only two or three floor plans that were flip-flopped throughout. So truthfully, I did not learn a great deal of advanced roof-framing techniques in the housing tracts, but rather what I did become was an expert in production methodology. I grew very fast and efficient.

Framing a big fancy Tudor house in Santa Barbara's Hope Ranch in 1979 was my first chance to build a tower roof and, after stick framing it in the air some three stories up, I swore that I would prebuild anything like that on the ground in the future and then set it as a finished product. This became my modus operandi going forward; all time-consuming roof sections were prebuilt on the ground and then set with a crane. This included dormers and the like. That same Hope Ranch job also provided the opportunity to develop my methodology of connecting two different height ridges in the same roof plane with a "broken hip" (RCS pgs. 79-81). **(fig 8-7)** The name "broken hip" came about when I realized that this short "piece" was nothing more than a short section of the full-length hip for the larger span. Its full travel was "cut" or "broken" by the lower ridge. These rafters have probably been called many things over time (extension hips, etc.), but I liked the name "broken

8-8 "Dog-leg" is a descriptive term used to describe a building that takes a jog of less than 90°

hip," so I started using this term and *A Roof Cutter's Secrets* helped spread it around. Nowhere in any of the Santa Barbara's library's limited collection of carpentry books could I find a single thing written about this roof situation, although they had been used in the more complicated Swiss Chalet style houses for centuries. So, like much that I faced in the late 1970s and early 1980s, I spent nights drawing them up and devising a methodology to employ in calculating and stacking them. Someday I would love to go to Europe to look in the attics of these ancient homes to see if I can figure out how the old craftsmen framed them.

On one big custom home in Santa Barbara foothills I had to install hips and valleys on a long straight Gable house that took a 45° jog (RCS pgs. 150-154). **(fig 8-8)** I nicknamed this situation a "dog-leg," deriving the name from an aviation phrase I once heard and had incorporated into my pilot lingo. "Dog-leg to final" is used to call out an angled intercept of the final straight-in course to the runway. I know many of you aren't familiar with pilot lingo, but imagine a runway at an uncontrolled airport (little country strip without a control tower) that is aligned North/South. The markings on the runway would be 36 and 18, which are short for 360° (North) and 180° (South). Typically, one does a racetrack pattern to align himself with a straight-in for one end of that runway depending on the favoring winds. At times, when there is no traffic in the area, an arriving pilot may choose to make a straight-in from many miles out rather than do the race track pattern. In this situation, it is rare that his heading to the runway is either dead-on 360° or 180° but typically at some angle off to either side.

The pilot would fly a heading to intercept the final course a mile or so out from the runway threshold. He would broadcast that he is a right or left "dog-leg to final" depending on which side of the final course he is situated. I liked the visualization, so we kept that name and "dog-leg" became accepted as the way to describe a house that makes a jog at any angle other than 90°.

Hip and valley rafters for a non-90° building jog have been called irregular hips/valleys since ancient times, as opposed to regular hips/valleys on a 90° building jog. I, not having much of a loving affection for irregulars, started calling them "bastards" in a derogatory sense. And once again, after using this terminology in *A Roof Cutter's Secrets* it seems to have stuck (RCS pg. 149). It has now been decades since I have heard anybody refer to these rafters as irregulars. Truthfully, irregular hip/valley is a more "use-specific" term, so this would be one instance where you could say I veered from my focus of naming or renaming roof-framing items to better suit the roof situation. It was originally done in jest due to the frustrating process of dealing with these rafters. It's too late to change back now. Many times I use the term "bastard" along with the situation in which it will be placed. "Dog-leg bastard hip/valley" would be a good example.

Since I faced the irregular hip/valley situation as a roof framer before I faced the unequal-pitch hip/valley situation, irregulars were the first to be dubbed "bastards," but later on I included unequal-pitched hip/valleys under this heading as well (RCS pgs. 162–183). Do note that an irregular hip/valley connects two **equal** pitched roof planes at any building jog angle other than 90°, whereas an "unequal pitch hip/valley" is the term used to describe a hip/valley that connects two **unequal** pitched roof planes no matter what the building jog may be. Typically, I refer to an unequal pitched hip/valley as an "unequal-pitch hip/valley" and save the term "bastard" for irregular situations.

As time went on, I had to devise or invent names for rafters in other roof situations in order to write about them in the original version of *A Roof Cutter's Secrets* (1988). Who knows what carpenters in Medieval ages might have called them since I sure couldn't find anything in my searches. Even the old-time carpenters of Santa Barbara were of no help since they had never seen them before either. Young as I was then, I was everybody's "go to" guy on roofs. All the roof-framing books available when I was young focused on how to use the steel square to layout commons or hip/valley situations. Not one book dealt with complex roof-framing situations or production methodology. This observation, in addition to my own crew wanting a copy of all my roof-framing notes as a resource, was the incentive for the original RCS. Little did I know that a gentleman by the name of Marshall Gross on the Right Coast was working on a roof framing book which would be published a few years ahead of RCS. His book, *Roof Framing* and *A Roof Cutter's Secrets* have been the industry's mainstays throughout the past 40 years. Both books may be written on the same subject, but they are exact opposites in their

8-9 "Dove-tail hip" describes a hip that splits to terminate on each end of a 45° clipped building corner

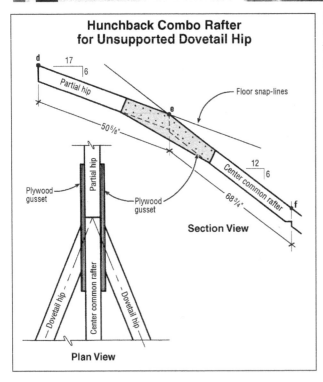

Hunchback Combo Rafter for Unsupported Dovetail Hip

d

17 | 6

Partial hip

50⅝"

Floor snap-lines

e

12 | 6

Center common rafter

68¾"

f

Section View

Plywood gusset

Partial hip

Plywood gusset

Dovetail hip

Center common rafter

Dovetail hip

Plan View

8-10 "Hunchback combo" describes a rafter that leaves the wall plate as a common rafter, but converts to a hip

approaches. Whereas Marshall's book was kind of like a math textbook, since he was a brilliant mathematician and a carpenter union teacher, my book was all about practical jobsite Keep It Simple, Stupid (KISS) methodology because I was a production roof cutter/stacker and framing crew foreman. Each book appealed to a different audience. The more heady guys may like Marshall's

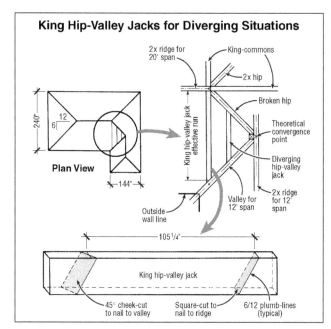

King Hip-Valley Jacks for Diverging Situations

Plan View

240'

12 6

144"

Outside wall line

2x ridge for 20' span

King hip-valley jack effective run

King-commons

2x hip

Broken hip

Theoretical convergence point

Diverging hip-valley jack

Valley for 12' span

2x ridge for 12' span

105 1/4"

King hip-valley jack

45° cheek-cut to nail to valley

Square-cut to nail to ridge

6/12 plumb-lines (typical)

8-11 A "king hip-valley jack" is a king common rafter that is cut or broken by a valley

book better, whereas your everyday framer who was looking for speed and efficiency loved RCS.

I framed one roof that had a hip which split to bear on a 45° clipped building corner, and assigned it the name "dove-tail hip" because it resembled the dovetail joint that I used to join two pieces of material into a single long ridge (RCS pgs. 115, 159). **(fig 8-9)** On another dove-tail hip situation that needed to be self-supporting, I gusseted a common rafter off the end of a partial hip and nicknamed it the "hunchback combo." It served as a common rafter down low, but converted to a regular hip segment at that point where the two dovetail hips intersected (RCS pg. 163). **(fig 8-10)**

Needing to write about the various different hip-valley jack rafters that one might find on a complicated roof, I coined the name "king hip-valley jacks" to name the special hip-valley jacks that were positioned at the end of the ridge where normal full-length king commons would have gone, and "diverging hip-valley jacks" to name the hip-valley jacks that ran from a broken hip to a valley (RCS pgs. 73–75). **(fig 8-11)**

When writing about "Bay window roofs against a wall" (RCS pgs. 237–239), I decided to name the two hips that are fastened to the wall "ledger hips." **(fig 8-12)** It seemed like a logical name since the word ledger is always used to describe a weight-bearing framing member that is attached to a wall. You could call a valley against a wall a "ledger valley" as well, and we did have one of these on a job in Park City, UT, a few years back.

I dubbed a valley that joined two different-size rafter materials an "offset

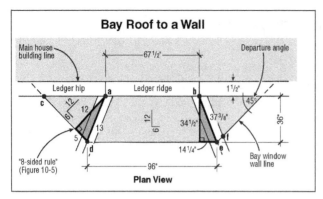

8-12 A "ledger hip" is a regular hip that is nailed against a wall surface such as a Bay window roof

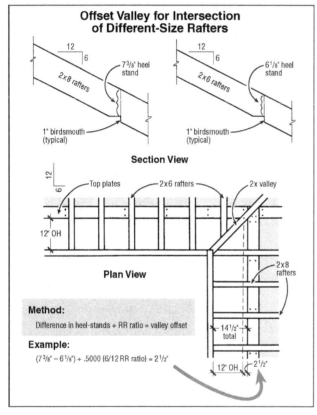

8-13 An "offset valley" joins two roof surfaces that were framed with different-sized materials

valley" (RCS pgs. 100–101). This name originated from the fact that this valley had to be offset from the true inside corner of a building by an amount that compensated for the plumb height difference between the two different-size materials. **(fig 8-13)**

On a big custom home job in Medford, OR, in 1997, we confronted several new roof-framing situations. One part of the roof had jack rafters framing

8-14 "Continuation jacks" are needed when a full hip is installed in the position of a broken hip

8-15 "Off-angled CA valley jacks" are layover jacks used to frame an irregular valley intersection

from a supporting hip to an associated secondary span ridge. I christened these jacks "continuation jacks" since their function was to continue the hip jacks that framed from the plate line to the supporting hip. I had briefly considered naming them "broken commons" since the supporting hip cut through a run of common rafters, but that name sounded too goofy. These "continuation jacks" are cut as regular valley jacks but are framed from a ridge to a supporting hip instead of a standard valley (RCS pgs. 105–107). **(fig 8-14)** In another part of the same roof, we installed California valley jacks to form an irregular valley intersection. I labeled these rafters "off-angle CA valley jacks" since they framed onto the supporting roof surface at an angle other than 90° as regular CA valley jacks do. Technically they are "CA style irregular valley jacks" but "off-angle" seemed to sound better at the time. "Irregular layover valley jacks" would have been a more accurate name choice (RCS pgs. 182-183). **(fig 8-15)** And the strangest of all on this job was a hybrid rafter that I named a "disappearing valley" for lack of anything better (RCS pg. 107).

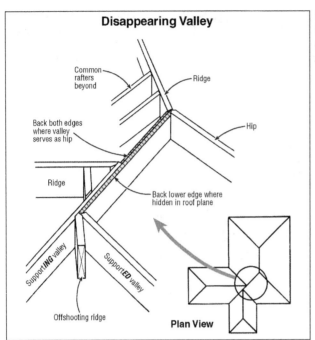

Disappearing Valley

Common rafters beyond

Ridge

Back both edges where valley serves as hip

Hip

Ridge

Back lower edge where hidden in roof plane

Support*ING* valley

Support*ED* valley

Offshooting ridge

Plan View

8-16 A "disappearing valley" leaves the wall as a valley, disappears briefly to reemerge as a broken hip

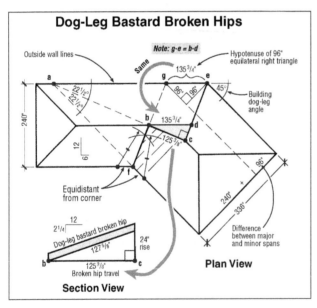

Dog-Leg Bastard Broken Hips

Outside wall lines

Note: g-e = b-d

Same

Hypotenuse of 96" equilateral right triangle

135 3/4"

a

22 1/2°
22 1/2°

g
96" 96"
e
45°

Building dog-leg angle

240"

b
135 3/4"
d
125 3/8"
c

12
6

96"

f

Equidistant from corner

240"

336"

12
2 1/4

Dog-leg bastard broken hip

24" rise

127 5/8"

Difference between major and minor spans

b
125 3/8"
Broken hip travel
c

Plan View

Section View

8-17 "Bastard broken hip" was coined for an unusual situation encountered on a job for S.R. Freeman

(fig 8-16) It was a real quandary as to what to call this rafter. It was a very unusual supporting rafter that served double duty as a valley down low and a broken hip up top. Since this rafter started from the plate line as a valley it only made sense to call it some type of valley. I am still not totally satisfied

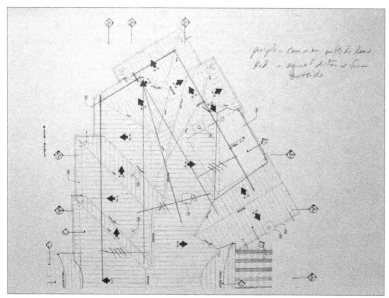

8-18 At times it can be difficult to find the controlling outside plate lines for a bastard broken hip

with the name I chose, but nothing better has ever come along since.

When I worked with Shone Freeman in 2000 on a very complicated roof in Monte Sereno, CA, we encountered a type of rafter that I had never seen before (see *The Complicated Roof* cover). It had the attributes of two different rafters, so I combined their two names and the "bastard broken hip" was born (RCS pgs. 154–158). That tricky little rafter was detailed in a new section of the revised *A Roof Cutter's Secrets* (2002+). **(fig 8-17)** The bastard broken hip requires a strong understanding of roof framing principles to find the controlling outside plate lines. **(figs 8-18, 8-19)** On another job, Shone coined the name "bee-hive tower" for a convex looking onion dome tower roof that he built in Los Gatos, CA (RCS pg. 227), **(fig 8-20)** and then he nicknamed the step-down intersections that a long straight hip roof makes as it works its way down a hillside "over-under intersections" (RCS pgs. 98–99). **(fig 8-21)**

One term that I use frequently is hip or valley "fill." This was a Los Angeles housing tract term that was substituted for "hip jack rafters" or "valley jack rafters." Many folks shorten up this mouthful of words and refer to "hip jack rafters" or "valley jack rafters" very simply as "jacks." Think of "fill" in the same light, like a nickname. "Fill" stems from the idea that jack rafters are used to "fill in" the holes occurring in a run of common rafters at roof intersections or hip ends. I use "jacks" and "fill" interchangeably.

"Sway-stick" is a term I made up for RCS to describe the long vertical temporary 2×4 or 2×6 that one nails on edge against the outside of a gable end wall to be used as a stacking aid (RCS pgs. 110–112). **(fig 8-22)** It is situated some 8 to 12 inches to one side of the building's center line and

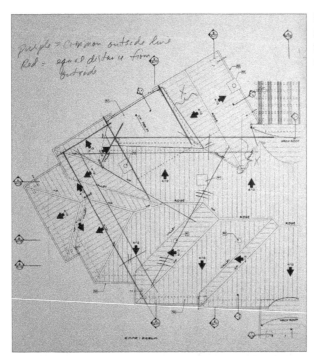

8-19 Complicated roofs often require the positioning of theoretical plate lines to solve situations

8-20 Shone Freeman chose the name "beehive tower" for a convex-shaped roof he built in San Jose

extends at least 6 inches above the associated ridge height. With it in place, the first pair of common rafters can easily be positioned plumb and flush with the outside edge of the wall. It also serves as an extra man when stacking solo as I described in RCS, all the while temporarily swaying in the ridge line end-to-end until permanent sway braces are installed. Once you

8-21 Shone dubbed the step-down intersections on a long straight hip roof "over-under intersections"

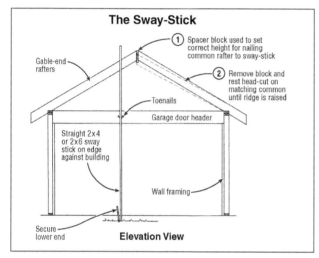

The Sway-Stick

① Spacer block used to set correct height for nailing common rafter to sway-stick

② Remove block and rest head-cut on matching common until ridge is raised

Gable-end rafters

Toenails

Garage door header

Straight 2x4 or 2x6 sway stick on edge against building

Wall framing

Secure lower end

Elevation View

8-22 A "sway-stick" is the temporary brace erected at a gable end to help set the first pair of rafters

have the roof skeleton up and braced both vertically and horizontally, the sway-stick is removed and the gable studs are installed.

So, over my lifetime, we have seen many new words added to the roof-framing lingo and I am certain there are many others that have been added that I don't have a clue about, but they will show up as time goes by. But when you think about it, we have only applied existing words to describe various things. Imagine how difficult it would have been for Adam to have named all the animals from scratch. Pretty smart cookie to have come up with words like zebra, giraffe, lion, gorilla, etc., when these words had never before even been in existence.

The difference between the right word and the almost right word is really a large matter — it's the difference between the lightning bug and the lightning. - Mark Twain

9

Filling Needs – the Headcutter and the Seat-cut guide stories

Strive not to be a success, but rather to be of value. – Albert Einstein

I find craftsmen generally to be some of the most ingenious folks on the planet. When something is difficult or time consuming, our brains jump into action to look for a simpler or easier way to do that something. Sometimes this requires a new method, sometimes this requires modifying an existing tool, and sometimes this requires inventing a totally new specialized tool. Take home construction for an example. Up until the Civil War days, timber framing was the standard method of home construction in the more populated areas. It was heavy, slow, expensive, and required master craftsmen to assemble all the mortise/tendon/peg connections. This method was followed by balloon framing, which attempted to address those timber frame weaknesses. Balloon framing used lightweight 2×4 milled lumber that was more economical and could quickly be assembled by normal carpenters using steel nails. After World War II, platform framing became the dominant method of building since its speed and simplicity meshed well with the industrialization of housing tract construction. Of course, there was overlap at each of these transitions, and some folks have begrudgingly clung to one method or another out of emotional attachment. But, as a whole, most builders have always been focused on producing the best product for the lowest cost as a result of our free market based economy. To do that, one looks at simplification, which cuts material costs, lowers labor costs, and shortens the overall building time.

Another example of beneficial progression is jobsite tools. They caused, paralleled, or augmented the advance in the various building methods. In the timber frame days, jobsite tools included a chisel, an adze, a whip saw, a brace and bit, etc. As the building methodology swung into balloon and platform style framing, those tools were replaced by the portable circular saw (1924 Skilsaw), the chainsaw (1926 Stihl), the radial arm saw (1922 DeWalt), the trigger switched pistol grip power drill (1917 Black & Decker), and the framing nail gun (1962 Pasload). We have come a long way since then, with these same tools being refined over and over to do more and more while a multitude of variations have been added. The tools we have today are truly amazing feats of engineering. Every one of them started from a singular idea to fill a need.

I have been blessed by the Lord to have my hand in the development of a variety of new tool ideas and roof-framing methodologies. These methodologies I shared in *A Roof Cutter's Secrets*, but the tool ideas are less well known because of the difficulty of getting them produced and marketed. Roof tools are much too specialized for any tool manufacturer to take seriously. Ever since roof trusses became the dominant roof framing method in the 1980s, there has been little rationale to look our way. So for this reason, those who "stick frame" roofs have struggled to find tools with which they can cut rafters efficiently. Relatively few have the good fortune to own a set of production roof cutting tools left over from the old days when cut and stack was the only way roofs were built. Yeah, while I might be one of those lucky few, I was never one to just let it end there – I desired that others to be able to gang-cut rafters just like I did. After all, what good was it to share the methodology of gang-cutting in *A Roof Cutter's Secrets* if a normal carpenter can't use the technique for lack of the specialty tools required to do so? This chapter is my story of the struggle to make this happen.

If one looks back at history, it seems like the Los Angeles housing tract era (1945–1975) was one of the most inventive time periods for both tools and methodology. I see it as the birth and rapid-growth stage of modern day house framing. So just as we humans make our biggest growing spurts during adolescence, so did home building during her adolescent stage. What helped spur this growth along to record levels was "piece work" or pay for completion. Using this method made every tradesman into an independent contractor. He was in charge of his own business which was just one task repeated ad infinitum. It ingeniously caused each person to be personally invested in how quickly they were able to complete their work task. If they could do something faster, they took home a fatter paycheck. A carpenter working by the hour does not have that kind of incentive. Of course, this could only work in a tract-building environment where a fair price for a set task was easily determined as opposed to doing individual tasks on a custom home. In today's world, these same types of motivated individuals would be the framing contractors. I still remember framing contractor Shone Freeman famously responding to someone who asked about receiving his pay check.

Shone said, "Don't worry you will get yours – I'm the only one piecing this job." I still get a kick out of his response when I think back, because it was so profound. Shone's whole way of thinking has been inventive, from how he operates his company to his actual jobsite methods. As a result of this originality, his company, S.R. Freeman Inc., owns a good portion of the high-end framing market in the San Francisco Bay Area.

THE HEADCUTTER

I had to pull Shone into this story because he unknowingly started me down the path that would lead to the "Headcutter" being invented. I believe it was 1996 when I first met Shone Freeman. He had just attended a roof-framing seminar that I had given at the San Jose, CA, *JLC* Live building conference and we had gotten together afterward to look over a set of blueprints for a complex roof he was just getting ready to frame. While Shone normally cut his own roofs, once he got busier with multiple jobs, he had started to use roof cutter Eric Krilonovich to do this task. Eric was in partnership with a Santa Cruz lumber company and did all his cutting at their yard. The completed roof-cut packages were then delivered to the jobsite. This would be the exact same thing I helped Dave Saunders set up at National Lumber in Mansfield, MA, a few years later. While we were looking over Shone's plans, he asked if I might be available to cut roofs for him now and then. He explained the roof packages he was getting from Eric were a bit "rough" as he put it. Shone went on to say that Eric gang-cut all his rafters using only a gas-powered chainsaw. I had never heard of this method before, so I was intrigued. Evidently, Eric stacked his rafters flat one on top of the other and cut them vertically as if the rafter pile was a glulam beam set on edge. He made the birdsmouth in the same fashion – freehand by eye. Years later, while serving as a volunteer in Central America, I would see this same kind of amazing steady hand ability as men would vertically cut perfect 1-inch-thick planks from a fallen tree simply by following a snapped line with a Stihl 064 chainsaw. They had no idea what a Granberg Alaskan Chainsaw Mill even was.

Anyhow, this chainsaw idea planted a seed. While I couldn't see free-hand cutting with a chainsaw as a viable option for most of us to accurately cut rafters, incorporating a gas-powered chainsaw in a fixed milling position like what Granberg did to make boards was a real possibility. A type of monster jig saw. Linear link had stuck a chainbar on a Skil 77 in the late 1980s and I had used their tool as well as the Prazi Beam Cutter to gang-cut ridge-cuts at some roof cutting demonstrations since I couldn't very well pull out my sidewinder blade and use it to gang-cut common rafter head-cuts as was my SOP, or JLC would have hung me from the highest beam. Besides I am sure some OSHA representatives were hanging out at these conferences. For all I know, they may have even had a booth there and probably would have relished the opportunity to hand-cuff and haul me off in front of all the

9-1 The Homelite XL100 is an obsolete 9-inch circular saw powered by a gas motor

9-2 I Initially thought of adapting a chainbar to fit the XL100 as Linear Link had done with the Skil 77

attendees. You certainly don't run a red stoplight with a cop sitting right at the intersection. By doing these demonstrations in the mid-1990s, I became acutely aware of the problems everyday carpenters were facing in applying production gang-cutting methodology on-site. While the swing-table saw base was readily available to help make the seat-cuts, making the head-cuts even with the Linear Link or Prazi was extremely inefficient. These tools lacked any real power to spin the chain, and the saw-foot was too small to adequately steady the long chainbar if much of a bevel was used. Additionally, in the case of the Prazi, no provision had been made to oil the cutting chain during operation and both apparatuses threw wood chips upward, often obscuring the cut-line. These devices were more suited for a shop or hobbyist, not the heavy-duty work of gang-cutting rafters at a construction site. I played with the idea of taking the gas-powered Homelite XL100 circular saw and mounting a chainbar on it like both Prazi and Linear Link had

9-3 The XL100 has a large beveling saw-foot

9-4 An early prototype of the "Headcutter" gets tested on the job

done, but in the end it made no sense, because these saws were obsolete and impossible to find. **(figs 9-1, 9-2, 9-3)** So instead, I decided to undertake a project to mount a regular "find anywhere" gas-powered chainsaw on a saw-table. Working on it in my spare time, I had a prototype ready within a few weeks, but it would take a year or more before I could get it out to the public. **(fig 9-4)** What was of great importance to me was that the saw-foot be able to mount quickly on the chainsaw's chainbar without the need to drill mounting holes. An accessory more or less. I also wanted the saw-table to be able to bevel well past 45°, so it could not only be used to gang-cut ridge-cuts, but also be used to gang-cut seat-cuts. Yep, a genuine "one tool does it all" solution to the age-old problem of gang-cutting rafters. I originally began by using a pair of large set screws for the chainbar fastening method, but later this was upgraded to a more beefy clamping mechanism when it went into production at Big Foot Tools, and a legitimate machine shop was fabricating the saw-table, not some guy on the tailgate of his pickup truck. My design utilized the top edge of the chainsaw bar to make the cut so wood chips were thrown away from the operator and the cut-line area stayed clean. While I had employed the "top edge of chainbar" cutting technique in other framing situations all my life, using it for the vertical milling of raked rafters was nothing short of a perfect fit.

I began looking at how to get my saw-foot to the general public and, being an ongoing customer of the chainsaw supplier Baileys, I approached them about carrying my saw-foot. Needless to say they weren't real jazzed about my idea, since they had just come out with a chainsaw cutting attachment (The Beam Boss) and felt my saw-foot would be in direct competition. While their attachment was similar from the aspect that it swung angles, the Beam Boss was only an aid for regular horizontal downward stroked cutting of individual beams and clearly was useless to support a chainsaw vertically like a gigantic jigsaw that cut using the top side of the chainbar like my saw-foot did. Baileys even said that if I did try to sell it, they would come after me with a patent infringement suit since they had just spent $50,000 to get it patented. A bit disillusioned, I bought a Beam Boss device and then stopped by Granberg International in Richmond, CA, to see Erik Granberg, whom I had come to know a bit over the years. Since Granberg held lots of different patents on their chainsaw milling equipment, I knew Erik was very familiar with all this patent stuff and could share some of his wisdom. Anyhow, I showed him my prototype and the Beam Boss and told him what had gone on between me and Baileys. He looked it over and said my saw-foot was a super idea and that the two devices had little in common. Erik told me to go get a patent for it, so Baileys couldn't bother me anymore. That lifted my spirits somewhat, but then I realized I didn't have the big bucks needed to get a patent.

After purchasing a copy of the book *Patent it Yourself*, I began studying about all this mumbo jumbo stuff one must do to get a patent. Thus began a process that would take some 5 years to complete. The book said that most patent applications are rejected the first time through, especially when prepared by an amateur. So I hoped for the best, but expected the worse.

While I had yet to settle on a name for the new tool, I felt a single-word name to be best and had "Ridgecutter," "Plumbcutter," or "Headcutter" on my possible name list. Although I planned to use the saw-foot for both head-cuts and seat-cuts, I needed more time until I was satisfied with its performance as a seat-cutter. I had some apprehension that folks who didn't know how to use the tip of a chainbar safely might injure themselves when it was used in a seat-cut application. So, for this reason, I felt it best to first introduce it as just a device to gang-cut head-cuts and, later on, when I had worked out all the seat-cut bugs, introduce its seat-cutting function as an add-on. I would write the patent so the saw-foot's range of bevel adjustment was from vertical (0°) to +70° off vertical so it could swing down and gang-cut seat-cuts for a 4/12 pitched roof. I didn't see the gang-cutting of seat-cuts as a high priority since regular swing-table saw bases for the Skil 77 were readily available. So other than having a custom chainbar maker in Portland, OR, fabricate both a 12-inch and 14 1/2-inch chainbar to mount on my Stihl 044 for initial testing purposes, I left this aspect of the device for later.

Being in the Bay Area, I spent my weekends at the San Francisco Patent Library researching "prior art" for my saw-foot device. "Prior art" is all the other patented devices that may be similar in some manner. For a new patent to be granted, it must be substantially different in functionality from anything else recorded. Sometimes you find something that is close enough to what you have just "invented" and the process ends there. One must do a thorough investigation because, when the US Patent and Trademark Office (USPTO) gets your patent application, they too will do the same thing and, believe me, being experts they typically find something that has similar features to yours and reject your application. It is pretty daunting as you flip through the volumes of patent records to see inventions dating back to the earliest days of our nation. The very first patent was granted on July 31, 1790, barely two years after the US Constitution was ratified. Recently, all the patent records have been made electronic, so now all the "prior art" investigation can be done online, but for some reason it just doesn't seem the same. It's probably just me. I had that same type of nostalgic feeling when I went to visit the Smithsonian museums in Washington, DC, in 2002. I had flown out from California to teach a roof-framing seminar at a *JLC* Live conference in nearby Providence, RI, and had tacked on a couple extra days to my return flight so I could go down to DC for a visit. It was something I had always wanted to do since I was a kid. Although I was on crutches at the time, I went all over the Washington National Mall and, of course, to the Air and Space Museum to see the history of flight. I looked at everything. What a special place. I suppose it was the closest I could get to a father I had hardly ever known. He had played an important role in the advance of aviation flight systems, and some of the planes he had helped design were either parked on the ground or hanging from the ceiling.

While I was working on the patent application, I was also hunting for another avenue where I might be able to sell my chainsaw-foot since the Baileys idea had not worked out. I decided that Big Foot Tool would be a great sales platform since they were specializing in tools for framers, so I got a hold of the owner, Bob Hutchings, and shared my tool idea with him. Bob immediately saw the usefulness of the tool since he had been a framer

9-5 Big Foot Saws started selling the "Headcutter" early in 1998 as patent pending

at one time and agreed to manufacture and sell it. Bob had made the timely decision to fill the vacuum in the construction market for a larger-diameter worm drive circular saw after Skil ended production of their 12-inch model 127. During the tract framing days (1945–1975), a Skil 77 was all a carpenter ever needed, so the demand for its big worm drive died. When custom home building came back with a vengeance in the 1980s, the building industry once again had a need for a large-diameter worm drive circular saw to cut beams, etc. The 16-inch Makita Bean Saw (late 1970s) was OK for some things, but was big and awkward for other uses. So in the early 1990s, Bob formed Big Foot Tools and began modifying the Skil 77 and 87 with larger diameter saw blades. Bob also brought back other tract style framing paraphernalia that had disappeared as a result of the big Los Angeles basin framing supply houses closing their doors.

I finally settled on the name "Headcutter" for the saw-foot and Bob started selling it as "patent pending" in 1998. **(fig 9-5)** I guess it came down to what sounded better. The names "Ridgecutter" and "Plumbcutter," while just as vague as "Headcutter," didn't have the correct ring. While rafter head-cuts can be anything from a plumb-cut made square, to a single 45° cheek, to a double 45° cheek, I was out of time and out of ideas. Looking back now, I probably should have named it the "Raftercutter" or "Gangcutter" so as to incorporate both the head- and seat-cuts aspects of the saw-foot, but hindsight is always 20/20. May rename it someday. A year or so later, I got notification that my patent application had been denied. When that

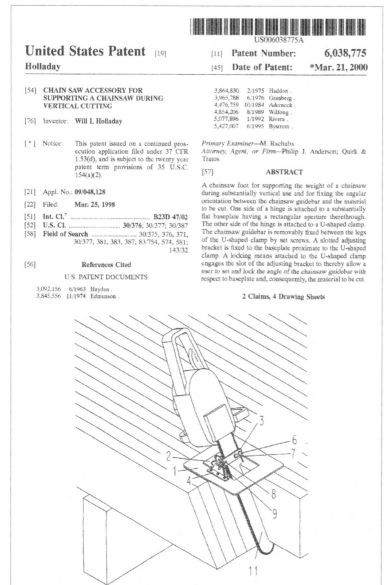

United States Patent [19]

Holladay

[11] Patent Number:	**6,038,775**
[45] Date of Patent:	*Mar. 21, 2000

US006038775A

[54] **CHAIN SAW ACCESSORY FOR SUPPORTING A CHAINSAW DURING VERTICAL CUTTING**

[76] Inventor: Will L Holladay

[*] Notice: This patent issued on a continued prosecution application filed under 37 CFR 1.53(d), and is subject to the twenty year patent term provisions of 35 U.S.C. 154(a)(2).

[21] Appl. No.: 09/048,128

[22] Filed: Mar. 25, 1998

[51] Int. Cl.⁷ B23D 47/02
[52] U.S. Cl. 30/376; 30/377; 30/387
[58] Field of Search 30/375, 376, 371, 30/377, 381, 383, 387; 83/754, 574, 581; 143/32

[56] **References Cited**

U.S. PATENT DOCUMENTS

3,092,156 6/1963 Hayden .
3,845,556 11/1974 Edmunson .

3,864,830 2/1975 Haddon .
3,965,788 6/1976 Granberg .
4,476,759 10/1984 Aderneck .
4,854,206 8/1989 Willong .
5,077,896 1/1992 Rivera .
5,427,007 6/1995 Bystrom .

Primary Examiner—M. Rachuba
Attorney, Agent, or Firm—Philip J. Anderson; Quirk & Tratos

[57]   **ABSTRACT**

A chainsaw foot for supporting the weight of a chainsaw during substantially vertical use and for fixing the angular orientation between the chainsaw guidebar and the material to be cut. One side of a hinge is attached to a substantially flat baseplate having a rectangular aperture therethrough. The other side of the hinge is attached to a U-shaped clamp. The chainsaw guidebar is removably fixed between the legs of the U-shaped clamp by set screws. A slotted adjusting bracket is fixed to the baseplate proximate to the U-shaped clamp. A locking means attached to the U-shaped clamp engages the slot of the adjusting bracket to thereby allow a user to set and lock the angle of the chainsaw guidebar with respect to baseplate and, consequently, the material to be cut.

2 Claims, 4 Drawing Sheets

happened, I decided that it was now time to get some professional help. Bob helped connect me with an "intellectual property" lawyer near his production facility in Las Vegas, NV. The lawyer changed a few words in the "claims" section of the application, charged me a pretty penny, and the revised application went sailing through without a stutter. **(fig 9-6)** I suppose I just couldn't figure out the correct way to phrase those very special words so as to make the USPTO inspector happy. In the early days of filing patents, the inventor simply scratched out what it was that he was patenting in simple words, but over time, patenting something has become a very specialized field. These patent lawyers are sure good, but they ain't cheap. This reminds me of an old story I once heard. As the story goes, a company had a huge computer complex that was not operating because of some glitch. After trying unsuccessfully in-house to find where the problem was hiding, they decided to hire a renowned specialist to come in and locate it. The gentleman arrived and after spending some time studying the plans, etc., went over to a particular area and marked an "X" with some chalk and told them "here is your problem." They thanked him kindly and directed their technicians to the area who quickly fixed the problem. The specialist then left and some days later the company received his bill for $1,000,001. They were confounded by the strange amount so they called the specialist up and asked why the $1? He responded the $1 was the cost of the chalk he had used to make the mark and the $1 million was for the knowledge to know where to put that chalk mark. I suppose the same was true in my case, only on a smaller scale.

Everyone liked the "Headcutter." Not only did it get used to gang-cut rafter ridge-cuts, but it found a home precision cutting bundled TJIs and structural insulated *panels* (SIPs) as well. I was jazzed that carpenters finally had an adequate solution to the age-old problem of gang-cutting head-cuts. By that time, I had begun work on the revised edition of *A Roof Cutter's Secrets* and, being inundated with complex roof-framing projects, I was forced to put finishing the Headcutter's seat-cut aspect on the back burner. In the end, it would be half a dozen or so years before I would be able to get back to it. When I did get back to it, I was able to quickly finish revising the issues that had concerned me, and the new revised prototype was ready to go. **(fig 2-41)** By then Bob had sold Big Foot Tools so I wasn't able to effect any more input into its production. Besides that, the updated Headcutter would have gone head-to-head with Big Foot's best seller, their 10-inch worm drive circular saw on a swing-table. Over time various carpenters did find that it could be used for seat-cuts so the word has gotten out. I still plan to offer a seat-cut kit for the Headcutter when I can find a manufacturing partner. I never did use the Headcutter at any of my *JLC* Live demonstrations since I wasn't allowed to crank up a gas-powered chainsaw inside the convention hall. Big Foot Tools usually had a booth at the conventions, so those interested could always meander over there to take a look at it.

The "Headcutter" works best for milling head-cuts when only about 2 to 3 inches of the tip extends below the rafter material. Therefore, it behooves one to find a chainbar length that works best with the rafter size and roof pitch you normally frame, or like me, have a variety of chainbar lengths available that will work with anything from 2×8s to 12-inch TJIs. When the "Headcutter" is used to make seat-cuts, it is best to put on the shortest bar that will make the required cut. This is a bit more difficult to accomplish, but shoot for a 14- to 15–inch-length maximum. This keeps the power head close to the saw-foot for better balance and less physical exposure to the moving chain cutters.

THE SEAT-CUT GUIDE

The "Seat-cut guide" arose out of another similar situation, but this time I found myself in the shoes of Third World carpenters. Over the years, I have spent a fair amount of time in Central America on various humanitarian aid projects. One of those projects offered me the opportunity to train up a bunch of young men in Western framing techniques. In tropical regions, nearly all the buildings are now built using concrete block walls, poured in place floors, and light gauge steel rafters/joists rather than wood, so the knowledge of wood style construction had long since disappeared. Most wood structures are unable to hold up long against the onslaught of vicious termites or the dry rot caused by humidity-induced fungus. The wood from Guayacan and Nispero trees are impermeable to both of these elements, but they were overharvested in the early 20th century without having been replanted. Unfortunately, being slow growers, it will be a while before they will again be seen in construction. Anyhow, the project was to build four small homes on an island in a remote Pacific archipelago for a fishing resort operator. It was indeed a rare opportunity. The company wanted these houses for their on-site management and had chosen wood construction based on esthetics. The wood to be used was Honduran Pine, obviously imported from Honduras. It had been pressure-treated with CCA (oxides of copper, chromium, arsenic) and had a light greenish hue.

Seeing as how I had traveled to this country by airline, I could only bring along one of my best friends, the Skil 77. Used chainsaws are restricted from cartage on commercial airliners due to a residual gas fumes fire hazard. The job was fun and the guys were good strong workers. In no time, they had picked up floor and wall framing basics and we were moving on to the roofs. We used an area out of the rain to rack up the rafters so they could be cut. All the roofs were Dutch Hips so there was a lot of hip jack rafters to be cut. Since I did not have any of my production roof cutting tools, we were forced to hand-cut all the rafters. Major bummer! This was something I had not done since I was a kid, yet in Second and Third World countries it was the everyday occurrence. This would truly be an enlightening experience, and just as giving demonstrations at *JLC* Live conferences had opened my eyes to see the typical American carpenter's dilemma in applying gang-cutting techniques without the tools being available to do so, this similar situation now led me to see the world through the eyes of a very poor carpenter just struggling to feed his family. He possessed few personal tools other than a hammer. Due to extremely poor wages ($12 to $15 per day) a crew of 5 to 6 guys might have one portable circular saw among them, if they were lucky. They certainly would never have the funds to get a chainsaw and Headcutter saw-foot in order to gang-cut rafters like we do in the States.

Even when hand cutting rafters, it is still best to use various production gang style techniques to save time and increase precision. Gang marking rafter layout on all the boards in a particular series of rafters is infinitely better than the age-old practice of using a full-length rafter template to mark each board individually. For those unfamiliar, gang marking is accomplished by placing all the rafter material for a series of identical common rafters on a pair of long, ground-level, rafter racks. This material would be positioned on edge, crown down, side-by-side, with the ends aligned. After calculating the rafter's length, a carpenter would use these measurements to lay out the location of head-cut, the tail-cut, and the heel-cut on the topside edge of the outside board at each side of the racked lumber material, and then snap perpendicular chalk-lines across the racked lumber to connect these marks. **(fig 7-7)** Next, the carpenter would gang-cut a saw pass at each of these snap-lines using his circular saw. To make the head-cut and a plumb tail-cut starter passes, the carpenter would adjust his circular saw's bevel to match the pitch of the roof, and with the saw blade set to its maximum depth, make a long, rip-style saw-cut across the top surface of the racked lumber material following the appropriate snap-lines. If the tail-cut was to be cut square, the tail-cut snap-line is followed with the circular saw set square (0°) instead of set at the roof pitch's bevel angle. Although the depth of these cuts will be far short of what is needed to complete them in most cases, they nonetheless provide an excellent physical locator to place the circular saw's blade when it comes time to finish off the cuts with the rafter boards laid flat.

With the head-cut and tail-cut starter passes made, the carpenter would adjust the depth of his saw blade to equal the vertical portion of the rafter birdsmouth's notch and make a saw pass across the top surface of the racked lumber material following the heel-cut snap-line. The heel-cut dimension is found by drawing out a full-scale birdsmouth notch having a 3½-inch seat-cut length and scaling the vertical leg. The saw's bevel would remain the same as was set previously for the ridge-cut (and tail-cut if plumb) and angle the same direction.

Now, if the carpenter has an aftermarket swing-table saw base mounted on a 10-inch worm drive saw, he could gang-cut the shallow-angled horizontal seat-cut portion of the rafter birdsmouth notch. But of course, most Second and Third World carpenters don't have this tool, so this cut must be made entirely by hand. At this stage, the tradesman would lay all the partially cut rafter boards flat on their sides, so he can finish off the starter cuts with his circular saw's bevel set square (0° on adjuster). The head- and tail-cuts at each end of the board are made first, typically using a handheld adjustable saw guide (a Quick Square® will substitute) or a plumb-cut template. **(fig 9-7)**

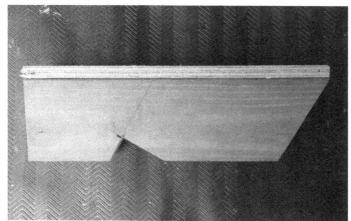

9-7 A rafter-cutting guide has an edge for scribing a plumb-cut and a notch that defines the birdsmouth

After those cuts are made, the carpenter must draw out the seat-cut on each rafter so he will have a cut-line to follow with his circular saw. To lay out the seat-cut correctly, the carpenter's best option is to use a template-style marking jig that characterizes the desired birdsmouth notch. **(fig 9-7)** This jig must include a top edge-of-board follower rail to position the depth of the birdsmouth notch correctly relative to the top plane of the roof. Once the jig is aligned with the previously made heel-cut, the carpenter scribes the seat-cut line. After removing the marking jig, the carpenter makes the seat-cut with his circular saw by following this scribe-line.

Accuracy for the seat-cut can be difficult to achieve by sight considering that the cut is very short in length, and the carpenter is making this cut freehand with his circular saw balanced precariously on the very edge of the board. Not only does the front of the saw-foot obscure a good portion of the cut-line, but dark-colored wood, especially pressure-treated lumber, and shadows caused by bright sunlight, can cause the cut-line to be practically invisible. All these things only serve to multiply inconsistencies in the finished birdsmouth notch. Variations in the seat-cut cause a poor transfer of roof load to the wall, make installing exposed frieze blocks difficult, create problems installing the fascia, and produce a wavy roof surface. Another common problem when making the seat-cut freehand, is overcutting the existing heel-cut. When excessive, the available rafter tail strength is greatly reduced.

So as we waded our way through hand cutting the rafters, my mind was looking for some way to speed up the process. Marking and cutting the seat-cut was the most time-consuming aspect, so I focused my attention on that area. I settled on the idea to make a "ride over" seat-cutting jig that would use the premade heel-cut saw kerf as a reference. With some scrap

9-8 This is the original fixed pitch seat-cut guide that I made to use on a job in Central America

pieces of light-gauge steel joist material, I fabricated a seat-cut guide device for our 2×8 rafters at 5/12 pitch. It positioned a short saw-fence perpendicular to the existing heel-cut so as to produce a 3¹/₂-inch seat-cut. To use the guide, all a carpenter had to do was slide the device's follower rail along the top edge of the board until the locator tang fell into the existing heel-cut saw kerf. Next, he would position a circular saw against the saw-fence, activate the motor, and push. It was simple and produced a perfect seat-cut every time. Gobs of time was saved since there was no birdsmouth to lay out and the actual cutting process was idiot proof. Since the seat-cut positioning was governed by the top-of-board follower in combination with the heel-cut alignment tang, the heel-stand on every single rafter was held constant. By incorporating a cutting stop on the saw-fence, excessive overcut at the notch was eliminated. By using the guide, I estimate we cut 30% from the time it would have taken to cut the rafters on those four island homes without it. Everyone on the job loved that little guide. **(fig 9-8)**

Its success got me thinking that a variable version of the guide would be a great help for carpenters in poorer countries, so I began to work on such a design. Since there are both right-side bladed direct-drive circular saws and left-side bladed worm drive saws, I had to make a choice between the two designs to pair with the guide. Being a California production framer I went for the heavy-duty worm drive saw and figured that if carpenter demand required, we could always produce a mirror-imaged unit for the direct drive circular saw style. I wanted the guide to be geometrically functional, so that when the saw-fence was adjusted to any roof pitch shown on the graduated

9-9 I designed the "Seat-cut guide" to be adjustable from 4/12 to 12/12 and produce a +/− 3$^1/_2$-inch seat-cut

common rafter scale, the length of the resulting seat-cut would be approximately 3$^1/_2$ inches long (an industry acceptable size). Unfortunately, to calculate this type of complicated movement mathematically was above my math level so I was forced to rely on the caveman "trial and error" method to solve the geometry. I made a cardboard mockup and kept varying the positioning of the saw-fence pivot point in relation to both the top-of-board follower and the alignment tang until I had an arrangement that gave me a 3$^1/_2$-inch seat through the range of most common roof pitches. I never got the geometry perfect but it was close enough. It went from a 3$^1/_8$-inch seat-cut size at 4/12 to a 3$^1/_2$-inch seat-cut size at 12/12. Acceptable in my world. I next built up a sheet metal version using the same light-gauge steel joist material that I had used to make the fixed pitch unit for the island's four houses. **(fig 9-9)** In time, I realized that the guide needed more birdsmouth size flexibility in order to accommodate thicker walls (i.e., 2×6) so I added an adjustment thumbscrew at each end of the top-of-board follower rail. By threading each thumbscrew in toward the saw-fence by an equal amount, the birdsmouth notch was deepened. This adjustment also made it possible for the guide to be used to make seat-cuts on hips/valleys. **(fig 9-10)**

At this stage I began to think about how I was going to get the guide produced and out to the guys who could benefit from it. From my previous contacts with tool manufacturers, I had learned that they were more open to consider a new idea if it had an accompanying patent so I pulled out my old copy of *Patent it Yourself* and started the long arduous patent-seeking process again. Since I was outside the USA as a volunteer at the time I was

9-10 Two depth-of-birdsmouth adjustment thumbscrews allowed for variation in the seat-cut size

quite happy that, this time around, I could do my "prior art" search on the USPTO website as opposed to at the various patent libraries scattered around the USA. After 4 to 5 months of pretending to be a patent lawyer again, my application was ready, so I sent it in, hoping for the best. Next, I sent my prototype to a friend who was a carpenter/machinist back East to see if he could fabricate a few professional samples that I could send around to various tool manufacturers. **(fig 9-11)** The samples turned out great but when he went to try one out on a roof they were framing he found it wouldn't work because their roof rafters were 2×10s and the guide could only be used with 2×8 rafters. He sent me an email to that effect, and I quickly realized that this was one parameter I had failed to take into account. I had based the guide on 2×8s rafter stock which was the common rafter size in California and failed to consider that, in both the Northwest and Northeast, they use 2×10s or 2×12s as rafter stock to handle the snow load. Well, like any idea, it takes real-world trials to work out all the bugs. After a bit more work, the design was modified so it would work with either 2×12s, 2×10s, or 2×8s rafter stock. The updated version used a 2×12 rafter as the base size but when the user needed to cut 2×10- or 2×8-sized rafters, he modified the guide's

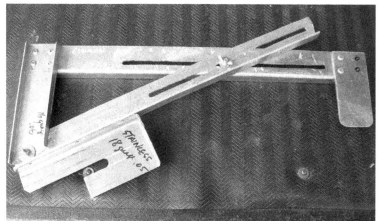

9-11 The "Seat-cut guide" prototypes were made from lightweight aluminum

9-12 The production version of the guide could accommodate the most common rafter material sizes

working range for these rafter sizes by installing a pair of stops at either 2 inches or 4 inches inboard from the top-of-board follower rail. To keep the geometry correct, I extended the pivot arm out 4 inches as well and installed a 90° extension to the saw-fence arm so it could still reach back and connect to the edge-of-board follower. The two depth-of-birdsmouth adjustment thumbscrews were preserved so one could fine tune the birdsmouth notch depth as required. **(fig 9-12)**

A year later I received a denial letter from the patent office. It just so happened to include the phone number of the inspector assigned to my application, so I called him up to ask for suggestions on how I might

9-13 The "Seat-cut guide" was granted a patent in 2015, some 3½ years after it was filed

US009120241B2

(12) **United States Patent**
Holladay

(10) **Patent No.:** US 9,120,241 B2
(45) **Date of Patent:** Sep. 1, 2015

(54) **PORTABLE ADJUSTABLE SAW GUIDE DEVICE FOR CUTTING A NOTCH**

(76) Inventor: Will Holladay

(*) Notice: Subject to any disclaimer, the term of this patent is extended or adjusted under 35 U.S.C. 154(b) by 99 days.

(21) Appl. No.: **13/419,183**

(22) Filed: **Mar. 13, 2012**

(65) **Prior Publication Data**
US 2013/0283993 A1   Oct. 31, 2013

(51) **Int. Cl.**
B27B 9/04   (2006.01)
B23Q 9/00   (2006.01)
B23Q 17/22   (2006.01)
E04F 21/26   (2006.01)

(52) **U.S. Cl.**
CPC . *B27B 9/04* (2013.01); *B23Q 9/005* (2013.01); *B23Q 17/2233* (2013.01); *E04F 21/26* (2013.01); *Y10T 83/8889* (2015.04)

(58) **Field of Classification Search**
CPC B27B 9/04; B23Q 9/0042; B23Q 9/005; B23Q 17/2233; B23Q 17/225; B23Q 17/2258; B23Q 17/2266; B23Q 17/2275; B27G 5/02; B43L 7/10; B43L 7/12; B43L 7/14; E04F 21/26; G01B 3/56; Y10T 83/8889
USPC 83/574, 435.11, 435.12, 435.13, 83/435.14, 743–745, 821, 829, 522.17, 83/522.18; 33/423, 452, 456, 463, 466, 33/468–471, 403
See application file for complete search history.

(56) **References Cited**

U.S. PATENT DOCUMENTS

288,613	A	*	11/1883	Bolles	33/456
746,468	A	*	12/1903	Crozier	33/423
830,322	A	*	9/1906	Hodge	33/456
912,605	A	*	2/1909	Osmonson	33/456
1,040,239	A	*	10/1912	Rarey	33/456
1,074,969	A	*	10/1913	Moore	33/423
1,187,272	A	*	6/1916	Demmrich	33/421
1,999,105	A	*	4/1935	Milla	33/453
2,080,792	A	*	5/1937	Simmons	33/453
2,632,483	A	*	3/1953	Jamack	33/499
2,735,455	A	*	2/1956	Forsberg	83/745
3,352,016	A	*	11/1967	Jablonsky	33/423
4,494,434	A	*	1/1985	Young	83/745
5,384,967	A	*	1/1995	Helmuth	33/456
6,594,633	B1	*	2/2004	Nyquist	33/452
7,269,909	B1	*	9/2007	Barbieri	33/419
7,302,763	B1	*	12/2007	Matthews	33/562
2012/0285028	A1	*	11/2012	Atwood	33/452

* cited by examiner

Primary Examiner — Clark F Dexter
(74) *Attorney, Agent, or Firm* — Knobbe, Martens, Olson & Bear LLP

(57)   **ABSTRACT**

A saw guide device for the rapid and precise cutting of perpendicular notches in framing lumber using a portable circular saw. The device consists of an edge-of-board follower rail, a support arm, and a pivotally adjustable saw fence. Externally affixed to the saw fence are a horizontal cut locator arm and a saw stop tab. The locator arm has a cut alignment tang and a saw blade recess slot. The saw stop tab has a thumbscrew adjuster. The device is positioned by the alignment tang, which drops into a previous cut. During operation the saw foot overruns the cut locator arm and is stopped by the tab. Thumbscrew adjusters are located at each end of the follower rail to allow for variation in depth of the perpendicular notch. Various angular scales are marked on the upper surface of the follower rail to aid in saw fence setup.

20 Claims, 8 Drawing Sheets

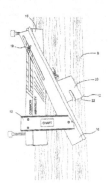

overcome his objections. He gave me some rewording ideas to make the "claims" acceptable but then I decided that maybe it was time to once again turn this process over to a true professional as I had done with the Headcutter patent after its first rejection. You can only pretend to be a lawyer for so long. A friend recommended a patent lawyer he knew so I called him up. When the lawyer learned I was a humanitarian aid volunteer and was hoping to get this device produced to help Third World carpenters, he was more than happy to help me with it. He quickly got a hold of the patent inspector and after a brief chat had the patent's "claims" reworked and it was resubmitted. A few months later the application was accepted. **(fig 9-13)**

After sending the guide and information around to all the relevant tool manufacturers, I came up empty handed. While they all liked the tool and thought it was a slick idea, it made no financial sense for them to produce it. Hand cutting rafters was just too small of a niche market. I can't blame them, they are in business to make money for their shareholders not fulfill the dreams of some crazy roof framer. Nothing new here. It's the same problem we have faced in roof cutting all through history – just too few of us to make it worth anybody's time. I will keep looking for a production opportunity or fabricating partner in hopes of getting the guide out for those carpenters in poorer countries, but I recognize that there are lots of great ideas that never make it to the market place. I realize how blessed I was that the Headcutter did indeed make it.

The definition of genius is taking the complex and making it simple.

– Albert Einstein

10

Framing is a Street Fight – treating and avoiding jobsite injuries

The thing about a street fight is that the street always wins.

– Vin Diesel *(Furious 7)*

If you stay in framing for any length of time you will get hurt – it is just a cold hard fact of life. The more time you spend in the trades, the more exposure you will have to dangerous situations that can cause accidents. And being imperfect people, eventually something will catch us whether it be of our own causation or that of another worker. If someone says they have never been hurt while framing, I would concede that they really didn't do much "hands on" framing. They either moved up quickly into a supervisory role with little exposure to the daily risks or they are flat out lying about how much time they spent framing. No one will ever live the life of a framer and remain unscathed. The harder you push – the more exposure and more injuries. Accept getting injured as a reality that you will face somewhere along the path and prepare for it mentally while doing all you can to minimize the risks. Hopefully, some of the thoughts I share in this chapter will help you do both of these. Although you may be blessed to go through life with relatively few major scrapes and bruises, your body will definitely still pay a price in the long run. While there might be an older car or two on the highway that has never been in an accident, most certainly there is not one that has been immune to everyday wear and tear. Things like wheel bearings, piston rings, valve seats, ball joints, timing belts, tires, etc., degrade with use. The more you drive the car or the harder you push the engine, the quicker these parts end up needing replacement. The same holds true for our bodies. The hard physical work of construction will cause your body to wear out and fail much sooner than that of computer Joe. If you don't want that to happen, then it is best you get a desk job. Framing certainly isn't for wimps. Then again there are some body types that simply resist the onslaughts of heavy labor with greater ease. I find these typically to be burly guys who are nearly as wide as they are tall. Certainly a sturdy 4×4 Ford pickup truck will take the bumps and ruts of heavy-duty off-road driving better than a Honda Civic.

And with that, let's dive right into this chapter's subject matter – what to do when you get hurt and some ideas to help avoid getting hurt in the first place. While I might not have recognized all the dangers that came with rough carpentry when I was young, ignorant, and had "superman" syndrome, my current near half-century association with the trade has probably earned me a minor degree in jobsite medical situations by the sheer volume of life experiences. God only knows how I hate seeing others get hurt, and I personally have been injured far too much. Bear in mind that I am not a medical professional, so I would never be so bold as to proclaim what I outline in this chapter is to be taken above the advice of a true professional, but then again I have learned quite a bit from these same folks over the years, for you see I am a certified Wilderness First Responder (WFR). One of my hobbies since my rowing days at Orange Coast College has been whitewater rafting. During my summers through the 1980s, while working as a framing contractor in Santa Barbara, CA, I served as a whitewater guide on most weekends for Kern River Tours or various private groups. **(fig 10-1)** A couple times I had the opportunity to serve as a boatman on seven-day trips in Idaho, but this would only work if I had a short gap between framing jobs. Back in those days there wasn't much of an industry requirement for emergency medical training beyond that of standard Red Cross First Aid and cardiopulmonary resuscitation (CPR). However, when I tried to get a job as an occasional Outward Bound School (OB) whitewater instructor in 1998, I came to discover I now needed to be WFR certified and have swift-water rescue training to boot. In the levels of the medical competency hierarchy, a WFR is just below an emergency medical technician (EMT), although for several treatments in the bush a WFR can do more than a regular EMT, unless the EMT has added the wilderness training component. I found the training to be very valuable since it was all scenario based. To date, I have done my best to keep the certification active, even though I have not instructed on an outdoor course since 2002. So if you want to know my medical background and credentials, there they are. Most of my suggestions come straight out the medical treatment guidelines that serve as a basis to renew my certification each 2 to 3 years. Do check out Wilderness Medical Associates (WMA) or Wilderness Medical Institute (WMI) on line if you would like to get this excellent medical response training yourself. I highly recommend it for anyone, especially if you are running a crew. With this type of training, you will be able to step up and help out in an emergency. My favorite reference guide for everyday

10-1 Guiding a class 5 route on the Upper Kern River (photo 1985)

medical issues is *Where There Is No Doctor* by David Werner. It is relied on heavily by medical volunteers in isolated Third World countries, and it serves as my "go to" medical encyclopedia.

Safety experts name the top 10 reasons for general workplace accidents in random order as: fatigue, stress, slips, trips, toppling objects, hazardous materials, repetitive motion, lifting, workplace violence, and collisions. These seem reasonable enough. The FAA has its "Dirty Dozen" which is a list of 12 common causes of errors in maintenance that lead to aviation accidents. They are: lack of communication; complacency; lack of knowledge; distraction; lack of teamwork; fatigue; lack of resources; pressure; lack of assertiveness; stress; lack of awareness; norms. While this list may have been written for the aviation industry, it appears to be tailor made for our field of construction as well. You will find many of the causes from this list evident in the accident accounts that I share throughout this chapter. OSHA names the construction industry's top life-taking accidents as: falls, struck by object, electrocution, and caught-in/between (in that order). From my lifetime on the jobsite I believe the most common injuries or accidents that we framers may see can be lumped into three categories: cuts, falls, and getting hit. Funny, those are the same three things one could possibly face in a street fight if you rule out guns – a punch, getting thrown, or a knife. So let's jump into the fight and explore what we can do to defend ourselves and survive. While this chapter most certainly is not an all-encompassing look at jobsite framing injuries, hopefully it will get you to start thinking a little bit about safety and the "what ifs." Undoubtedly, the most important part of safety is having the right mindset. It cannot be replaced by the fanciest safety gear on the planet. As in defensive driving, you must place your own safety first, and after that look to protect those in your sphere. You must think like an aircraft pilot who takes in everything that is going on around him. He is constantly on the lookout for a place to put the plane down if the engine should fail or a way out if the weather should get bad. You too must keep that "what if" running in your brain all day long. Or, as they teach in martial arts – "never let your guard down."

CUTS

Let's begin our discussion with cuts and punctures. Everybody has gotten little cuts and scrapes on the job. These normally do not require professional medical attention unless the cut goes deeper than the fascia layer (tough layer of connective tissue just below subcutaneous fat), and you are unable to clean it well or the laceration will not stay closed after cleaning. Think PRESSURE, CLEAN, and BANDAGE. Direct pressure with a clean cloth is the first course of action to stop the bleeding. Most of us just go back to work after the bleeding stops, but, in truth, at this point, the cut/abrasion needs a good cleaning to remove anything left in the injury that might cause it to become infected. Construction jobsites are dirty environments. To accomplish this task, start by washing your own hands with soap and water and then do the same for the area around the cut itself. Certainly don't want to add germs/bacteria to the cut. Next, grab a pair of disinfected tweezers and pick out any foreign matter, and finally irrigate the laceration well with copious amounts of drinkable grade water. Typically, on the jobsite, this will be with a hose bibb valve located somewhere. Don't chintz on the cleaning process since the more thorough your wash job is, the less likely the cut will get infected. Medical suppliers manufacture handy syringes for this type of wound irrigation, and I have one in my First Aid kit. A syringe allows me to give the laceration a good pressure wash. **(fig 10-2)** I also like to clean my lacerations/abrasions with a 1% povidone iodine/H_2O mix, since various studies have shown that it can be helpful to wound healing. For most abrasions I use a disinfected tooth brush to scrub out all the crap. This may hurt a bit, but the pain is short lived. When done with the cleansing, cover the injury with a sterile bandage of the appropriate size to keep the injury both clean and dry. A swipe of antibiotic ointment on the gauze pad of the bandage is an added bonus. As you change the bandage each day, keep an eye out for infection. If all goes well, the laceration will scab over quickly and, by the second day, have created a protective barrier. While a certain amount of wound site pain, warmth, and redness is to be expected as part

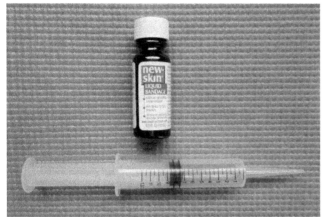

10-2 Pressure wash a laceration using a small syringe. Use a liquid bandage on small exposed cuts.

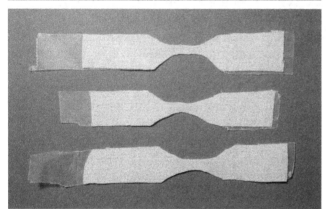

10-3 The edges of open cuts can be drawn together with homemade medical tape butterfly closures

of the body's injury response, these can also be signs of infection, especially when the injury is accompanied by oozing pus, swelling, red streaking, a fever, swollen lymph nodes, etc. Hot compresses applied 4 times a day can help, but many times I simply reopen a laceration if it seems to be infected and do a second round of aggressive deep cleaning to try and remove the junk I must have left in there the first time around. If I don't see a quick improvement after that "do over," it's time to visit the professionals. If a wound is small, and particularly if it is on my hands where a bandage won't survive for very long, I use a liquid bandage product named "New Skin." It works well in most cases to keep the cut clean, but you may need to apply it several times a day if the injured area sees heavy use. **(fig 10-2)**

For shallow dermis-depth lacerations that don't want to stay closed, try using some butterfly closures or steri-strips. When none are handy, I have many times cut my own butterfly closures from 3/8-inch-wide medical adhesive tape. **(fig 10-3)** Although many folks use Super glue to close a wound, this is not advised. Its composition is different than the skin glues used in the hospitals and can burn your skin.

During my time framing in Santa Barbara, CA, I recall that a guy on another job fell and ended up impaled on a vertical piece of rebar left exposed for some block wall tie-in or something. It was a long time ago, so I can't remember where he was impaled, but the crew did the right thing by sawing off the rebar that had punctured him and heading to the hospital with it still impaled. I must say, I hate rebar for just this reason. On many small custom jobs, common sense safety practices are simply not followed. Even without OSHA safety regulations, anyone with half a mind should know that the exposed ends of vertical rebar are safety risks and should be covered if not immediately formed into whatever project they are there for. When I come on any job and I see vertical rebar unprotected, I bend them all over flat. It may piss off the concrete guy but nobody on my crew is going to end up impaled on a stupid piece of rebar. For embedded objects (other than simple splinters), it is always best to leave whatever is embedded in place and transport the injured individual immediately to a hospital emergency room, unless the object is somehow restricting breathing or, in the case of an object embedded in a limb, is preventing you from controlling bleeding. Then again you have to balance pulling it against the option of throwing a tourniquet on above the injury to stop the bleeding. This may be OK if you plan to be at a hospital in 30 minutes but do keep foremost in your mind that, if a tourniquet stays on for a long time period, you will permanently lose whatever is downhill from it. A long-term tourniquet will always remain a "life or limb" decision. Tourniquets are used in most limb surgeries and do often stay on for an hour or two, but their application is done by folks who are highly experienced professionals working in well-equipped operating rooms. Double trouble are items embedded in the torso or the eyes, since both are extremely dangerous situations – stabilize in place and get to the hospital pronto. Think back to a knife fight. While surface slashes are bad news (super bad if an artery is hit), a knife thrust into the central region of the human body can hit the heart, the kidneys, the liver, etc. If the protrusion into the lung area was a stab/retract injury, it will most likely cause a pneumothorax where the lung collapses because outside air enters through the puncture hole wound and fills the vacuum cavity around the lung. With the pressure equal on both the inside and outside of the lung, it will just hang there. A protrusion into the lung area can also cause a pneumohemothorax where the sack around a lung fills up with blood or a mix of blood/air that restricts the lung from working. For any hole into the chest cavity, slap a piece of plastic wrap over the hole to seal it off so that no more outside air enters the lung cavity. One item you might want to add to your First Aid kit. What – no jobsite First Aid kit? You might want to rethink that one. **(fig 10-4)**

Now, most of us have had both little and big splinters embedded in our fingers or hands, and these are best treated by using a sterilized needle to

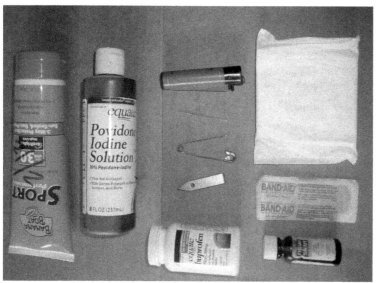

10-4 The basic medical supplies I keep in my jobsite First Aid kit to handle small common injuries

dig out and expose its uppermost end followed by yanking out the pesky item with a pair of sterilized pin-point type tweezers (i.e., Uncle Bill's Sliver Gripper Tweezers). Rubbing alcohol makes for an easy sterilizer. Remember to wash the area around the uninvited invader first before going on the attack to remove it so you don't introduce more germs into the opening. Sometimes splinters are embedded so deeply they cannot be reached easily. In this case, soak the area in an Epsom salt solution to draw the invader closer to the surface where you can do battle with him. Occasionally when moving lumber we get bit by a dagger splinter that most often resides along the corner edges of a board. Most often a dagger splinter pierces us and is withdrawn when we quickly yank our hand away from the board bite. The pain of a dagger splinter mimics that of a standard splinter, so often we believe we have something embedded in our hand/finger. Before you start excavating and come up dry, use the old "jobsite X ray" trick where one places a small flashlight on the opposite side of the finger from where the splinter may be and direct the light beam through the finger. If something is there, you will see it. My little Solitaire LED Mag light works great for this task on fingers since its lens is so small that no light escapes to the side to diminish its effectiveness. **(fig 10-5)**

Puncture wounds including splinters that go deep are actually worse than a larger cut to the skin's surface, because they drive germs/bacteria through the body's protective skin layer. If crap makes it past this defensive "border wall," we will have a more difficult time dealing with these Trojan horse

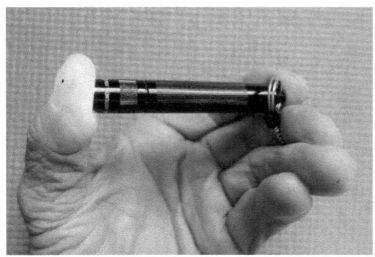

10-5 A small high-powered flashlight can check for embedded splinters in your fingers like an X ray

invaders. Unfortunately, most of us are not surgeons who can open up the punctured area to clean out all the crap that just got injected in, so your best option is to allow a puncture wound to bleed a bit in hopes that this may carry the invaders out. Soaking the punctured area in Epsom salts may help as well, but if an infection does kick off, run to a doctor quickly so you can get some antibiotics. Puncture wounds are not something you should dilly-dally around with since you can end up with a dangerous infection in no time. In the late 1990s, while helping my brother frame a Prow roof on his cabin, I got stabbed by a dagger splinter from an LVL. It nailed me in the palm of my right hand. Nothing showed up in my "jobsite X ray," so I washed the entry site good and went back to work. The next day my whole hand was inflamed, I had red lines streaking from the area, and it was so painful I couldn't use it. Off to the Medical Center I went. The doctor cut into the area to look for splinter remnants. Finding nothing, he shot me up with antibiotics and prescribing an oral series as well. If my tetanus vaccine hadn't been current, I know they would have also hit me with that (normal recommendation is a booster every 10 years). It turns out that the dagger splinter had injected some invisible grime into a subterranean blister below the callus at the base of my index finger and the germs had just gone crazy multiplying in the perfect petri dish environment. The doctor told me that he had once seen something similar happen to a guy's fists the day after a bar fight. Forewarned, I have since removed bare knuckle bar fighting from my "to do" list. Splinters seemed to have been less of an issue when I was a younger and we used "real" wood, not all this paste up "imitation" lumber of today (LVLs, PSLs, OSLs, LSLs, etc.). These products might be high tech, but I still

10-6 Never leave boards with protruding nails lying around the jobsite

hate to work with them. Most new-age carpenters use work gloves to protect against splinter bites, and I must admit that a few years back I wussed out and started using them when I had to move a lot of "fake" lumber.

Another embedded type injury one occasionally may see on the jobsite is a puncture injury from a framing nail. Most often this comes from stepping on a board that has some nails sticking up. **(fig 10-6)** I am a stickler for a clean jobsite. If you knock a board down and it has nails in it, then you must immediately either pull those nails or bend them over. It barely takes more than a few seconds to do this. Until those protruding nails are dealt with, that board is nothing more than a Vietnam era punji stick trap. If you visualize all protruding nails being covered with the same type of filth the Viet Cong tainted their punji stakes with, you too will probably become as anal as I am about making sure they are never seen on your jobsite. I did step on a nail protruding from a block once and was fortunate that my foot healed without incident. Must have been a clean nail. Normally, when I was only working from the top plates up as a stacker I was fairly immune to this kind of injury, but when I started leading custom home framing crews there would always be a certain amount of time that I had to spend working at ground level before I could get up in the air where it is safe. Anyone who has ever worked with me knew that leaving a 16d punji block around on the job was a quick way to get fired. An individual's normal reaction to this type of injury is to quickly pull one's foot off the nail/nails and sit down to take a look at the puncture wound. As mentioned earlier, try to get the nail hole to bleed some to help carry out any injected germs. Then clean and bandage it as you would with any wound, and make sure your tetanus vaccination is up to date.

10-7 The guys in Central America work in sandals or rain boots

Over the next few days keep a sharp eye out for infection. Some folks like to use work boots with a steel shank to avoid jobsite 16d punji block injuries, but my response would be that, by keeping a clean jobsite, you have eliminated the hazard, and an individual can walk around the job in sandals as some of the guys I taught in Central America would do. **(fig 10-7)** I was forced to wear work boots on some big commercial jobs but I must say I felt like an elephant walking around up in the air not a quick-footed squirrel. Steel-toed boots are another safety item that I seriously have questions about their benefit. With enough downward force they can chop your toes right off. Of course you will have to decide whether it is better to have your toes cut off or deal with the mashed mess that may remain if you don't use them. My idea is to stay away from situations were something that heavy can fall. While we may hand set some smaller beams with Genie lifts or human muscle, all the big heavy stuff is done with a crane. In all my years I can't remember ever smashing my toes badly on the jobsite, but dropping things on them in the kitchen is another matter. And while I am off on this tangent of crushing and cutting things, if you wear a wedding ring or any jewelry, take it off before you go to work. A smashed ring can act like a guillotine or get hooked on something and drag you into a bad situation. Remember in the 1999 film *Payback* starring Mel Gibson, how he yanked out the drug dealer's nose ring to get his attention. Well things on the jobsite can do the same thing, so don't have anything on your body that can get hung up on something. I personally don't have or wear any jewelry at all. Since my days were all spent on a jobsite, what good would it do for me to wear them to bed at night?

Very rarely, one might get nailed by the pneumatic nailer. It happened once when I was framing a two-story house on a sloped lot in the Oakland

Hills with Dave Sylvester. Dave was outside using an extension ladder to bump nail the exterior sheathing on one of the sloped sides of the building. It had rained recently, so the ground around the house was fairly muddy and, after a while, one of the ladder's legs started to sink slowly into the mud and the ladder began to slide to the side. Dave was a long way up the ladder and, not wanting to go down with the ship, he instinctively grabbed for a nearby window opening in order to pull himself to safety, but in the frantic leap he somehow accidentally bump nailed his left hand to the wall. He ended up standing on the window sill, torso plastered face first against the building like a rock climber with his palm securely nailed to the wall. Luckily one of the guys worked part time as an ambulance EMT and he quickly used a block of wood and his cat's paw nail puller to remove the nail so Dave was freed up, then off to the hospital they both went. After a thorough examination, it was determined that the nail had missed everything of importance in his hand. The Lord's blessing. It did slow Dave down for a couple days, since he was forced to work one-handed. Since my days as an apprentice carpenter, I have only rarely nailed off sheathing; I always assigned the task to others. We had one guy on Dave's crew who was an absolute magician at gun nailing sheathing, but evidently this day he wasn't around. Treatment plan for an injury of this type parallels our earlier models – get the bleeding stopped with pressure while you are on the way to the hospital. There they will take care of the next two steps (clean, bandage). I always like to prenail my exterior wall sheathing before standing the walls, not only because it is faster, but also to avoid risky situations just like this. Unfortunately, especially with hillside framing, this isn't always possible, and one is forced to hang and nail the sheathing from the outside using ladders, pump jacks, or the like.

We all have heard of or been a part of terrible jobsite circular saw cut injuries, and I, having spent nearly half a century in the battlefield, have seen my share. Let's look at a few and see what we can learn from them. In 1979 when I was working as a framing foreman in Santa Barbara, CA, one of the guys on the crew, Davido, opened up his thigh badly with a Skilsaw. It required several skin graft surgeries to repair. While I wasn't around when it happened, because he was on a weekend side job, I do remember that it really put a huge damper on our framing crew performance since Davido really functioned as my partner. But more than that, it affected me psychologically. While I had known of and seen other construction accidents up to that point, this was the first major one that happened to someone I knew well and who was like a brother. From what I recall, Davido was cutting a piece of siding between a pair of saw horses when the saw blade bound up and ran back at him across his thigh. We all know intrinsically that, while this cut can be accomplished with some tricky balancing, it is a very risky situation and should be avoided. This is why it is listed in my list of *10 Commandments for Skilsaw Use* (see chapter "My Two Best Friends"). Certainly Davido, who was already beat tired from a long hard week framing, fell prey to what is known in the aviation world as the "Get-home-itis syndrome" as Saturday wore on. "Get-home-itis syndrome" is where one gets so tired that you throw caution and sound decision-making to the wind, just so you can be done with whatever it is that you are doing and go home. If you haven't faced this yet in your career, you will, so be forewarned.

Most likely, the lower blade guard of Davido's Skilsaw was pinned back and quite possibly, if it had not been, the kickback cut may never have bit him. Anyhow, it is impossible to know for certain. While pinning up the lower guard may be against OSHA regulations, it was a common practice in my day and something I have done all my career even after nearly losing my own thumb in the mid-1980s from blatant violations of my own 10 command-ments of proper Skilsaw use (story to follow). With the lower blade guard of a Skilsaw in the down position, one has problems cutting beveled cheek-cuts or trimming a board by anything less than ½ inch. So the common cutting task of "take an 1/8 inch off this board" cannot be made one-handed with a Skilsaw when the lower blade guard is down. To follow the OSHA regulations correctly, one would need to set up a cutting table having a clamping device and then use your second hand, which normally grasps the piece of wood, to now sustain the lower guard in the up position while this cut is made. So clearly anyone can see that this is not something that can be done with ease when you are up in the air stacking a roof solo. So for this reason, we always worked with our lower guards pinned up or removed, and were extremely careful in how we handled our Skilsaws.

First aid treatment in the situation of a major cut such as what happened to Davido's leg is no different than what is done on a minor cut, except that we as initial caregivers will only be doing the pressure part of the injury equation, while the professionals at the hospital will do everything that follows (clean, etc., bandage). So, as a response to an injury of this type, quick-ly slap a clean cloth and apply pressure to the injury while heading for the hospital's emergency room. The injured individual can apply direct pressure to the cut while you drive. They will automatically want to do so anyway. Keep the extremity that has been cut elevated above heart level. Therefore, in the case of a leg injury, have the injured individual lie down so you can prop the leg up, all the while keeping that pressure applied. If the individual loses consciousness due to blood loss or other reasons, get somebody to apply direct pressure to the injury site while you drive the vehicle or vice versa. Since typically on a jobsite no one will be carrying around a clean cloth on their person, a sweaty T-shirt or something similar is thrown on the cut immediate-ly until it can be swapped out with something clean from the jobsite First Aid kit. Women's supersized sanitation napkins work great as the clean cloth on a bad cut. I keep a few stashed in my First Aid kit.

On one job in Montecito, CA (early 1980s), my carpenter apprentice/

laborer was trying to make an angled cut on a block of wood with his Skilsaw blade guard pinned up, and the saw kicked back and ran up the board nearly cutting his thumb clean off. It is instinctive for the hurt individual to smother the cut and that is exactly what happened in this case. Dave Sylvester, my framing partner, tossed him a T-shirt and off to the emergency room they sped. There just so happened to be a hand specialist on call at Cottage Hospital who patched him up well and he regained full use. I do not allow new carpenters to work with their saw guards pinned up. Only after they have developed good saw technique and have gained a lot of experience will I back off and allow them to decide for themselves. The difficult cuts are always reserved for the more experienced guys with lots of saw time. And that being said, even experienced guys like myself can do stupid things and get hurt as I will now share in my next story.

This must have been a few years after the previous story on a job up in a part of Santa Barbara, CA, called the *Mesa* (table). I had just finished piecemeal cutting all the roofs on a tract of two-story condominiums when the framing contractor asked if I wanted to stay around for a few more days and piecemeal frame all the drop ceilings. I saw that I could make some good money if I was fast, so I accepted. Being tall, I have a definite advantage when framing in 7-foot drops since I don't need a ladder much and can move quickly. These drops were required to hide the installed waste lines from the upstairs bathrooms. Unfortunately, the plastic pipes from above turned into the wall framing fairly low in respect to the bottom surface of the drop so I had to do a lot of notching to fit the wall ledgers around the pipes. Now realize, I am fast at notching. For a pipe that infringed into the level of my ledger I would make two quick cross-cut passes in the ledger at each side of where the pipe dove into the wall and then drop-cut between those two cuts for the bottom of the notch which parallels the ledger. It might take all of 5 seconds. As the day wore on my back started aching a bit and I was getting tired so instead of bending down to make the drop-cut notch on stickers in a safe manner on the floor, I stayed standing and began placing one end of the ledger on the floor while grabbing the other end of the board 18 inches my side of the part to be notched and made the drop-cut. Most of you can see this one coming. Yes, I was busting commandment #2 of my own *10 Commandments of Skilsaw Use* – never put your hand anywhere behind a Skilsaw. I suppose my stupid rationalization for breaking my own Skilsaw operation rules was that my hand was located so far away from the drop-cut that it was out of the danger zone. Anyhow all went well for a while but on one drop-cut the blade bound and even though I let off on the trigger instantly the saw shot up the board and in less than a microsecond cut across the top side of my left thumb. This can only happen if the front of the saw-foot is allowed to lift up off the surface of the wood, and, evidently, I had unknowingly let that happen. That is all it takes for the saw to take off at full gallop in reverse. Besides this flagrant disregard for the rules, I must not have been bracing the elbow of my right hand, which was holding the Skilsaw against my body as I should have been, or it would not have been able to jump back. This was a second flagrant violation of my *10 Commandments of Skilsaw Use*. Anyhow, I grabbed my T-shirt and slammed it on my cut thumb, yelled for the contractor, and off to the hospital we went. Truthfully, I was indeed blessed in this accident because the saw blade's teeth walked right across the bone stepping over the extension tendons and an artery. The blade did sever the sensation nerve on the back of the thumb, and, distal to the cut, this nerve did die. This was in the days of the old-style steel blades that had big gullets between each tooth. The whole incident did give me a bit of a head trip, as I realized how important our hands are and how the Lord had mercifully protected me, in spite of my own stupidity, by placing that gullet so exactly as to cause the least amount of damage considering the situation. Without a thumb I would not been able to finger nails or the multitude of other framing tasks where all our fingers are called upon. With time it healed up well enough, but it would take many years for the sensation nerve from the inside of the thumb to grow up and around to take over some of the sensory work done previously by the nerve I had ruined. The loss of feeling in my thumb would be a constant reminder going forward through my life to adhere without exception to my Skilsaw operating rules.

The worse cut type accident I personally know of happened when I was working in the Los Angeles housing tracts. I did not know the individual, nor was I anywhere close to the accident site when it happened, but from what I was told the big 18-inch cross-cut saw blade came off the spindle of the Delta overhead radial arm saw and buried itself in the chest of the operator. Sadly, the gentleman died and most likely left a wife and kids to fend for themselves. I don't know the details on why it actually happened, but, undoubtedly, this accident has played a big part in the subconscious fear I now have for these big saws that sound like a jet engine when they spin up. Medically, outside a miracle, there is not much one can do in such a traumatic accident of this magnitude even if it were to happen in an operating room.

FALLS

Falls are by far the biggest contributor to injuries and deaths in the construction industry. The 2015 US Department of Labor statistics show that 21.4% of all private industry worker fatalities come from the construction industry where the leading cause of these deaths is falls. In fact, the number one violation cited by OSHA in 2015 was for improper fall protection (29 CFR 1926.501). These statistics are as good a motivator as anything to take this facet of framing seriously. Greg Medcalf, our California high school state finalist heavyweight wrestler, became a bar bouncer during and after college. He told me years later that as bouncers they would never get into a fisticuff with anybody, simply grab and toss them into something or down on the floor. Nothing hits harder than smacking a concrete floor, a wall, or a table. During high school wrestling practice, all us heavier guys (175, 191 weight classes) had to tussle with Greg as part of training, so I vividly recall how much "fun" it was to be smashed into the mat by him. WMI notes that any high-impact collision or a fall onto the buttocks, back/side, or head from above the height of 3 feet has the inerrant energy required to do major spinal damage, possibly resulting in paralyzation. So for these types of situations, our first response on the jobsite should be to stabilize the individual in the position you find them (if at all possible). Grab their head with both hands to freeze it in a normally aligned position and call 911. If the individual is standing, ask them to lie down but do not help them do so. When they are lying down, move in to stabilize their head. Sometimes the individual who has made a tumble ends up in a cock-eyed position, so he must be moved into a neutral alignment position but, unless you have had some training in doing this correctly, you can risk severing the individual's spinal cord if indeed his/her spine column is damaged. Best to wait for the paramedics to arrive and they will take care of moving him/her around. Then it is off to the hospital to get X rays, scans, etc.

Now with this being said, how many times have we all taken a major spill and then jumped right back up to keep on working with no ill effects. So why such restrictive First Aid recommendations? It comes down to that the medical profession prefers to be more safe than sorry and they don't like lawsuits. I respect that. Lifetime paralysis is not a joking matter. One of the guys on our rowing team was paralyzed after the car he was driving was struck by a drunk driver. What can anyone really say to him except to cry inside. I believe most people who have injured themselves after a fall know it. They sense something isn't right. I remember the story of a surfer who had gotten dumped by a wave into the ocean floor. When he came ashore, he immediately laid down on his back on the beach and used his hands to move sand around his neck in order to stabilize it while asking someone to go call 911. Smart guy. One dilemma we face on the jobsite is that you can't force anyone to go to the hospital if they just fell and feel totally fine. All we can do is suggest. I suppose we must look at each specific fall situation to decide how hard to push anyone against their own will. In WFR training we learned how to "clear a spine" of any damage in a wilderness setting but, in an urban jobsite setting, this procedure is not authorized since expert medical attention is only minutes away. Certainly, signs of damage like back pain, or a lack of circulation, sensation, or motion (CSM) in any of the extremities are a good clue that you should push very hard to convince the individual to lay down and permit you to steady his head, while calling for the paramedics. I must say that being young definitely plays in one's favor to avoid suffering the ill effects from a fall. As a kid I would take such brutal disastrous spills while rough housing that I was nicknamed "lumps," but I never suffered a major injury. If I did even one of those same crazy things nowadays I would end up in a casket.

One winter morning in Berkeley, CA (2002), Nick Ridge, who is absolutely phenomenal up in the air, was walking the roof sheathing on a two-story house and slipped on an unseen patch of ice. He went right off the roof eave and smacked into an outside concrete patio slab and bench some 20 feet below. Nick landed mostly on his left side bent over the bench. He shattered his left hand, severed ligaments in his left elbow, and had massive hematomas in his hip. I personally believe he is lucky to be alive. In Central America several years back I arrived just after a painter fell 12 feet from some scaffolding to a concrete sidewalk. Unfortunately having hit his head he died almost instantly. We can all spot at least one error in Nick's roof sliding incident and that is the lack of a 2×4 nailer around the perimeter of the sheathed roof at the fascia line. This might have stopped his ski slope slide, but then again maybe Nick had just removed all the nailers the night before in preparation for the roofer to paper the roof. For those of you in cold climates, ice on the sheathing might be a common occurrence, but for us in coastal California it is almost never seen, so it would not be something one would have foremost in his mind as a hazard. What is probably a much more common cause of a slip on the roof surface is sawdust. While cutting roof sheathing produces some good sawdust, the most slippery type sawdust comes from 2×6 T&G spruce decking. It has some type of waxy component. We would never sheath a roof above 4/12 pitch without a push broom handy to sweep the roof surface clean after every cut. A stream of pressurized air from the nail-gun hose would accomplish the same thing. What I hold as paramount to avoid falls of this type is the correct sole on one's shoes. Besides general comfort, I always test the sole's grip on any pair of shoes that I might be considering to purchase. Stores that sell outdoor gear like REI often have little rock piles where you can test out how the shoe's soles perform at extreme angles. And it goes without saying that one should never work up high with the soles of your shoes dirty. Dirt, mud, and sand all create a slippery layer that separates your shoe's sole from the wood surface. Also, when you are up high, don't wear super loose clothing that might get caught on something and cause you to stumble. From the safety standpoint, I suppose that our half-nude tract-framing uniform of shorts and tennis shoes had some safety benefit after all, because there was almost nothing there to get hung up on anything. OSHA has a list of safety equipment required nowadays for when one works at heights, and I had the chance to try out some of it on various commercial framing jobs for Dan Daley. None of it was around when I was younger and I doubt I would have used it anyway because of its steep price and physical restriction to movement. Most small-time framers don't have the funds to equip their crew with this gear, so they do it the old-fashion way. Sometimes I wonder if safety gear makes folks less safety conscious since they believe they are now invincible. I have frequently observed that the guys with the lower blade guard on their Skilsaw handle it in a rather careless and sloppy manner. On top of this, safety gear can fail. Now I am most certainly not saying that you should not use safety gear, but rather don't let it lull you into thinking you don't have to be concerned about safety anymore. Learn to operate any tool in such a fashion that, even if it didn't have any safety gear attached, you would not get hurt. Then safety gear simply becomes a second line of defense.

A good rule is to always take responsibility for your own personal safety and don't do anything unless you feel confident about the work situation. One trick I do to help make walking 2×4 thick wall plates a bit safer on a section of a house that is totally open and exposed, like a cathedral ceiling or open beam, is to simply add a temporary 2×4 ledger along the inside of the rafter wall flush with the top of the double plate. This widens the wall plate out to near 2×6 thickness which is a whole lot easier to plate walk than a 2×4 wall. Another idea when sheathing a very steep pitch roof in addition to 2×4 nailers every 4 feet up the angled surface is to toss a ½- to ¾-inch rope over the roof ridge that is tied off to something on the far side of the roof or house like a window header or tree. Then a guy can tie it around his waist at such a length that there is no way he will go off the roof. Not as fancy as these cool retracting-type restraining lines, but it gets the job done none the less.

While big falls from height are bad news and can often end your active career, as it did for my Orange Coast College instructor Hank Resse, more often we framers will face smaller floor-level stumbling falls. While walking the second-story floor joists on a job in the Berkeley, CA, hills I tripped on a nail head that had been left sticking up above the surface by someone that needed to be fired, and down I went through an opening in the floor. I caught myself with my arms, but the maneuver ended up tearing my right rotator cuff. Always sink your nails until the head is flush. Another tripping risk in modern day framing is all the blooming cords and hoses that everybody stretches like booby trap trip lines all over the darn place. I try to teach guys to be considerate of the other crew members with whom they are working. It seems like such a simple request but, more and more, I find that this hardly enters folks' heads. It doesn't dawn on them that, with all their cords and hoses going every which or way, they have created an obstacle course for everybody else who wishes to traverse that area. It takes no more than a few extra seconds to rig the hoses and cables to their work areas from such a direction that they stay out of the high traffic areas and out of everybody's way. Same goes with leaving scrap 2× cutoffs lying around where you were last working. When done with some project, clean up your work area. Besides my nail trip "free fall" through the floor joists incident, I have tripped over wood cutoffs laying around on the floor several times that have caused major shoulder injuries requiring surgery. One time I tripped on a 2×4 scrap and fell forward. I landed on my outstretched hand and the force separated my shoulder. Another time, I tripped and fell backward while carrying a heavy tool under my arm. I caught myself on the free outstretched arm, but once again the force caused major shoulder damage. A habit of leaving scrap wood lying around is definitely a fireable offense because of the safety hazard it presents to the crew.

Despite being a wrestler through high school where I learned to fall correctly, then later taking a little Judo and Jujitsu, I still screwed up on both of these tripping falls. In a pinch, none of this training did me any good because my reflexes just sent my arms out to brace before my mind could even grasp what was going on. In grappling training I was all primed to fall correctly knowing the other guy was about to throw me or knock me on my butt, but on the jobsite I am in a totally different mindset. Maybe if I spent 20 years rolling around the mat it may have become second nature like they all claim, but I still wonder. I remember Nick Ridge's older brother who was some kind of high-ranking Black belt in Karate giving Nick a rash about his two-story fall, saying that if it had been him who had fallen, he would have just rolled out of it. Right! Maybe if he had planned ahead to make the jump but a slip and ski slope slide is something different. On top of that, his older brother had never worked carpentry or played around on the roof. I feel that we will have to do some testing and unknowingly throw a bunch of karate guys off a two-story roof in various positions to see how they fare.

So what should one do with a stumble-and-fall injury at floor level that injures an arm, a shoulder, a leg, etc.? Sometimes it is very hard to know if the injury is minor and will go away on its own in a couple weeks or if it is something major that will require prolonged care or even surgery. As we live life and experience injuries, each of us will learn how to balance the feeling and intensity of pain to an injury's seriousness. For example, I knew immediately after each of the various falls detailed above that I had injured my shoulders badly because of the type of pain and where it was located. Other indicators to help one consider an injury's seriousness are: swelling; tenderness; a pop at the time of a fall; funny joint sounds upon movement; altered CSMs (circulation, sensation, motion), etc. As with any type of musculoskeletal injury immediately stop, slap ice on the painful area, and elevate it to above chest level. These two responses work to slow inflammation (edema) which will help to lessen the pain and speed the healing. Instant cold packs are a great item to have stashed in your First Aid kit for these occasions. A 4- to 6-inch compression wrap can be used between ice treatments and for several weeks after the injury as needed to control swelling. Remember to apply the wrap on limbs from far to close (distal to proximal in medispeak). The biggest benefit from icing an injury is seen during the first 48 hours after the injury, but it can be helpful out to several weeks. Use a 20-minute cycle (20 on/ 20 off). Ibuprofen at 800 mg 3 times a day (maximum dosage) is also recommended to help with inflammation and pain. You can combine this with acetaminophen 1000 mg 3 times a day (maximum dosage) if you are still experiencing pain. These two should be taken alternatively every 4 hours – never take them both at the same time. Limit their use to a 10-day run since these medications are hard on your liver. It stands to reason that you will need to back off using the injured part for a while so it can heal. Use pain as a guide to how much you should do with the injured area. Pain is the body's way of telling us to "cool it." The above-described musculoskeletal injury treatment plan can be easily remembered using the word mnemonics of "**RICE**" which stands for **R**est, **I**ce, **C**ompression, **E**levation, and "**PFA**" which stands for **P**ain **F**ree **A**ctivity.

If you can't put weight on the limb, it is an unstable injury (i.e., can't use your foot to walk) and you should head off to see an orthopedic doctor. He normally will shoot some X rays or send you off to get an MRI in order to see what you tore up or broke.

Once I had to frame a dormer on a 12/12 pitched Gable roof from the inside using some job-framed scaffolding. I can't remember exactly what happened now some 40 years later, but somehow I ended up stumbling 5 feet straight backward into the butt end of a fixed 2×4. Needless to say, it was not a fun day and I ended up with several cracked ribs. Unfortunately, there is not much one can do for this except to wrap the chest. Every breath for the next several weeks was painful. A chest strike such as that can cause a closed pneumothorax (air entering lung cavity internally) from a rib fracture tearing the lining inside, so if your breathing increases in difficulty, head for the hospital.

HITS

Getting hit by something can cause the same type of musculoskeletal damage that we looked at in "Falls." Although less common, they still happen. I had a wall fall on my leg and tear up my knee. I got hit by a crane slung load of TJIs, which damaged my shoulder. These would be treated as outlined previously. Unfortunately, some of the most common hits we receive we give to ourselves. Over my life I must have lost a dozen or so fingernails as the result of a hammer strike that went afoul. While that may seem like a lot of errant strikes, when compared to the sheer volume of nails that I might have driven in my career we find that it is really no big deal to have lost 10 to 12 fingernails in +40 years. Bear in mind that, for my whole life, I have done nothing but hand nail. I only used a pneumatic nailer for sheathing and then it wasn't even me using it but another crew member. And unlike most framers who either moved up into a "bags off" supervisory position after a reasonable time, or left the trade entirely, I never left the daily "hammer in hand" swinging aspect of framing. I couldn't – I was addicted to it. In the end, it was only disabling injuries that forced me out. Just for fun, I looked at how many nails I might have driven in my life. I recall that during my stacking days in the tracts I would typically eat through nearly three-quarters of a 50-lbs box of 16d nails per 16-inch OC house roof (3200 nails in a 50-lbs box). I would do one roof in a 10- to 12-hour marathon day. Not to be undone by a poor memory, I sat down and mathematically counted up all the nails an individual would drive, to stack, block, brace, and run gable studs, on a standard 2000-square-foot tract house of that rafter spacing. I came up with about +/−2360 nails per house, which concurred with my three-quarter box recollection. When that daily amount is run out mathematically for just 1 year of working 5 days a week, it would be some 5 tons of 16d nails. If that same house had rafter spacing of 24-inch OC, the nail count is about +/−1600 nails per house (half a box per day) or 3.1 tons of 16d nails per year. When I shifted over to custom home framing I probably held to half a 50-lbs box of 16d nails driven on most days. When I added this all up for my life I found it to be such an amazing amount of nails hand driven that I now fully understand why my body is so worn out. The yearly amount could be as high as +400,000 nails in any given year or a possible maximum lifetime amount of over 10 million nails hand driven after subtracting out for my 3-month Alaska summer bush-flying diversions spanning several decades, my forced time off for injuries, and the time I spent overseas as a volunteer. So I averaged hitting a fingernail in 1 out of every +/−1 million nails driven, which is really not bad at all. Wonder how many pneumatic nail guns lifespans it would have taken to shoot that many nails?

The vast majority of my finger whacks came from either ricochets or distractions. Remember in the 1991 movie *Robin Hood* how easily Lady Marian distracted Robin Hood (played by Kevin Costner) with just a simple puff of air in his ear when he was demonstrating his super archery concentration abilities. Unfortunately, my nailing distractions were not caused by a pretty blond gal blowing in my ear, but by much more mundane circumstances. For example, while working for Hal Benhardt, I was up on a long 6×16 ridge beam installing exposed vertical blocking between top sitting rafter beams. I had the block positioned between the beam rafters and was holding it with my left hand while striking each end alternately with my 28-ounce hammer to drive it down. Someone shouted a question to me mid swing and I responded by looking toward him just enough that my swing went awry hitting my left thumbnail and opening it up like a ripe tomato. Blood went shooting out the sides of the nail. It was ugly. Thank goodness it was a tapping swing rather than a full force swing or it is doubtful my finger would have survived. Eventually it did heal up. The first course of action for a smashed fingernail is ICE and pain medications. If there was any exterior bleeding then obviously that must be stopped with direct pressure. If you can still move your finger around normally, you will probably recover OK. If you have any issues with CSM, it would be best to have a hand doctor check it out. If not, most of us go back to work when the pain becomes manageable in 10 to 15 minutes. I know it is hard to do while you are working, but try to ice the damaged digit on a 20-minute on/off cycle for the first 48 hours after a finger smack.

The best way to avoid a distraction fingernail strike or, for that matter, any distraction-caused tool injury, is to teach your crew to take into account what someone is doing before butting in. Wait for the person to pause what he/she is doing, whether it be using a saw, hammer, or nail gun before you hit them up with a question or request for their help. When it is absolutely imperative that I stop someone in the middle of a tool operation activity for some reason (i.e., doing something incorrectly), I have found that gently placing my hand on their shoulder or upper back in a momentary lull is a good way to get their attention in a subtle and safe fashion. Everyone seems to recognize this as a sign to stop what they are doing. Cutting their power or air supply is another way that works well if they surprise easy. Now, if you are the tool operator, learn to block out all sound and visual distractions when you are hammering or operating a tool. The only exception to this would be the "hands on" foreman (like me) who must operate in two different worlds at the same time – one world is the particular task I may be doing at the time (i.e., running frieze blocks) and the other world is a kind of omnipresent shadowing of what everybody else on the crew is doing. We lead carpenter types must be able to absorb all that is going on without permitting it to distract us. I was blessed all my life to have incredible partners who most of the time stepped in to resolve lesser jobsite issues so I could stay focused. They always ran interference. Other distractions can be carpenter's dogs and loud music.

Many of my ricochet fingernail smashes have come from hand setting a nail in a super confined space. At times when setting a nail, the hammer handle may glaze or bump something due to the tight space. This small disruption is all that is needed to send your hammer head off course so it contacts the thumb or forefinger of your nail set hand instead of the head of the nail as planned. One can get all types of pool table like ricochet strikes from oddball nailing situations. I rarely give risky nailing situations to others since I feel it is something that leaders should do. These types of tight-space nailing situations are an excellent place to apply a pneumatic nailer if it will fit. If not, give a slide hammer a try (a.k.a. pea-shooter). If neither one is able to do the job and you must hand nail, then expect some fingernail damage now and then. For some tight spaces, one can spin the hammer head around and finish driving a set nail in a tight space with the claw and I would do that often.

Over the years, I developed a technique that seems to lessen the overall injury of a smashed fingernail. What I do is immediately apply pressure on the injury site by clamping it between the thumb and forefinger of my good

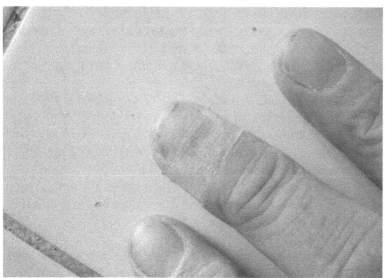

10-8 Pressure at the site of a fingernail strike seems to help curb the extent of under nail bleeding

hand. Although this hurts like hell, I keep the damaged area clamped for 15 minutes just like it is an external wound that is bleeding. My theory is that, in doing this, the internal blood vessels will bleed less into the space under the fingernail, and the resulting hematoma under the fingernail will be smaller. After 15 minutes have passed, I wrap the finger snugly with some medical tape at the damaged level in order to continue to apply some modest pressure to the damaged area for the next day or so. **(fig 10-8)** Since using this procedure, I have not had to melt a hole through the top of my fingernail into the nail bed a day or so later in order to relieve the pressure from the hematoma. While few of us leading a crew have the luxury of time to dunk our injured finger in ice water every so often, we generally can spare 15 minutes to "pressure clamp" the injury and apply some tape. If the pain grows over the next day, it is because of pressure built up under the finger-nail. Heat the "eye" end of a sewing needle to red hot and place it on the fingernail over the middle of the hematoma. **(fig 10-9)** Don't apply much pressure or you will go right through the fingernail and into the nail bed which will spike your pain. You only need to go through the nail's keratin layer. Expect a gush of fluid in most cases and then an immediate lessening of pain when the pressure is released. A new fingernail will grow in below the damaged one and slowly carry it out. Try to keep the old fingernail on through the whole grow-out time period in order to protect the tender nail bed that would be exposed if it was to fall off. I use various methods to keep it attached from epoxy glue to tape. **(fig 10-10)**

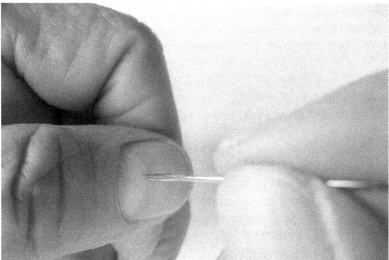

10-9 Heat the head of a sewing needle to red hot and then perforate the nail to relieve pressure

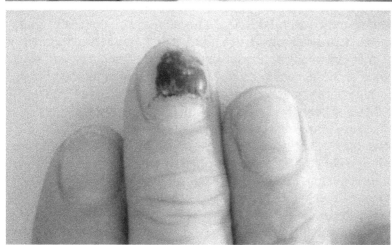

10-10 As the new nail grows in, keep the old nail affixed as long as possible to protect the nail bed

A very serious type of hit is a flying object to the eyes, and, for this reason, I always suggest that all my crew wear sunglasses or clear safety glasses on the job. Not only is there the risk of your own nails ricocheting up at your face by an off-angle hammer strike, but also friendly fire from other crew members. This alone is a good reason not to lump everyone in one small working area. While I attended the Orange Coast College construction program I did maintenance and construction at the crew base during the school year and framed full-time during the summer break. I often did little side jobs to help folks out as I could fit them in. One of these was a quick weekend job to spice up a friend's bland concrete driveway with some side-to-side stripes of regular brick pavers. While I was making parallel saw passes 9 inches apart across the driveway with a diamond blade mounted on my Skil 77, my helper Eric was busting out the concrete in the middle with a sledge hammer. I should have noticed, but he was not wearing any eye protection. A little while into the demolition process he felt like something had shot up into his eye, so we stopped to take a look. A quick examination showed a small speck of something embedded in his cornea which was not good. We shortened a foam coffee cup down to about 2 inches high and set it over his eye and held it in place by wrapping a T-shirt around his head so it covered both the cup and his good eye like a blindfold and took off to the hospital. If one eye is injured it is always best to cover both eyes until cleared by medical professionals. Since both eyes move in union, the injured eye will naturally want to copy what the good eye is doing, which is not very helpful when you don't want the injured eye to move. An eye specialist was able to surgically remove the speck, and Eric suffered no ill effects. The speck ended up being of small sliver of metal from the striking face of the sledgehammer.

Some years later in the early 1980s, while framing custom homes in Santa Barbara, CA, we had two other jobsite eye injuries that only served to fortify the importance that everybody on the jobsite should wear some type of eye protection. In one of these incidents a pneumatic nailer misfired, sending a nail out to the side of the tip toward one of my carpenter's eyes who was stabilizing the material being fastened. The nail hit just below the eyeball on the uppermost reaches of the cheekbone, saving his eye from what could have been a terrible accident. I suppose nail guns have gotten safer nowadays, but in the old days we always seemed to get a couple misfires per day. On another custom home we were framing in the mid-1980s, a very skilled framer named Mark Trabucco was running CJs. Mark framed using a rigging hatchet and was a real whiz with it. With one end of the CJs nailed in place and having just finished eyeball cutting the "run wild" end to length, he was nailing off the loose ends. Evidently, a nail he had installed went awry or bent so he spun his hatchet around to make a swing using the blade and knock it out so he could redo with another nail. Unfortunately, the nail, instead of following the arc of his hammer swing, shot up into his eye puncturing his eyeball causing fluid leakage. His brother Andy quickly grabbed him and off they went to the hospital. One good thing about Santa Barbara, CA, is the high quality of doctors in town and Mark recovered without suffering any long-term ill effects.

Before we totally depart from the subject of eyes, let's touch on the standard operating procedure First Aid treatment for airborne particles that may end up on the surface of your eyeball. While wearing eye protection may help defend against direct missile strikes to the eyeball, airborne sawdust or dirt can still make it into your eye unless your eye protection is a scuba dive mask. Most know not to rub their eyes when particles find their way in, since this will only scratch the cornea by moving the particle around. Flooding the eye with water to float the particle/s out is the preferred starting point. I personally use one of two methods to accomplish this. In the first method, I fill a glass with water, then, looking down at my feet, I place the opening of the glass around my eye like a swimming goggle and tilt my head back. This immediately submerges my eye underwater. Blinking a bit in this underwater eye position can be helpful. In the second method, looking straight ahead tilt your head to the side of the affected eye and gently pour water into the eye so it drains out the side away from the tear duct. Never rinse the eye out toward the tear duct. Doing this several times usually washes out most particles of sawdust and dirt. It helps to have a partner for this method, but it can be done solo. Another quick and easy method that works in a waterless environment is to grab the top eyelid of the problematic eye and gently lift it out and set it over the lower eyelid in an effort to brush off anything that stuck to the underside of the lid with the lower lid's eyelashes. A last ditch effort if a particle is still seen floating around on the eyeball surface is to dab it off gently with a cotton Q-tip but this does require a partner, preferably one with a steady hand. Even once the particle has been removed, the eye will often still feel like there is something in there. Normally, this is because the cornea was scratched slightly by the floating particle. This will heal quickly, but this is the very reason you never want to rub your eye when it feels like there is something in it.

Another less common hit is the missed swing of sledge hammer or framing hammer contacting the shin bone. While a strike such as that can easily deliver enough force to break the tibia, it most often gives the errant swinger a large swollen bump and much pain. Once again, use the mnemonics of RICE and PFA to guide you through acceptable First Aid practices. Don't forget to incorporate some ibuprofen as an anti-inflammatory and painkiller. If the leg can't bear weight and CSMs are compromised, then the problem is more serious and you should seek professional medical care. If the hospital is a short distance away, it is probably best to just transport immediately, but many times it does help to alleviate the pain and lessen travel stresses if you spend a few minutes to immobilize a suspected broken bone first. If the limb looks deformed, gently traction it into its correct anatomical position before applying the splinting materials. For a long bone injury such as the tibia always immobilize the joints above and below the suspected break. On most jobsites, one can usually find (or cut) something that can serve as splint material. A pair of 1×2s, some scrap pieces of PVC pipe, or even a short piece of rolled roofing paper will all serve as the rigid splinting structure. These items should be well padded, and, normally, if everybody chips in some clothing items, you will scrounge up enough cushioning to make it comfortable. For binding a splint into position, things like lumber tie down straps/rope or a T-shirt ripped into strips can fill this need. **(fig 10-11)**

10-11 A few examples of jerry-rigging leg splints from one of my WFR refresher classes

Smacks to the head are another real hazard on the job. Unfortunately, in the old days, head injuries were not given the care they deserved simply out of medical ignorance. I remembered when I played football in high school, I got knocked out during repetitive head-to-head tackling practice. As I came back to consciousness, I looked up to see our toothless coach, Mr. Spud Murphy (pro lineman and longshoreman in the 1960s) smiling down at me. As I was pulled to my feet, he handed me a new helmet (since I had cracked the other one), and immediately stuck me right back in the exercise lineup to face every member of the team as they charged me in rapid sequence. Little knowing how dangerous a concussion really was, this was the standard method used to toughen us up for the game. On the jobsite, most head injuries typically happen from things falling on our heads or possibly because of a lifted sling load of material giving us a wallop. As I discussed in the chapter entitled "The Minimalist" falling items can be avoided by always keeping your crew on the same building level so no one is working above anyone else. And if someone is up high on the roof and someone is down at ground level for some reason (visiting the portable toilet), always shout before you toss something to the ground to alert anyone who may be below that they should to take cover from an "incoming." A hard hat can go a long way to avoiding head injuries from "small" objects falling from above, but anything large will just break your neck. As I described in that same chapter, hard hats have their drawbacks, and I quite frankly have received all my head strikes on account of their visual restrictions. One sad memory from my Santa Barbara, CA, days happened on a commercial job in Ventura, CA, when a scaffold plank several floors up broke with a guy walking in the middle. The two ends of the board flew up and like clapping your hands smashed into his head front and back. A hard hat did him no good at all, and he died instantly. So every safety device has its limit. Since that scaffold plank-busting episode, I have been very careful in choosing my scaffold planks. I look for near FOHC (free of heart center), clear, no-knot type planks and then double them up on almost every situation above 4 feet from the ground.

Any head strike can be dangerous, but of utmost concern is when the individual loses consciousness as a result. Since the brain fits snugly inside the skull, any swelling or bleeding inside this space causes the intracranial pressure (ICP) to rise, which can damage and alter brain function. So any time after a head strike, the individual starts acting strangely and/or their level of responsiveness is going downhill, know that the ICP is gradually increasing, and it is a high-priority emergency. They may eventually fall into an unresponsive state unless advanced medical help is received. Signs like a worsening headache, vomiting, vision problems, sleepiness, or being disoriented, irritable, or combative are definite signs that their brain is in trouble and you best get them to the hospital for a check out. The First Aid procedure for any head injury would be to treat any accompanying contusion, monitor for signs of deterioration, and facilitate transport.

Another type of smack is getting hit by electric shock from a frayed or broken electric cord. If you happen to be standing in a wet area when you get belted, it can cause some serious physical damage. The electric power tools of today do a good job of preventing electrocution by being grounded or double insulated with plastic handles. If you are working in the rain, some of these protections are diminished since a layer of water will serve as a conductor even on a plastic handle. In California we would shut down the job and head home at the first sign of sprinkles since rainy days were so few, but in places like Oregon, Washington, or Southeastern Alaska, where the standard daily weather menu is rain, one must work in the light drizzle or nothing would ever get built. In wet conditions, I always kept my Skilsaw dry under a small piece of plywood. In Central America, we would tarp the working areas if possible. Standard First Aid procedure to help someone who has been slapped by electric shock is to first, make sure the power source is turned off and then verify that the individual's heart is pumping and he/she is breathing. If not, start CPR (you have taken a class in this haven't you?) and call 911. Keep your patient warm until the paramedics arrive and only move him/her if absolutely required. I hope nobody stays working when thunderstorms are in the neighborhood. We had a policy when I taught outdoor courses with Outward Bound that if lightning was within 5 miles (count after lightning is seen until the sound arrives – 5 seconds per each mile away) we would disperse everyone and get into what is call a "lightning position." Basically it is squatting low on a foam sleeping pad. On a construction site, your "lightning position" would be to either go sit in your pickup truck or head inside a completed building of size. I remember a guy was struck and killed by lightning on a concrete pour in Ventura, CA, when I was framing in Santa Barbara, CA. Lightning is so rare on the California coast that most of the locals aren't familiar with its danger. It doesn't need to be a direct hit to cause great physical harm, since 55% of all lightning injuries result from ground current, while an additional 35% of the injuries come from splash lightning where the strike skips off one item to hit another. The "take away" from all this – pay attention to the condition of your tools and electrical cords, and avoid playing in thunderstorm type rain.

LIFTING INJURIES

While lifting injuries don't exactly fall in the categories of Cut, Fall, or getting Hit, they may very well be one of the most common jobsite injuries aside from wood splinters. Anyone who spends much time in "hands on" construction will most likely suffer to some degree from bouts of low back pain during their career. This pain can arrive from a single event of pretending to be Hercules and lifting something way beyond rational, but most often this pain arrives from normal wear and tear. If loading and unloading, twisting, bending, etc., wear out the ball joints on our car/trucks, should we not expect these same movements to put some wear on our spine. Most certainly, spending many decades bent over at the waist nailing all day long combined with bouts of hauling material around the jobsite can't work in one's favor. The lumbar region is that area of the spine most often injured, and this is simply the result of body mechanics. While a single extreme lift can blow a disc (typically L4-5), all five disks of the lumbar region lose elasticity and compress through the aging process as they lose water content and dry up. Heavy use does much to accelerate this decline. In a "degenerated" condition, not only are the disks more likely to tear, bulge, and herniate, but their diminished height also changes the facet joint geometry and these joints wear out rapidly because of misalignment. Generally speaking, the most common source of low back pain comes from muscle spasms as your musculature faithfully tries to protect an overused or strained area. This pain generally stays localized in your low back area. This can be treated with rest, anti-inflammatory pain killers (ibuprofen), hot showers, and heat pads to relax the muscles. Most episodes will resolve themselves after a week to 10 days of rest (no framing). A doctor may also prescribe a muscle relaxant (flexeril) to see if it helps. If you have a couple decades of "hands on" daily framing under your belt, your back pain might also be caused by a torn disk (annulus fibrosis), a disk bulge, or facet joint osteoarthritis. These three possibilities are difficult to diagnosis without MRI imaging, but "time in the trade" can be a good indicator that you might have some degenerate disk-related issues that might be acting up. Many bulging disks or disk herniations go unnoticed unless they are pressing on a nerve root. If that happens, you will have radiating pain down into your buttocks with the worse cases causing sciatica pain down your leg and toe drop (can't flex foot upward). These should definitely be seen by a spine specialist. Many times these issues can be handled with good physical therapy, while other times it may require surgical intervention, which effectively ends your framing career. While some guys are just built better structurally to handle lifting (short, stocky), prevention is still the key to avoiding back injuries. If you follow a good physical training plan to keep your core strong, lift with your legs not your back, don't try to be macho and lift too much weight, use a weight lifter's back support belt when lifting, and invest in a telehandler, you may grow old without groaning about your back like some of us.

Another lifting injury many framers experience is a hernia. Straining while lifting is a major cause, but then again sometimes hernias just arrive with age or an individual has an inherited inclination. Most often they are of the inguinal variety and little can be done to prevent them aside from using a weight lifter's back/stomach belt when lifting, utilizing proper lifting technique, and limiting your lifts to a weight that you can do without excessive straining. While keeping your core strong goes a long way to preventing low back pain issues, it does little to help avoid an inguinal hernia, because the inguinal canal is on the edge of the protective shield of stomach muscles. A hernia is not generally a jobsite emergency unless it becomes very painful, causes vomiting, or makes it difficult to have a bowel movement. If it becomes large, it can be gently pushed back inside while lying down with your feet elevated but at this point I would expect that most people would be considering a visit to the doctor. If the inguinal hernia starts to cause pain in the scrotum area, it should be seen by a doctor. While sometimes it is possible to live with a hernia, many times it requires surgery to close off the weak area with a mesh insert.

HEAT/COLD INJURIES
Since we carpenters work in an outside environment, we face additional injury risks associated with temperature extremes. Since most of us have grown up dealing with the climate in our particular region we already know how to dress for it throughout the year, but what may bite us is when we move off to work in a totally different part of the country from what we are accustomed to. Going from the dry Southwest to the heavy humidity of the Southern Coast or vice versa can be quite the challenge. Take me, for example. I grew up in Los Angeles, CA, so I was well versed in handling hot dry summer heat and mild winters, but when I began to work in colder climatic zones like Oregon, New England, or Alaska, I had some learning to do. Usually one can just copy whatever everybody else is wearing or doing in that climatic zone and you get along fine, but bear in mind it will take your

body between 10 and 14 days to acclimate up/down when you first arrive. After confronting winter cold on a jobsite many years back, I came to find out that I had Raynaud's disease. Since then, it has required that I either be extremely careful in colder climates or avoid them altogether. While Raynaud's disease may be a rare affliction, hypothermia and heat exhaustion are more in line with what one might see on the jobsite in extreme temperature situations.

Dehydration is a major culprit of problems in both hot and cold injuries. Typically this happens because we just aren't replacing the liquids we are losing fast enough in hot climates or we don't feel like drinking liquids in cold climates. One major problem is that the thirst mechanism doesn't get triggered until your body is already at a 1.5-quart water deficit, and then the thirst mechanism is easily turned off by just taking a few sips when you really should be downing some serious liquids. Our brain is the most water-sensitive organ, and, considering that the human body is made up of 70% water, even a small water deficit will put our brain at risk. Headaches, lightheadedness, fatigue, and irritability are clear signs of this deficiency. Dehydration in hot climates is accelerated by wind, humidity, diuretic drinks (coffee, tea, alcohol, and soft drinks), sunburn, and improper attire. Heat challenges go through a three-level worsening progression. First, we see heat stress (body temperature 99.5–100°F) which reduces job performance, dexterity and coordination, decision-making skills, alertness, and caution. This can progress to heat exhaustion (101–105°F), which exhibits symptoms like fatigue, nausea/vomiting, giddiness, cramps, rapid breathing, and fainting. The worst level is heat stroke (>105°F), which is a life-threatening emergency because the body has now reached the point where it is unable to cool itself and organs start dying. It is kind of like a nuclear reactor going into meltdown. Heat stroke exhibits as mental confusion, disorientation, bizarre behavior, and coma. An altered mental state is the difference between heat exhaustion and heat stroke. This person needs medical help quickly. Be aware that, if the heat challenge or heat exertion is severe enough, an individual can easily go direct from a first-level heat stress straight to heat stroke without passing through the heat exhaustion symptoms. Normally, on any jobsite, a heat problem would be caught long before it becomes dangerous either by the individual him/herself or other members of the framing crew. While on rare occasions I have seen guys touch on the border of heat exhaustion, I have never seen or known of anyone who made it to heat stroke. We lead carpenters should be attentive enough to the outside air temperature, an individual's attire, and their performance that heat problems should never happen. On hot days, make sure the guys are drinking enough fluids and ask about their urine output. Is it "clear and copious" as WMA likes to say which demonstrates they are downing enough liquids. Electrolyte deficiency is another issue that we used to worry about when I was in the Los Angeles housing tracts during the summer, and I, like many, took salt tablets. Since those days, I have learned that an electrolyte shortage is nearly impossible if an individual is eating throughout the day. While I would only snack lightly during my tract framing days, the gallons of Gatorade I downed kept my system balanced so the salt tablets were unnecessary. If you do see one of your crew developing some heat problems, do the following three things: first, have the individual stop working since physical activity is an internal heat producer; second, get the individual out of the sun and into shade or air conditioning to lessen the external heat input; and third, have him drink cold fluids. In extreme cases you may also need to spray the individual with water or immerse him in water to lower his body temperature. It may take a while for them to feel OK again, so don't push it. Realize that as folks get older they have a tougher time dealing with heat challenges, and also keep in mind that hot humidity is much more difficult for the body to deal with than hot and dry since your sweat can't carry body heat away as efficiently through evaporation. A favorite habit of mine in the Los Angeles housing tracts was to pour cold water over my head. It would definitely knock my body's temperature down a notch or two real quick. Other times I simply held a cold bottle of liquid against the side of my neck or under my armpits to lower my body temperature.

I had to laugh when Vin Diesel said to **Dwayne Johnson** at the beginning of *Furious 6*, "I don't do cold weather" because I can totally relate – I hate cold weather too. Not only is it plain physically uncomfortable, but it really puts a damper on jobsite performance. I have a Yupik Indian friend in Crooked Creek, AK, who holds to the opposite opinion of cold. Where she lives, it gets down to −60°F, but she argues that the discomfort one feels in a cold climate can easily be remedied by just putting on more clothing, while in a hot climate, once you are stripped naked, there is nothing more you can do to relieve the discomfort if you are outside. She may have a point in the respect of comfortability, but to be dressed up like a bloated astronaut on the jobsite certainly doesn't facilitate agility and efficiency. In any case, injuries like hypothermia and frost bite can be a major concern in some areas of the USA if you work outside during the winter. Hypothermia affects the ability of the brain and muscles to function, so we quickly become unable to care for ourselves or even recognize that we are in trouble. From there, it quickly spirals out of control. WMI names four degrees of hypothermia. First, it starts off as a general cold feeling with the body beginning to shiver while retaining normal mental function. The next degree is given the designation "mild" hypothermia, and here we see an individual start the "Umbles" which are "stumbles, mumbles, fumbles, and grumbles." At this level, we see a lack of fine motor skills, slurred speech, an increasing inability to do complex tasks, and general apathy. At the third level, "moderate" hypothermia, the "Umbles" worsen and an altered mental state becomes evident. "Severe" hypothermia is the final degree. Its symptoms are listed as a deteriorating mental state that can progress to unresponsive, a decreasing heart rate and respiratory rate, and the shivering stops to be replaced by muscular rigidity. On par with the treatment of heat challenges, the treatment for cold challenges incorporate a similar three-prong approach. In the earliest stages of a cold challenge, the ones that might be encountered on a jobsite, adding extra clothing and moving the individual to a warmer windless environment will counter the external component, while heightened activity can be used to increase internal heat production. Obviously, any wet clothing should be removed and replaced. When adding clothing to provide supplementary insulation, emphasize adding to those areas of the body where the circulatory system is relatively close to the skin first, like the head, the neck, and the hands/feet. The third prong of cold challenge treatment is to get some food and a warm sweet drink into their bodies to provide energy for the internal furnace. "Feed em and beat em" is a little phrase that concisely summarizes early stage hypothermia treatment. At more advanced stages, external heat is added to the individual's arm pits and chest area in the form of heat packs or warm water bottles to augment the body's heat production, but I would hope that, long before this, the hypothermic individual would have been pulled off the job and taken to medical care. It may take 24 hours for an individual to completely recover from even the milder levels of hypothermia, so don't be too quick to send them back outside on the job. Might be better to send them home until tomorrow.

Hypothermia, like heat challenges, is best treated by avoidance. When I worked in New England, I saw how the building technique had been modified just to accommodate the cold snowy winters. New homes were framed up as shells and closed in during the warmer months with the interior framing saved for a wintertime project. During the winters when the interiors were finished, huge jet blast propane heaters were brought in to keep the interior warm. Unfortunately, the homes I worked on in Central Oregon that occasionally stretched into the winter months weren't designed so accommodating, and many times we ended up shoveling snow off the subfloor after a storm blew through, so we could continue framing. Here, at least, the contractor always kept a huge blast propane heater going so we could warm up as needed. Similarly, when I worked for National Lumber we had a 55-gallon burn barrel going all the time to keep our hands warm. My rafter cutoffs made perfect fuel.

WORKING SOLO

There is an interesting book out by John Carroll entitled *Working Alone: Tips and Techniques for Solo Building*. While I respect John as an accomplished builder, I personally find the concept of building solo foolish from the safety standpoint. While a finish carpenter or cabinet maker might be able to get away working solo since their work entails fewer risks and they are indoors, it is my opinion that a framer should work with a partner or on a crew. We partner up in most anything else that carries risk like scuba diving, backpacking, swimming, etc., – why would we not do it for framing, which probably carries a higher chance of injury than all these activities combined? If something goes wrong and someone gets hurt, his/her partner will be on hand to help and call 911. While I would cut or stack solo in the Los Angeles housing tracts, there were always a lot of guys around within shouting/visual distance doing some other task in the framing assembly line if an emergency arose and help was needed. If I was stacking a roof, ahead of me might be another stacker, ahead of him would be the roof cutter milling rafters, behind me was a guy running fascia. On the other side of the street where the houses were framed out, one might see the plumber at work in one house, while to his side in another house an electrician was busy running the wiring. While I did work solo a lot when I was a custom home framer, it was mainly a way for me to do tasks that required total concentration without the distraction of running a crew. I would always snap, plate, and scratch walls or mark and gang-cut rafters after the crew had gone home or when no one was around on the weekends. Granted there was a slight risk of injury in these endeavors, but it was nothing when compared to stacking a roof solo on some secluded house in the Santa Barbara or Oakland, CA, foothills where a fall might have left me lying there until someone showed up the next day. While this new generation of carpenters is blessed to have portable cell phones for an emergency call, we had nothing like that in the old days and only a very small percentage of the jobs even had a jobsite land line type telephone. So typically, we were incommunicado until we were back at home in the evening. I suppose I still operate that way, although I have moved up in the world and do now have a cell phone, although I do not carry it on my person and only rarely is it turned on. But then again, what good does a cell phone do if it gets damaged during your injury-causing fall, or you don't have cell coverage, or you got knocked out from a head injury. Unless you are so crotchety of a guy that no one will work with you, go find a partner for the sake of safety alone, if not also because two decent guys working together can easily outdo two guys working separately. In rowing, the double skull is much faster than any two guys in separate single skulls. "Two are better than one, because they have a good return for their labor: If either of them falls down, one can help the other up. But pity anyone who falls and has no one to help them up." (*Ecclesiastes* 4:9–10)

THE PSYCHOLOGICAL EFFECT OF INJURIES

Something few of us ever think about until it happens is the psychological effect of an injury. I believe sometimes it causes more grief than the injury itself. When I injured my knee on the jobsite in 1979, it didn't really faze me much mentally, because I could still frame fine up to and after the surgery. Perhaps it took away some of my fleet-footedness but my bread and butter were still solidly intact. It was a few years later in the early 1980s when I cut my thumb badly that I really struggled psychologically because it caused me to realize how dependent I was on both of my hands to perform my job. The Lord did bless me and I got full use of my injured hand back, but that occasion did introduce a scary "what if" into my superman psyche. Since my self-worth was based on what I could do "from the top plates up," I found myself overcome with the anxiety of losing it by injury. Dread of this type is not good because it generally tends to move people toward overreacting, which is even more likely to cause an injury. So rather than just relaxing and doing what they have always done by muscle memory, folks become overly conscious of every little thing. I spent some time soul searching about this incident which ended up bringing me back to my trust in Christ. I accepted that it was He who had given me my skills "on loan," and, therefore, He had the right to take them back anytime He so desired. I am thankful for however long that period is. This experience helped to deepen my relationship with the Lord and was good preparation for the other curve balls that life would toss my way. It was at this time that I started focusing on expanding my world to include things other than just rafters. In other words, I set out to "get a life." I began attending city college night classes on a wide range of subjects, and started guiding whitewater rafting part time. It was an unwit-tingly good move and the right thing to do. With my major back injury some 6 to 7 years later in 1987, I jumped right into a second career, but now, having the source of my self-worth spread out over a variety of interests, I suffered no mental anguish. After intense physical therapy, I did make it back to framing roofs. It would be in late 2014, some 42 years after starting my career in construction and some 27 years after my initial back injury in 1987, that my low back would take me off the roof for the remainder of my life. Sure, I miss it. Not a day goes by that I wish I was back up on the top plates, but I thank the Lord for each one of those precious days that I was up there. A big part of my ability to handle the life change this time around were close friends and, in particular, the love of one woman who I most certainly don't deserve.

So the point of this little section is to make folks aware, who don't already know, that not only will a major injury be a challenge physically, it may also send you for a loop mentally. The more devoted and dedicated you are to your trade, the more profound the effect. I believe it was 2002 when I got a call from Sarah, Nick Ridge's wife, asking me to talk with Nick because he was having a rough time mentally after his two-story roof fall. Now understand that Nick is very dear friend who by far is the most focused roof guy I have ever known – he absolutely lives and breathes roofs. I believe he may have every book or video on roof framing ever produced going back to the parchment paper days and even understands all this age-old European roof gibberish that makes me want to take a nap to every time he tries to explain it to me. Nick was not only struggling with that same loss of purpose that I had battled 20 years prior, but he was also distressed about how he was now going to financially support his family. Nick's whole life had been roofs and now he was facing the possibility that he might not be able to build them anymore. This worry was eating him to the point that he even forced himself with his arm in a cast and still limping from the damage to his left hip to go back up on that same roof from which he had fallen and walk the ridge. Like getting back on the horse after it just bucked you off, Nick needed to make sure he hadn't lost his amazing ability up high (he hadn't). In my chat with Nick I reminded him of just how much talent he had in other areas if he didn't heal up as hoped (drafting, building instructor, physical therapist, physical trainer, and more). He could spread his source of self-worth out over a whole sea of talent. Needless to say, Nick is still "Mr Roof" of the East Bay Area, CA.

So, like any good investment counselor I suggest that everyone in construction first off, "diversify your (skill) portfolio" or "don't put all your eggs (skills) in the same basket." Start another career or two that don't require all your body parts. These new adventures will not only break up the monotony of life, but I have found they will also sharpen your mind. Hobbies do the same thing – I know framers who love to golf, fish, sailboard, mountain bike, etc. Second, set aside some money specifically for if/when you may get hurt. This will help alleviate the financial stress that comes with any major injury. Six months living expenses is a good starting point. And finally, make lots of close friends – the kind that will be there when you need them. These three things will go a long way to helping you build a bridge to cross that big rut in the road if it should ever appear.

> Who can hope to be safe? Who is sufficiently cautious?
> Guard himself as he may, every moment's an ambush.
>
> – Horace

11

The Domino Principle and the Downhill Slide

There is only one thing more painful than learning from experience and that is not learning from experience.

– Archibald McLeish

There was a movie I enjoyed when younger entitled *The Domino Principle* starring Gene Hackman. It had a simple message of how one simple event can affect something else, which in turn affects something else, etc., until the whole mess spirals out of control. I won't ruin the movie for those of you who haven't seen it by detailing the plot, but I felt the title was very fitting because it brought to mind a game I played as a boy in which you stand up a whole bunch of dominoes on end next to each other like people in a single-file line waiting to check out at the grocery store cash register. You could weave this line just about anywhere, but you must keep the spacing between the dominoes about half the height of the domino. When you had all the dominoes set up, you would give the first domino a gentle flick to upset its balance and watch as it fell into and knocked over the second, which in turn fell into and knocked over the third, etc., until all the dominoes were down. It was amazing how fast it all happened. Like a wave. Anyway, it is a good illustration of how jobsite injuries have affected my life.

As Peyton Manning once said, "Nobody really wants to hear about anybody else's injuries. Or how your back feels. Whose back doesn't hurt?" I love that quote since Peyton is really saying "shut up and deal with it like everybody else." I totally agree with him that moaning does no good, but, on the other side of the coin, there is much that can be learned from the how and why of an injury that can be of great benefit to those in the game.

From real life experience I have found that an injury and/or the treatment of an injury can raise the likelihood of other injuries happening down the road. This cascade of events (the Domino Principle) will eventually take you down unless you are able to recognize that a domino is about to fall and stop it. Since injuries are such an integral part of a career in framing, I believe that most folks will find this chapter to be both interesting and beneficial. Its purpose is certainly not to glorify injuries or compare my injuries with those of anyone else, but rather to share a few lessons from the medical situations I have faced in my life. I feel that it is infinitely better to learn from the mistakes of others than to make them yourself. Maybe if I had read something like this when I was younger, I would have made better decisions along life's path. Certainly we will never know, because what is done is done, but I would like to think it might have made a difference. I like a fool never let off the accelerator even when pieces were failing right in front of my eyes. Certainly you have heard that a horse when pushed by its rider will run until it falls over dead. Well, unfortunately I am both the rider and the horse in that cliché.

Health is something that one seldom thinks about when young, at least I never did. Somehow I just assumed I would be immune from getting injured during my life as a framer. After all, I had made it through 4 years of multiple high school sports and 2 years of college sports with little more than some cauliflower ear from wrestling and a nose surgery to repair a deviated septum from taking too many balls in the face as a water polo goalie. I figured I would be pounding nails until I was 70 years old, at least. The Lord had blessed me with a mind and body that was well suited for the demanding work of a framer. I loved to work hard, move fast, carry lots of lumber, swing a hammer, climb walls, run around the top plates, etc. Workers' Compensation Insurance statistics name framing as one of the most dangerous careers an individual can choose. The longer one participates in it, the higher the chance you will get hurt and end up disabled. Kind of like the more tours you did in Vietnam, the more likely you were to come home in a body bag. Well, those unkind statistics finally caught up with me as I neared 60 years old. While I had lasted more than four decades before injuries forced me into the disabled ranks, the Lord had sent me many little wake-up messages along the way, prodding me in no uncertain terms that I had pushed my body well beyond the limits He had designed into it and that I should get out. But being blinded by my love of slapping up homes with trick roofs, I chose to ignore them. Now, instead of having a workable body for my "golden years," I will have to wait until heaven to be able to do the things that most old folks do.

Various guys have asked me how long should they stay in the field as a "hands on" framer? I typically just blurt out "get out by the time you turn 40." But, truthfully, this is a hard question to answer with a "catch all" rigid time frame since every person is so different physically and each works at a different speed and intensity. In my case, I came from the Los Angeles basin piece-framing days of the 1970s where we treated our job as if we were competing in the Olympics and went "balls to the wall" all the time. You didn't make any money if you weren't fast, so top speed was the norm. Besides that, if your work wasn't up to the level the job supervisor was expecting – you were gone; your slot was filled instantly from the long line of hungry guys just back from 'Nam.

The older seasoned carpenters in the tracts (they did all the pickup items) counseled me to only frame a handful of years and then get out. At tract production warp speed and intensity, guys burned out fast. Well, as time came and went, I didn't feel any worse for the wear. Actually, I was just starting to get fairly good at what I was doing and their advice didn't seem to make any sense. Besides that, what else could a poor boy like me do to earn good cash money? Bear in mind that this was some 20 years before the computer age when a construction job was really the only game in town unless you wanted to flip hamburgers at Jack in the Box (I did that, too). In retrospect, I should have listened to those wise souls because they sure knew what they were talking about. They knew that down the road I would end up a "walking train wreck" if I spent too many years as the "framing junkie" that I was then.

> "In particular, the reverse assembly line and the increased speed of construction deskilled the building trades and debilitated builders. For the maximum efficiency of the reverse assembly line, a worker must focus on one repetitive task to the detriment of other skills or job satisfactions; no longer problem solvers, carpenters become nailing machines... The speed of production also amplifies the abuse of the builder's body because more lumber must be lifted and more nails pounded in the same amount of time, such that "light framing [became] the purview of the young and exploitable." – David Monteyne (*Framing the American Dream*)

I still remember my first day on the job working for a custom home builder in Santa Barbara, CA, named Hal Benhardt. He had hired me as his framing foreman. It was late summer 1978 and I had just arrived in the area having recently left Los Angeles, CA, via a side excursion to stack roofs in Lompoc, CA. That first day I was snapping, plating, and scratching first-story walls for a fancy home he had designed. Hal showed up at the job mid-morning to make sure everything was working out OK. The first thing he said after watching his new employee for a few minutes was "Will, you don't have to go that fast. You are not a tract framer anymore. We are building custom homes." Needless to say, his words didn't do any good, because I only knew one speed and I stayed at that same insane speed all my life right up to the day injuries forced me out of service. Hal stayed a good friend and father figure until he died in the 1990s. **(fig 11-1)**

So back to the question, "What is a good length of time to stay in the trades as a 'hands on' daily framer?" If we use my life as a reference, I believe that by 40 years old it would be a wise idea to move from being "in the game"

11-1 I was framing foreman for custom builder Hal Benhardt (1932–1999) in the late 1970s (photo 1987 – courtesy Reta Benhardt)

to the "sidelines." Switch to a gentler "bags off" supervisor role or become a builder so down the road you will still be able to play catch with your grand kids; pull on/off a "pull-over" sweater over your head; walk through a Trader Joe's store without the need for a walker; and stoop down to tie your own lace-up shoes. Heavy work only accelerates the body's natural degeneration process as you will clearly see in this chapter's story. When I was 40 the doctors said my spine looked like that of an 85-year-old man who had done hard labor all his life. If you started framing later in life, say during your 20s or 30s, or are a short stocky guy with big strong joints, you might be able to squeak in a few more years past 40, but at the same time, while you might not be as worn out as some of us who started framing in our teens, your body will still have aged. By 40, you don't heal very fast anymore and can't sustain the type of work intensity that a younger framer can. You certainly don't see any Navy SEALs in their 40s still playing an active role in secret combat operations (ops). By 40, they have either said goodbye to the service or have moved into administration or training slots. Whatever you do – please don't be like me, who believed that the laws of nature didn't apply.

One event that has stuck with me all my life happened when I was still fairly young. I became a framing contractor in 1979 and normally led just a four-man crew. **(fig 11-2)** My company (Will Holladay & Co.) became

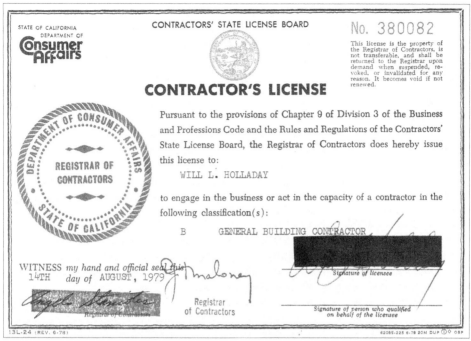

11-2 I started my own framing business in late 1979, and we were always flooded with fun jobs

well known in Santa Barbara, CA, for doing custom homes with complicated roofs. I wasn't your typical contractor who bid jobs, but chose instead to just work by time. Any general contractor (GC) who wanted us to frame a house simply paid me and my crew direct by the hour and stuck us on his Workers' Compensation Insurance. I never made any percentage on my guys' wages, just my personal straight-time pay. By doing it this way, I didn't have to mess with the all the crazy paperwork and office time involved with employing guys or wasting days bidding jobs. I could have earned much better money as a bidding contractor, and I should have at least charged a percentage on the job or my guys, but I have never been a money-hungry guy or a business man. I had tried bidding and didn't like sacrificing my jobsite time to sit behind a desk or the stress that came from not knowing if the bid would work out or not. I just loved my work as a framer and was content to simply be out on the job each day pounding nails and leading the crew. Kind of the like the difference between a sergeant and an officer. I made a good sergeant. I had no desire to be a lieutenant who had to screw around with all the paperwork and the higher ups. I liked running the ops.

Anyhow, I would only take on one framing job at a time. If you wanted us to do a job, you would have to wait until we finished the one we were on. That usually wasn't too long since we were extremely fast. The Lord always kept the jobs lined up. Often carpenters would stop by the job looking for work and hoping to become part of the crew. Rarely, did I need additional guys as we hardly had any turnover, but I do remember one time when a carpenter in his mid-40s stopped in looking for work. I decided to give him a chance, so I hired him and sent him up to help the other guys sheath the roof while I was doing something else. Some 10 minutes later I saw his truck drive off and I asked the other guys what had happened. They said he had tried to help out for a few minutes but quickly realized that his time for this type of work had passed so he climbed down from the roof and drove off. It really broke my heart, because in that minute I felt the pain that that gentleman had had to face by accepting that his days of hard core framing were behind him now. I realized that someday I too would have to face that day and it hurt. The big difference between he and I was that he was a much smarter man to have recognized when it was time to get out. I still wish he had swung by when he left so I could have said something. This, like many other little hints that Our Lord sent my way I refused to see. "To everything there is a season, and a time to every purpose under the heaven" (*Ecclesiastes* 3:1).

If you plan to spend any time as a framer, expect to get injured. Few walk away unscathed. I believe what Joe Montana, that great San Francisco 49ers quarterback of the 1980s, said when asked about his multitude of physical problems is fitting for we framers as well. He said "Unfortunately, most of us leave this game with things that linger." The big difference between football players and we framers is the amount of our paychecks. While football players are compensated millions for getting beat up, we just make a simple hourly wage that has only dwindled over time when compared to inflation gains. While football players have great retirement plans that take care of lifelong injuries, we end up just barely surviving.

Thinking back over my life, it seems like everybody I know personally who spent much time as a hard-core framer has at least one lifelong injury as a result of the job. Most have several. Some of these I talked about in the chapter entitled "Framing is a Street Fight." Without naming names, a guy that I have worked with on/off since the early 1980s tore up the cartilage surface of his humerus, has a bulging disk, and will soon have a knee replacement. Another from the same time period has had both hips replaced. Others I know well have gotten torn up by a tool attack, have broken bones and shredded ligaments from falls, have severe lower spine issues, have rotator cuff damage, or have hernias. I can already hear many of you quietly saying "What about Larry Haun – he seemed to have gone untouched from orthopedic injuries as a framer?" Many have asked me this. While Larry did help me when we were revising *A Roof Cutter's Secrets* in 2000, I didn't know him well enough to comment on what if any jobsite scars he carried. I recognize that he lasted a very long time in construction but know that any comparison between him and others like I would be like trying to compare

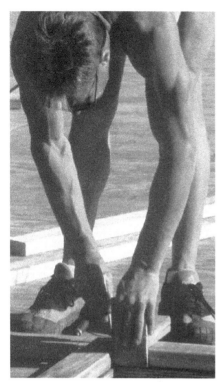

11-3 The normal Los Angeles housing tract framing attire in the mid-1970s was shorts and sneakers

apples with oranges. Larry is some 20 years my senior, and, as a carpenter, he moved quickly into operating a large framing company together with his brothers. He did not stay a daily "hands on" framer for years on end like us. Why would he? Larry after all was a bright UCLA graduate, a superb carpenter's union and community college teacher, and a gifted writer. We/I were none of these. Larry was involved in the early days of Los Angeles, CA, building boom as things heated up and the production process-es were being developed (1950s). He and his brothers specialized in framing large projects like apartment building complexes, etc. I, on the other hand, became involved in the housing tracts after the framing production process had been refined to its utmost efficiency (1970s), and was never anything more than a nail-pounding carpenter. I am one of the guys a framing company like the Haun Brothers would have hired. Larry was a well-rounded builder and proficient in most aspects of construction from dirt to finish. When he framed, he was more of a wall framer by his own admission. I, on the other hand, was a cutter and stacker of single-family tract home roofs who moved on to do basically the same thing in the custom home market. I have little knowledge of construction outside of framing and concrete. Our two time periods, job resumes, and job intensities were very different. For example, just compare the way Larry and other guys of his period dressed in full commercial union job attire consisting of pants, shirt, and boots to the way we of the later tract-framing days dressed in only shorts and sneakers. **(fig 11-3)**

I have personally averaged one major injury ever 4 to 5 years with a disproportionate amount of them coming in the decades of my late 40s and 50s. You might contend that I was an unsafe worker and, for that reason, I was injured many times, but you will not find anyone who has ever worked with me agree to that. My injuries as you will see farther along are things that could have happened to anyone, and no amount of safety precautions other than staying out of construction entirely could possibly have avoided them. We are all imperfect beings and we all make mistakes. Even the fancy

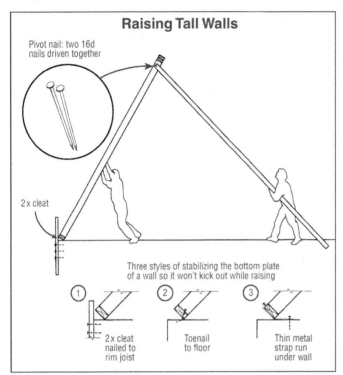

Raising Tall Walls

Pivot nail: two 16d nails driven together

2 x cleat

Three styles of stabilizing the bottom plate of a wall so it won't kick out while raising

1. 2 x cleat nailed to rim joist
2. Toenail to floor
3. Thin metal strap run under wall

11-4 Three methods to keep a wall from sliding off the edge of the decking when raising walls

Boeing jetliners that have such stupendous safety records incorporating multiple redundant systems and can fly themselves still crash every now and then. It is just part of life. We can help reduce the risk but we can't eliminate it. Safety has made big strides on the job since my youth but still "stuff happens." I think it is very telling to notice that the vast majority of my injuries came as I aged and tried to stay in the game with the young bucks. My body had withstood a good deal of beating over the years, and the accumulation made things weaker and more prone to fail when stressed.

One option many framers take in their late 30s is to switch into finish carpentry. This is a great move for a person who has the aptitude for detail work and possesses great patience. Unfortunately, these are two characteristics I don't possess in much abundance. I would rather split rocks with a sledge hammer than do finish work – I find it way too slow and boring. I suppose I am not happy unless I am going "Mach 2 with my hair on fire" as Kelly McGillis said to Tom Cruise in the classic movie *Top Gun*.

One piece of advice Hank Resse, my mentor at Orange Coast College, gave me was to buy and keep a private disability insurance policy. Just another example of some good advice I failed to follow through on. Actually, I did get a private disability policy as he suggested and kept it for at least a dozen

11-5 Blocks nailed to the rim joist as restraints allow a wall to be shuffled right or left after it is stood

years but dropped it when times got tough and I needed money. Unfortunately when things got better, I never restarted it, believing erroneously that the dough I forked out each year for the forced government disability plan (Social Security Disability Insurance – SSDI) was sufficient.

It was early in 1979 that I faced my first major jobsite accident. It was on a big job for Hal Benhardt, and there were maybe 5 to 6 carpenters/laborers on site. We were in the process of standing walls. I train my crews to always use a half-dozen 16d toenails driven in from the edges of 2×4 stickers nailed flat vertically into the rim joist of a raised floor to serve as a stop when lifting walls. This is one of the several different methods an individual can use to prevent a deck-framed wall from sliding off the floor edge when it is stood. **(fig 11-4)** Typically, I also toenail the bottom plate to the subfloor if the wall can be positioned in its final location but occasionally this is not possible and the wall must be framed a few inches one way or another from its final position owing to the fact that plumbing or hold-down bolts are in the way. Obviously, in this case you would not nail the bottom plate to the subfloor so the wall can be slid into position when raised. **(fig 11-5)** This was the case with this wall – It would need to be repositioned slightly after it was stood. This wall was a big ridge wall, some 14 feet tall and 28 feet long, that followed the building's outside edge for about 12 feet of its length before running inside for the remaining 16 feet. The guys installed three edge-of-deck restraining stickers to keep the 12-foot section from falling off the floor deck, while on the inside section they nailed some kicker blocks to the subfloor to restrict that portion from sliding. Anyway, for some reason, they forgot to add toenails to the edge of deck stickers as I had taught them and had only used end-nails driven through the stickers into the floor's rim joist. While end-nails may be good in shear, they have very little tension holding strength (pull apart resistance). Toenails, on the other hand, are great in tension and, for this reason, I use them in many situations including stickers like these. As is normal procedure, we always frame up as many walls as the floor space will allow and then come together as a group to raise walls. I checked over each wall to make sure nothing had been forgotten, but did not verify their sticker block nailing. We then went skyward with the big wall and were well overhead when the three edge-of-deck stickers pulled loose, and that part of the wall that was situated on the building edge slid off the deck, causing the whole wall to spin out of our control and fall. Everybody except me was able to find a window or door hole to duck through as it came down. I unfortunately was positioned at a part of the wall where there were only studs and while I had tried to back out rapidly to clear the top of the wall, I didn't quite make it and got hammered by the wall. My leg took the brunt of the force and was twisted in an unnatural position causing major knee joint trauma. I was able to limp around OK and finish the day, but went to see the Workers' Compensation (WC) assigned doctor the following morning. Because something was flapping in/out of the joint space and there was pain on various manipulations, the doctor suspected a major tear to the lateral meniscus. Bear in mind this was in the days before magnetic resonance imaging (MRI). I also went to a private doctor I knew who concurred with the WC doctor's prognosis with respect to the meniscus tear but thought that I also had severed the anterior cruciate ligament (ACL) because of the large movement forward of the tibia in relation to the femur during the Lachman and Drawer tests. He explained that repairing a torn ACL was a major open knee surgery and required a minimum of 6 months to recuperate.

Since this was a California Workers' Compensation injury, the surgical repair had to be done by their anointed doctor (some states allow you to choose the doctor) who removed the flapping piece of meniscus but left the ruptured ACL untouched. The surgery was done during the winter so that my time away from the jobsite would be less of a burden on the crew. I found out years later that WC doctors only do the bare minimum to get you back to the job as soon as possible. They care little of the patient's long-term outcome. What is paramount in their minds is holding on to their approved WC doctor status and the steady inflow of new patients this provides. By helping WC make a quick exit from any injury incident and keeping the remedial costs per incident down guarantees that they will be continually approved as a WC doctor. I was pretty ignorant of medical issues back in those days so when the doctor told me that I was good to go, I signed off on the injury release form that WC was pushing. Signing that form was an error that has cost me dearly financially and is the very reason that I now have a steel right knee. If the ACL had been repaired, the joint would have been very solid again and very likely would have lasted my whole life. As it was, the knee joint slopped around just enough to eventually cause more meniscus damage that would lead to three future surgeries in 2002 and a total knee replacement in 2015. All this could have been avoided. WC only cares if they can make it past the five-year statute of limitations for injury responsibility, which in my case was a good bet since they saw I had very powerful leg muscles that would stabilize the weak joint.

I have learned a lot since those days:

1. First off, **never never never** sign off on a WC injury if it is a major thing. Let it go to the state's Workers' Compensation Appeals Board for them to decide your outcome rather than the insurance company.
2. Get and keep copies of all your X-ray and Magnetic Resonance Imaging (MRI) reports, your X-ray and MRI images, your surgery reports, and your doctor visit notes. Hang on to these as long as you live. Remember Patrick Swayze carrying around his whole medical dozier in the movie *Road House*. You do the same.
3. Look for a doctor who has been fellowship trained in sports medicine to provide primary care for any injury. If surgery is required, seek out an orthopedic surgeon who has done a post-residency fellowship (an additional year of advanced training) in the specific area that must be repaired (i.e., spine surgery, joint replacement). Only use physical therapists whose primary focus is rehabilitating college or pro athletes
4. For any major injury, always get a second or even a third medical opinion from a good non-WC doctor, even if you have to pay for it out of your own pocket.
5. As I will show later on, make sure that only the very best radiologist reads your X-rays or MRIs. If the one who reads your MRI is WC assigned, consider getting a second read somewhere else.
6. Don't believe anything a medical professional tells you until you have researched it yourself at a university's medical library or through reputable sources on the Internet.
7. Keep your SSDI coverage active. If you are a self-employed individual and you take a major business loss that wipes out income for 5 years do show some income that will allow you to keep enough insurance-qualifying "points" in the system to remain covered. More on this farther along.
8. Carry a private disability insurance policy if at all possible.

The arthroscope having just been introduced as a surgical instrument was used for my knee surgery and I was back to work in a few months. My knee joint would always remain weak after the injury and I noticed a major loss in my running speed. Unbeknownst to me, both of these issues were because I had no functioning ACL. As a result of this knee weakness, I inadvertently began to incorporate my low back a bit more when lifting heavy things. This unconscious and unrecognized abuse came to a head a short 8 years later in March 1987 while I was lifting one end of a 6×12 beam to shuffle it onto an adjacent rafter-cutting rack. The beam might have weighed 200 to 250 lbs total weight, which is heavy but not outlandish with a guy at each end. While I, like everybody else, had had a sore back occasionally after a long day's work, I had never considered this soreness to be anything of much importance, so I was totally unprepared when on this standard lift I was overcome by intense low back pain. A MRI taken subsequently showed major disc degeneration disease (DDD) and with broad-based bulging disks at each of the five levels of the lumbar spine with a torn annulus fibrosis and herniated disk at L4-5. This certainly had been brewing for a while and WC even went so far as to drag a few previous builders for whom I had recently worked into the insurance fray. I had sciatica and buttock pain, so this showed some nerve roots were being compressed. The doctors pulled me off line and told me in no uncertain terms that I must stop framing because my back could no longer handle the lifting, bending, twisting, etc. This injury was a game changer. I was prescribed rest with physical therapy. Unfortunately, once your back starts downhill, there is no turning back. All one can do is try to slow its decline with physical therapy (PT) and lifestyle modifications. To properly stabilize my spine I began sleeping on a 4–inch-thick high-density foam mattress pad that was set either directly on the floor or a solid base. This would remain my modus operandi going forward. Having learned from the last time that I had been injured not to sign off on the WC release waiver my case eventually went to the California Workers' Compensation Appeals Board in 1990 where I was named 30% disabled with an added stipulation allowing for further lumbar spine medical care as required.

Even though I was in bad shape physically, we somehow finished the current framing job, but it would be the very last job I would ever do with my own crew as a framing contractor. With great sadness I laid off my crew and sent them off to fend for themselves. I then put my California Contractor's License on inactive status (eventually giving it back entirely when California jacked up the fees), and began the long road of recovery back to some level of normalcy through physical therapy. I had now been in construction some 15 years and was in my early 30s. During my time off, I organized all my notes on framing into the 1988 book *A Roof Cutter's Secrets,* which was primarily intended as a way to help out my dear crew whom I had abandoned to the wolves. In truth, they all picked up jobs rather quickly as many builders saw it as an opportunity to nab some very talented workers. I also decided to start a second career as a pilot with the hopes of eventually landing a flying job in the Alaskan bush. I would realize that dream in 1989 and I ended up flying most summers in Alaska for the next 25 years. But truthfully I missed being a roof framer immensely so it wasn't long after my back started feeling somewhat better that I devised a plan to return to the "ring," this time as a "traveling" roof cutter and only do "lighter" duty things like pushing my fancy roof saws across the racked lumber (reminiscent of the old tract roof cutting days). I decided to call myself a "roof-framing consultant." Well my idea didn't really

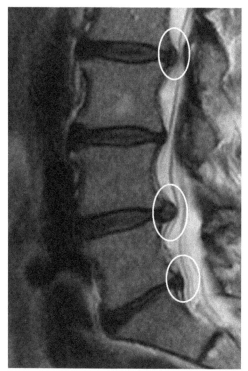

11-6 Disciplined therapy allowed me to keep framing despite DDD and herniations in my lumbar spine

work out as I had hoped, because everybody would always need me to stack the roof I had just cut since stacking was the hardest part. So in no time I was back to doing the same old thing I had done all my life, only this time I was traveling around and running other contractor's framing crews on complicated jobs instead of my own crew. I did enjoy working in a wide variety of places and made all kinds of new friends. My old framing partner Dave Sylvester who had left Santa Barbara, CA, in the early 1980s for Oakland, CA, got a hold of me and the East San Francisco Bay Area became my home base for several decades when I wasn't in Alaska. There were lots of homes to build in the Oakland Hills after the Tunnel fire in 1991. In retrospect, it was the camaraderie of a good crew that had always kept me going. If it had not been for Chuck Cline or Dave Sylvester, plus many others, I may have very well faded away from construction long before I had even turned 40. It was that sports team spirit and the challenge of a match (framing a custom home) that I just couldn't walk away from. I suppose that 8 man rowing team spirit never did leave my veins. **(fig 5-1)** I was a true "framing junkie."

My back issues held fairly stable through the 1990s into the 2000s and all debilitating flare-ups were treated with corticosteroids and occasionally a modification to my daily PT regime. Several MRIs were taken during this period that showed the annular tear had plugged up and a portion of the L4-5 herniation had reabsorbed. The spine doctor was very pleased and credited the injury's relative stability since 1987 to my disciplined PT regime and rigid body mechanics. **(fig 11-6)** Years later I would learn that if an annular tear was doing better by 4 months after starting therapy, there was a good chance, baring serious injury, that the plug could make it to the maximum heal up strength landmark of 4 to 5 years (www.chirogeek.com). It was also encouraging to know that sometimes a herniation may be reabsorbed in part or totally and, in my case, this reabsorption had unloaded some of the pressure on the nerve root. Because of the badly degenerated disks in my low spine, the geometry of contact at the facet joints had been thrown way out of kilter, so these joints simply wore away their protective cartilage covering, causing an osteoarthritis condition called facet joint disease/syndrome. In this condition, any low back movement causes the diseased facet joints to become inflamed due to their bone-on-bone grating, which sequentially causes a protective spasm reflex of the muscles along the spine. Facet joint disease is the most common cause of all recurrent low back problems. The associated pain can be so intense that, at its peak, the symptoms closely imitate those of a disk herniation. I found that by lying flat for several days often allows the muscle spasms to calm down. The doctors also prescribed Flexeril, a powerful muscle relaxant, to aid in shortening these muscle spasm pain episodes. Facet joint disease is obviously not something that can be cured, only endured. Many times facet joint disease is treated by corticosteroid injections directly into the affected facet joints themselves with the possibility of following up with rhizotomy to kill the associated pain-sensing nerves.

In the mid to late 1990s my right shoulder started killing me to the point where I was forced to switch to driving nails with my left hand. I had had no traumatic injury that I could pinpoint but that didn't mean much since we were doing heavy-duty lifting all day long. I went to see a low-cost medical center doctor who shot my shoulder up with corticosteroids and sent me on my way. An MRI should have been taken to reveal the damage, but I must not have had a medical policy in effect at the time and probably didn't have the funds to spare, so I simply did without. What I did do was begin a "heal yourself" style swimming routine after work in an effort to try and bring that shoulder back to life. While I hate swimming, I know of no better physical therapy for shoulders than the freestyle and backstroke. While it was miserably painful to try and swim, I kept after it and in a few months I began to see some improvement and a lessening of pain. I believe it took nearly a full year until I was finally able to go back to full-time right-handed nailing. While everything worked out OK for me in this case, do go see an orthopedic doctor and get an MRI taken for injuries of this type, even if you have to borrow funds to do so. My self-medicated physical therapy, while having a positive outcome in this case, could very well have made it much worse. Looking back now after suffering other shoulder injuries later on that were diagnosed using an MRI, I most likely had torn my rotator cuff somehow.

In late summer 2001, my ACL-less knee failed while I was attending a National Outdoor Leadership School (NOLS) backpacking cross-training program to gain authorization to instruct land courses in addition to river courses that I already did. Unfortunately, because this was nonpaid training, the injury's medical care responsibility fell on me. It actually should have been covered by the 1979 WC knee injury case if I had not signed off on the release form. This current failure was a direct result of the poor medical treatment I had received back then. This time in to see a doctor, my 22-year-old torn ACL and some lateral meniscus tearing were discovered in an MRI. The doctor silently cussed out the surgeon who had done the shoddy 1979 surgery and I was scheduled for both ACL reconstruction surgery, using a piece of my hamstring tendon, and the repair of a torn meniscus. Unfortunately, this surgery would not turn out so well, and the surgeon would need two follow-up surgeries to rectify all the meniscus issues. After his third surgery, he said that in time I would need a knee replacement. Great! If I knew then what I know now I probably would have done things much differently. Nowadays I do all kinds of medical investigating before I ever agree to a plan of action with a surgeon. By the time the doctor finished his third surgery, he had totally removed both my lateral and medial meniscus. Pretty stupid thing to do since the job of the menisci is to spread out the transfer of weight from the femur to the tibia. Without these menisci, the body weight is transferred by the two femoral condyles to the tibial plateau as point loads which, through everyday use, especially physical labor, will eventually bring on painful osteoarthritis as the end of bone cartilage wears through condemning one to a total knee replacement (TKA). By cutting out all the menisci, the knee's ability to absorb shock loading was erased, which effectively ended running and jumping for the remainder of my life. This was very sad because running was such a joyful part of my life. Years later I would learn that the best sports-oriented knee surgeons sew up meniscus tears if at all possible in order to save these crucial elements rather than simply cutting them out if they are damaged. This "sew up to save" methodology allows an individual to return to preinjury condition in most cases. I also came to find out that a donor meniscus can be transplanted when an existing meniscus cannot be saved. Both of these procedures could have been used in my case, although I may have had to fight with the medical insurance company to get a meniscus replacement surgery covered.

I did suffer some nerve damage from the initial ACL reconstruction surgery because the surgeon cut through the superficial peroneal nerve branch which provides sensation for the lateral side of my lower leg. It would take some 6 to 7 years for other peripheral nerves to grow into the area and weakly take over the sensation function that had been lost. During these years, I would get cut or scratched several times in the desensitized area and never even know it happened until someone told me that I was bleeding. Probably the worst by-product in terms of long-term effect from the surgeries was the poor placement of the replacement ACL ligament. I did not know at the time, but if the replacement ligament is not positioned correctly in the femoral or tibial tunnels, joint wear is accelerated because the articulation is abnormal. From National Center for Biotechnology Information research, nonanatomical placement of the replacement ACL ligament is the leading surgical error in ACL reconstruction. I surmise that it must be rather difficult to drill from the inside of the tibia and hit the correct spot on the tibial plateau with the exit hole. Anyhow, the positioning of my ACL ligament was so bad that in hyperflex my tibia would pull at least 1 inch forward so I never could kneel very well after the surgery. The poorly positioned ligament also limited my range of motion (ROM) to about 120° maximum. Even with the best of surgeons, every surgery has its risks so that is why it is always best to avoid them.

This experience taught me how important it is to choose the correct doctor and physical therapist for any injury needs. Physicians and therapists who are not athletes or who do not specialize in dealing with athletes have little understanding of how an athlete thinks, his high motivation level, or the importance his body plays in his job (I consider a framer to be like an athlete). This knowledge many times changes how medical professionals treat an injury, so for this reason I believe it is better for us to see physicians who have been trained in sports medicine and/or use physical therapists whose primary focus is rehabilitating college or pro athletes. Athletes have a tendency to push too hard in physical therapy. We just figure that the same overpowering work ethic that carried us to success in competition will do the same in helping us get back to the job quicker, when in reality it is detrimental. What the body needs is time for the healing process to work, it cannot be rushed along. If by chance a surgery is required to repair some condition, look for a specialist who has done a postresidency fellowship in that surgical area (i.e., spine surgery, joint replacement). Fellowship-trained surgeons are highly skilled in their field, having completed an extra year of intense training under the tutelage of the experts.

Just as I had done during the healing period for my low back injury in 1987 when I wrote the first edition of *A Roof Cutter's Secrets,* it was during the healing period for the first of the three knee surgeries in 2002 that I started writing my second book, *The Complicated Roof – A Cut and Stack Workbook.* Its purpose was to be a real-world jobsite application of the principles found in *A Roof Cutter's Secrets.* I worked on the manuscript in a "stop and go" fashion for 7 years, and by 2009 it was available in the market place. It was a very tough book to write since I had to recreate the thinking process I had utilized to cut and stack two very difficult roofs I chose as the book's examples. I wanted to reveal how the mind of a roof cutter and stacker worked in order to help guys have the confidence to approach difficult roof projects.

In any case, I was back to framing fairly quickly after the knee episode, but a trip-and-fall accident in 2004 sent me into surgery for a torn rotator cuff repair on my right shoulder. While it is possible that my weakened knee and awkward walking gate from the 2002 knee "destruction surgery series" played a part in this stumble, tripping on the unseen head of a nail that some idiot had left high would have caught anyone. It is possible that someone with two good knees might have been able to catch himself better than I did but it seems unlikely. I had heard stories from others on how painful the recovery from a torn rotator cuff could be, so I was blessed that mine wasn't too bad, although it took nearly 18 months for all the little idiosyncrasies to disappear. I had met the orthopedic surgeon who did the repair as the result of a roof cutting job I did for Nick Ridge in Larkspur, CA. Since it was a big beam roof it took me several days to cut, so I got to know the owner who would stop by every night to check things out and help detail the edges of the beams. After learning he was a hotshot shoulder and knee surgeon I became one of his patients until he retired in early 2017. Dr. John Keohane is still a good friend, and I praise the Lord for arranging our lives so we could meet up. He would end up operating on me a total of five times over those short 13 years.

A year or so after the 2005 shoulder surgery, while working on a commercial job in Redmond, OR, I got hit by a crane slung load of material, damaging my left shoulder. I went in to see a doctor in Bend, OR, who sent me off for an MRI. The read came back showing some damage but nothing of huge consequence. I found this surprising because this shoulder was more painful and had worse ROM than the earlier torn rotator cuff injury to my right shoulder. This is when I would learn a very important lesson about MRI reads – some radiologists are just way better than others at their trade. As obvious as this may be, consider that the outcome of a bad read negates an individual receiving the correct diagnosis and associated medical care to help his/her condition. This is what happened to me in this situation, and I was sent on my way as the result of a bad MRI read. Being one to always get and keep a CD copy of my MRI imaging, I dropped in to see Dr. Keohane when I was back down in the San Francisco Bay Area and had him look over my shoulder. After doing various diagnostic shoulder manipulations and giving the MRI imaging a cursory look, he sent the CD over to his radiologist for a read. Low and behold, this second read came back showing a SLAP lesion (superior labral tear from anterior to posterior) and torn rotator cuff. A far cry from the read made by the radiologist in Bend, OR. Small cities just don't draw the same quality of medical professionals as a large megalopolis does. Needless to say, this read matched with what Dr. Keohane believed to be the damage taken from my symptoms and the ROM test results at his office, and exactly what he later found on the operating table in 2007 when I had the repair done. Dr. Keohane sewed up the torn rotator cuff and repaired the SLAP lesion using a screw anchor with attached stitching. All I remember about the shoulder recovery this time around was that it hurt like hell for a long, long time and the physical therapy was brutal, but I had to do it or else end up with a frozen shoulder. Time has a way of putting our hurts behind us and, in 18 months, the whole miserable ordeal was but a memory. I had learned a great deal from the experience, especially since I had to pay for everything out of my pocket when it should have been covered by Workers' Compensation as a jobsite injury. From then on, I have been extremely skeptical of any MRI read unless it is done by someone who I know is an exceptional radiologist or is recommended by an orthopedic surgeon whom I trust. As in roof framing, it takes someone with lots of experience and God-given ability to be able to visualize all the problem areas. Indeed, this same situation of a bad MRI read would play out several more times in my life, twice on MRIs taken in Central America and once on an MRI taken in San Luis Obispo, CA. In each of these three cases where the radiologist's skill was unknown to me, I sent a CD with the imaging off to be read by a radiologist in the San Francisco Bay Area whom I trust, Dr. Sonja Moelleken. I have found that the best surgeons also know how to read MRIs and will always do a second read themselves. My spine doctor, Dr. Paul Slosar and Dr. Keohane both do/did this. Dr. Slosar doesn't even read the radiologist's report most of the time, since he prefers his own interpretation.

From 2007 on, I have experienced a constant cascade of injury events or body parts failing one right after another. The great "recession" began in 2007 and the accompanying construction slowdown seemed to coincide on par with my physical tumble. In 2007 I was seen for shooting nerve pain originating from my neck and diving into my right shoulder. An MRI showed DDD and facet joint disease at all levels with a bulging disk and foraminal stenosis pressuring the nerve roots at C4-5 and C5-6. Fortunately, traction therapy with strengthening exercises has been able to control the pain so I can live with it. So much for doing all the trick overhead framing like skylights, coffer ceilings, arched hallways, chandelier domes, etc. With all my spinal degradation I now measured 1½ to 2 inches shorter than I was in my late teens. In the summer of 2008, I had a major low back pain episode that put me down for a while. I helped lift the tail of a De Havilland Beaver float-plane off the beach in Alaska but unfortunately the effort crushed a large divot in the L5 vertebral endplate. Bad pain. I walked around bent over with a cane for many months like Rip Van Winkle, but eventually the pain began to subside, so the planned epidural intervention was avoided. The right knee that had survived the three surgeries in 2002 was slowly becoming arthritic and quite painful on the lateral side by 2009. In that same year, I would fall out of a chair and damage my right shoulder "again." This time it was a SLAP lesion with partial biceps tendon tear and subluxation of the biceps tendon, in addition to a partially torn rotator cuff. Being low on funds, I would leave this injury medically untreated, but did start doing the same shoulder therapy I had been assigned for the two previous shoulder surgeries in hopes that strengthening would help.

In 2010, I had a surgery to repair a right inguinal hernia that appeared out of nowhere and was causing a lot of pain. The surgery didn't come out so well and I ended up with a trapped nerve branch and couldn't stand upright. A few months later, another surgeon went back in and resolved the issue by cutting the entrapped nerve above where it became entangled in the installed hernia mesh. The result was a loss of sensation in my lower abdomen on that side.

In 2011, I began to have major problems with my right hip. After X-rays were taken, it was determined that I was suffering from acute chronic trochanteric bursitis. At times it was so painful that I could not even walk. It was treated with corticosteroid injections and strengthening/stretching exercises. Evidently, this new condition had been brought on by my bad right knee being out of alignment. My right knee had slowly become "knock knee" as the lateral side of the knee joint wore through its articular cartilage and the joint spacing collapsed. In medispeak, it is called valgus deformity. I learned that whenever a joint is not properly aligned for some reason (e.g., injury or birth defect), poor geometry will negatively affect the joint both above and below the damaged joint. So, as fate would have it, my bad knee was now throwing my right hip out of kilter and degrading that joint. If allowed to continue very long, this deterioration could cause me to end up with major hip problems. *Déjà vu* from how my low spine had deteriorated as a result of my original knee injury in 1979 and I wasn't about to let another domino fall. As much as I hated to do it, I set about checking with various hospitals to see what kind of packaged price they would give me for a TKA so I would know how much money I would need to raise. Unfortunately, I had no medical insurance at this time, since I had been priced out of the market as a bad-risk individual on account of all my medical issues, so I would need to pay cash at the time of service. I also did some investigating into using stem cells to treat my right knee's damage but found that it was too far gone to have much of a chance at success.

Also in 2011, I would trip on an uneven surface but catch myself from falling all the way to the ground by grabbing an overhead pipe with my left hand. Unfortunately this simple movement yanked loose the SLAP repair done in 2007 and caused new damage. The MRI report was a mirror image of the current damage to the right shoulder (SLAP lesion with partial biceps tendon tear and subluxation of the biceps tendon in addition to a partially torn rotator cuff). I was now on a first-name basis with the San Francisco Radiology center and, in their kindness, they gave me a punch card cash pay discount. The new left shoulder injury was added to the long list of "to do" surgeries and was now paired with its partner in ongoing daily physical therapy. Washing a car or things like that I would have to avoid since those circular movements were tough. You may think that this chapter is turning into a horror story, but hold tight, we are just beginning.

That same wonderful year of 2011 I was back in the hospital for both a left side inguinal hernia repair and a Spigelian hernia at the belt line. I have no idea why I was suddenly being plagued by so many hernias all at once. I certainly wasn't fat, I ate very healthily, was in good physical condition (if you looked beyond my orthopedic damage), and never smoked – four things the

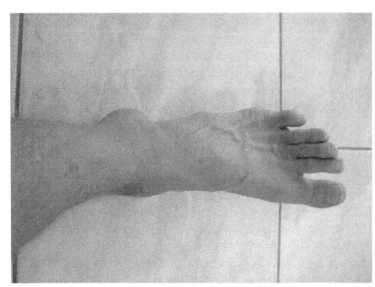

medical professionals list as possible contributors. Up to this point in my life, I hadn't had a hint of trouble hernia-wise. Since the inguinal hernias appeared outside my stomach muscle shield, all the core exercises that I did/do for my lower spine were of no help in prevention. The belt line hernia was caused by some connective tissue ripping horizontally from lateral to medial for who knows what reason. While there is the possibility that I might somehow be genetically prone to these hernias, it was more likely payback time for all the grunt lifting I had done over the previous four decades. I was just getting old and although I could still physically do the work of a young buck all my body's tissues were weakening and could no longer handle the stress of my profession. Unfortunately, there is not a darn thing anybody can do about aging, and aging was forcing me out. I ended up with nerve damage after the left inguinal surgery when the surgeon accidentally cut through the nerve that had purposely been cut through on the other side to end the nerve entrapment syndrome. I would have no sensation in my lower abdomen for many years until some peripheral nerves grew into the area to help out a tiny bit.

2012 brought with it a foot entrapment fall that fractured the distal fibula in my left foot, sprained my left ankle (grade 3), and tore the medial meniscus on my good left knee. The fracture healed quick enough, but the cantaloupe-sized sprain would take several years to reduce to a halfway normal size. **(fig 11-7)** The meniscus tear only hurt if I bumped my foot, so I put it as number four on the "to do" surgical list after the knee TKA and the two damaged shoulders. I had no major injury in 2013, but serious right knee pain when walking was a good sign I needed to get after its replacement.

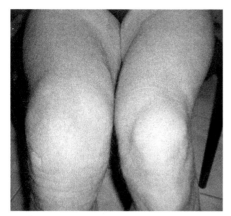

11-8 A rare allergic reaction to the joint lubricant Synvisc required the knee to be aspirated

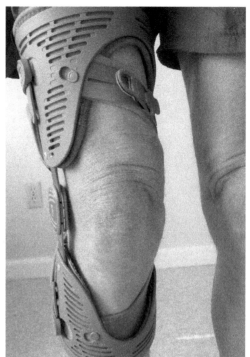

11-9 An unloader brace is a great option when only one side of a knee joint is worn out

Money was the only thing holding this back from happening since TKAs are not cheap even when one pays cash. We tried a series of Synvisc (hyaluronan) injections to lessen the pain and they worked super although the relief was short lived. On a second series, I had an allergic reaction and the joint had to be aspirated. **(fig 11-8)** It was the first time the doctor had ever seen or heard of that happening. Needless to say, that ended this joint-lubricating treatment, so we tried a unloader brace (www.ossur.com). These braces work wonders if you have one side of the joint still good and able to accept the transferred load, but unfortunately both sides of my knee joint were bad, so it gave no relief. **(fig 11-9)** After several years of physical therapy on my shoulders, they had stabilized to a level that I could use them OK as long as I stayed away from certain movements. Now and then, a corticosteroid injection was helpful. People thought I was plumb crazy to be doing things with two separated shoulders, but we do what we have to.

While my general health was good, I was a "walking train wreck" orthopedically. I knew I could not continue on much longer in active construction, so I started looking for a teaching job. The phrase "If you can't do – you teach" comes to mind. I could have done more Alaska flying, but with my

CREDENTIAL NO. 9 4 HOL 001

No. 363957

The California Community Colleges

WILL L. HOLLADAY

The Board of Governors of the California Community Colleges, acting in accordance with the authority vested in it, awards to the person named above a

COMMUNITY COLLEGE INSTRUCTOR, PARTIAL FULFILLMENT CREDENTIAL

This document, earned by meeting the provisions established by law and the requirements established by the Board of Governors of the California Community Colleges, authorizes the holder to perform all services permitted by these provisions and requirements.

SUBJECT MATTER AREA: BUILDING, CONSTRUCTION AND RELATED TECHNOLOGIES***

President, Board of Governors
California Community Colleges

David Mertes
Chancellor
California Community Colleges

ISSUED: October 10, 1989   EXPIRES: June 30, 1992

11-10 I was issued a temporary credential so I could apply for a teaching job at Cuesta College in 1989

back issues I had to back away from that as well. Alaskan bush flying requires a lot of heavy lifting to load and unload the aircraft, which was something I should avoid. Back in my younger days, we were loading/unloading 200-lbs totes full of fresh-caught Sockeye Salmon or 50-lbs boxes of flash-frozen fish all day long. I was way past that now. Besides this, I had Raynaud's disease, which limited my time in Alaska to just the few warm summer months. I would have liked to have taught construction skills at the Community College level where I had learned so much back in my youth. Unfortunately, I didn't have the correct level of schooling to make my resume attractive, so I received little if any response when I applied for available building instructor positions. Back in 1987 when I was struggling with a change in careers as a result of my low back injury, the State of California had issued me a provisional teaching credential just so I could apply for a Community College teaching job in San Luis Obispo, CA. **(fig 11-10)** I didn't get the job, obviously, so I took the route of a becoming a "traveling roof cutter." That certificate would have been helpful now, but since they had stopped issuing them years before, I emphasized that I had given many presentations at the *JLC* Live conferences and had taught carpentry skills in Central America as a humanitarian aid volunteer

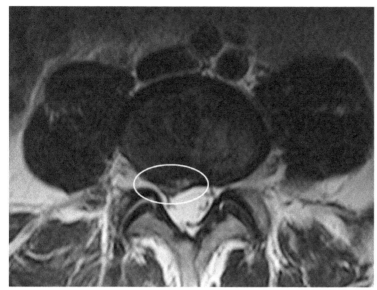

11-11 This 8-mm disk extrusion was enough to put me in a wheelchair and end my framing career

MRI imaging shows right and left sides reversed

to get a few points on my scoreboard. Evidently, there were just a lot of good younger guys out there who were qualified as teachers.

After several years of searching for a teaching job, a rural high school in Idaho with a technical department hired me to revive their dead building trades program. I started there in the fall of 2014 but unfortunately within a month of starting I herniated my L4-L5 disk while working with the students on a project. The massive extrusion clamped off the sciatic nerve causing me to lose the use of my right leg, forcing me into a wheelchair. Talk about excruciating pain. I had no choice but to resign from my long-awaited first full-time teaching opportunity and we traveled out to California where my attending doctor, Dr. Slosar, would do a microdiscectomy surgery the day before Thanksgiving to unload the nerve and get me back on my feet. Some deficiency in my right foot would always linger. In one fell swoop, this disk extrusion ended my construction career. **(fig 11-11)** The Lord had allowed me to do what I loved for over four decades, but now it was someone else's turn for I would never again be able to bend down, lift, squat, push, pull, etc. Some folks ask me why my surgeon did not fuse the L4 and L5 vertebrae. Here is another example of stopping a domino from falling. Dr. Slosar, who is one of the USA's most respected spine experts, knew that for nearly 30 years I had handled a miserably deteriorated spine condition through ultra-disciplined therapy and rigid body mechanics. He knew of few others who had that kind of motivation and passion to live a normal life. If he fused just one level when four levels are bad, the other three levels would fail in short order because of the increased demand forced on them by the loss of the one.

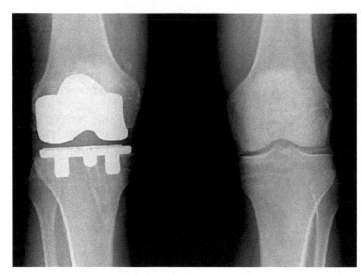

11-12 Bone grows into the textured undersurface on "cementless" implants as opposed to using glue

Tibial drill hole for the earlier ACL surgery can be seen below the tibial plateau implant

So given the choice between a four-level fusion having only a 50% chance of a positive outcome versus taking each pitch as it comes along, we chose the latter. He knew me well enough after 20 years of ongoing treatment to know that I would be unhappy with a total lumbar region fusion. Most likely, someday, we will have to resort to that, but, until then, I shall pray for as much time as possible. I had been partially disabled since my 30s – now I was definitely fully disabled physically. It was during the recuperation following the spinal surgery that I started work on this book *From the Top Plates Up*.

Because of the lifetime medical care stipulation set forth in my 1990 WC case decision, my spine surgery was fully covered. A little bonus from becoming a teacher in Idaho was that I had been enlisted into the school's group medical policy and because of COBRA continuation insurance coverage I was able to keep the policy, expensive as it was for 18 months. As a result, I used this insurance in the spring of 2015 to get the TKA done on my right knee. The deductible was astronomical, but it was still better than any other option. By this time I had already spent several years researching implants, etc., and decided to go with a cementless model for the replacement. Since I was still relatively young and active compared to the age group where most TKAs are installed, I figured that cementless fixation was a better choice. The cementless requires the highest level of surgical skill, since the cuts have to be absolutely perfect with no space between the bone and implant to effect correct ingrowth. Gaps can't be filled with glue as they are on a cemented version. Kind of like the difference between the finish work on a piano compared to the rough framing on a house. My TKA would be the only cementless version Dr. Keohane would do in his distinguished 40-year career. **(fig 11-12)** He is a master surgeon so his work came out like art but unbeknownst to anyone I am one of the miniscule percentage of people who have an exaggerated inflammatory response to surgery and developed arthrofibrosis and synovitis in the knee joint as a result. Arthrofibrosis is an overgrowth of scar tissue that ends up pulling everything together and freezing up the joint movement. Synovitis is an inflammation of the synovial membrane that encases a joint and its job is to produce a lubricant to help facilitate articulation. So by fixing one problem with the TKA, it brought on two very painful new ones. I could not sit with my knee bent for long, I could not pedal a bike up any incline, and it was all I could do to go up and down stairs. The pain was caused by the patellar tendon region being all choked up with scar tissue, and the inflamed thickened synovial membrane only compounded it.

It was at this point that I decided to pull both of my damaged shoulders off the "to do" surgery list altogether. I had been thinking of having one of them repaired as soon as possible after the TKA, while I still had medical insurance coverage but, with my knee doing poorly, I really wasn't in the mood for any more pain. The idea of adding a miserable shoulder recovery to the unrelenting pain from these new knee issues probably would have put me over the edge. At my age, they do not do a SLAP repair but simply cut the biceps tendon and screw it to the head of the humerus in a procedure known as tenodesis. I wasn't really jazzed about that idea but understood that with my shredded, subluxing biceps tendon it was the only option. Since 2005, I had spent more time recuperating from surgeries and injuries than I had spent on living life. How much longer did I have to live anyway so as to tie up 3 years of that short time span with shoulder surgeries and recuperating from them. I wanted to live life again.

In 2016, as I helped replace some dry rotting wood on a tree house that I had built some 7 years prior, I developed acute lateral elbow tendinosis in both elbows. I was breaking free some floor decking screws by hand before using a pistol grip drill with a screwdriver tip to extract. While I had to apply some force to loosen the screws, it seemed absurd that this activity could so easily tear my extensor tendon. My helpers had no problem with the activity. Sadly, just like the hernias, this was payback from a lifetime of overuse and a first-hand view of the gradual programmed cell death that comes with aging. The pain from this injury was so bad that I could not use my hands in any manner for several weeks. We injected the painful tendon area on both elbows with platelet-rich plasma (PRP) on two separate occasions and mixed in physical therapy, but still more than a year later the pain lingered, although it was greatly reduced. Since there was no way I could afford to have this cutting-edge tendon treatment done in the USA, we did it when I was down in Central America. There I would also have PRP injected into the torn biceps tendons on both shoulders. I am definitely a believer in PRP as a follow-up aid for soft-tissue injuries like tendons, ligaments, etc., which don't seem to be improving. These areas do not have a good blood supply to the injury sites so after the initial inflammatory response period of just a handful of weeks they just stop healing. PRP kick starts the healing response again for another 4 to 6 weeks. PRP can be injected into an area three times, spaced every 4 to 6 weeks, so say the experts. One shot is beneficial on 50% of the injuries, a second shot is needed for improvement on 40% of the injuries, and on 10% of the injuries a third shot is required to see some benefit. So it is not a magic pill, and not everyone will see the same results but it's worth a try. A doctor had started me on daily mix of glucosamine and calcium supplements years before to help with my joints, but after the tendinosis fiasco he added 10 grams of collagen daily in hopes that this might help slow my connective tissue deterioration. Only time will tell if this will have any effect.

In 2017, I raised enough funds to have Dr. Keohane do a "lysis of adhesion" surgery on my TKA knee and clean up the 5-year-old torn medial meniscus in my left knee. In a "lysis of adhesion" surgery, the surgeon goes in and removes all the scar tissue overgrowth that has formed. Hopefully, this will free the joint so it can move more easily and thus lessen the constant pain. In what would be Dr. Keohane's very last surgery before retiring, he skillfully cut out all the arthrofibrosis he could reach, including removing part of the inflamed synovial membrane. The trouble with a person like me who is prone to arthrofibrosis is that the body sees any surgery as a new "injury" and immediately begins to create scar tissue to help "heal" the area and the "clean out" will have been in vain. Same with the removed synovial membrane – it can grow its way right back. I will leave all in the Lord's gracious hands. "Be anxious for nothing, but in everything by prayer and supplication with thanksgiving let your requests be made known to God." (*Philippines* 4:6)

While I struggle with various other nonorthopedic medical problems that can be linked to work-related causes like Raynaud's disease (repetitive motion, frostbite), leukopenia (contact with sawdust, solvents, fumes, etc.), tinnitus (jobsite noise), and innumerable basal cell carcinoma or squamous cell carcinoma skin cancers (sun), the major contributor to my downfall has been just plain overworking the human body. I took a wonderful gift from God and beat the living bejeebers out of it. Like many of you, I only rarely worked a normal short 40-hour work week, especially in Alaska where, during the season, 14-hour days 7 days a week is the norm, but what brought me down was not the large number of hours worked, but my inability to lower the intensity or even to walk away from the hard physical labor part of framing, even in light of old age and a rapidly deteriorating body. I am sure the psychologists have a name for it like "workaholic" or "obstinate" but, whatever it is called, don't follow me down the same path. The payback is a bitch.

Lastly, don't put too much faith in the SSDI program to help you out if you end up disabled. Their inefficiency and partiality is absolutely astounding. While I have paid premiums into SSDI for over 45 years and have four times the number of medical disabilities needed to qualify for the program, I was denied when I applied on grounds that, while I obviously can't participate in jobs requiring any physical labor, they felt I could participate in the labor market as some type of part-time electronics assembler. On principle I agree – anyone, even folks who are quadriplegics, can do something, but the intention of the program is to help an individual who can no longer ply his/her lifelong profession due to medical reasons retrain or survive doing something else. Like everything else the US government has done, SSDI has morphed into another welfare hand out program ripe with fraud. My wife believes that the SSDI system is rigged or at least heavily biased since we know of a skill-less, Spanish-speaking illegal immigrant who was somehow granted full medical disability after working only a handful of years due to a relatively minor injury to one finger. Meanwhile, my wife has a husband who paid into the SSDI program all his life, has extensive damage to every limb of his body plus major spinal problems, lives in daily pain, has trouble dressing himself and getting around, sold his personal belongings to pay for medical care, yet was rejected while this other guy who has no real medical damage kicks back chugging *cervezas* (beer) on full disability paid for by her husband and others. So my advice is to plan ahead and prepare for a long-term disability privately as if the SSDI system didn't exist and if, by chance they accept you when you apply as a disabled person, count it as a blessing. Statistics show that one in eight of us will end up disabled.

With respect to SSDI always keep your qualifying points current if you are a self-employed individual. One way folks often get rejected is because they have a shortage of current credits. This can happen easily if you have a big business loss in one year and then spread it out over a handful of years negating income. With no net income on which to pay the Social Security (SS) tax you do not accumulate points (credits) during those years. I have seen it happen. So make sure that in your most recent 10 years of work, five of them have an income high enough to accumulate the maximum 4 points per year. In 2016, it was $1300 per credit or $5200 for 4 points. On your 1040 schedule SE, you must pay the tax on at least that amount to get the credits. Another way to look at it is that that tax amount is your yearly disability insurance premium. Without those points (20) you can't even apply to the SSDI program no matter if you had been current for the 40 years prior to that point.

Workplace statistics show that injuries to the back (36%), shoulder (12%), and knee (12%) compose the largest percentage of injury cases, and my life plus the lives of other framers I know verify those statistics. I did not write this chapter to scare everyone away from framing but rather to demonstrate through my personal story how easily one injury leads to another and then to another just like a line of falling dominoes. And these dominoes will continue to fall until you recognize what is happening and take action to stop the process. Don't be blind like I was. In many cases, it is simply calling it quits or transitioning to another career; in other cases, it is repairing an injury before it affects another body part or begins the arthritic response. While the physical part of any injury is miserable and certainly nothing to downplay, my biggest struggle has been emotional, for I greatly miss the active part of my life which was "my life." To see someone out running now often brings tears to my eyes. To see guys stacking a roof puts my heart in my throat because I want to jump up there and help. I know there are a lot of people who are worse off physically than I am, and I would never minimize that. Many have lost arms, legs, and much more defending our country or on the job. I hold them in the highest regard, they are all better men than I am. But then again, I want you to know that we face a high risk of injury in our field and it is best to be prepared. Certainly Our Lord can use even an injury for the good. "And we know that in all things God works for the good of those who love Him, who have been called according to His purpose" (*Romans* 8:28). Looking back, it is highly unlikely that I ever would have ever written *A Roof Cutter's Secrets*, *The Complicated Roof*, or this book, *From the Top Plates Up* without injuries slowing me down. I certainly am no writer, so it takes immense discipline and effort to put my thoughts on paper. There are a million and one other things I would rather be doing. The funniest thing is that, in over 40 years of framing, I have never been seriously injured when I was up in the air, it has always been the ground that was my enemy. Maybe I should have just stayed "From the Top Plates Up."

If it weren't for the rocks in its bed, the stream would have no song.

– Carl Perkins

12

Teaming up with the Perfect Carpenter

All I have seen teaches me to trust the Creator for all I have not seen.

– Ralph Waldo Emerson

I t was the summer of 1977 when I accepted the Lord Jesus Christ as my Savior. I can't remember the exact date, but I do remember it was a late summer Saturday evening probably in early September. After having worked the week (Monday through Saturday) stacking roofs in a housing tract in Pomona, CA, I was on my way down Highway 57 to Costa Mesa, CA, to get together with a few of my former crew team compatriots. My stepmom, knowing how I liked music, had mentioned to me months before that Calvary Chapel Costa Mesa held a free rock concert every Saturday night during the summer. I'm sure I thanked her kindly for the recommendation, but attending a "Jesus freak" concert wasn't high on my "to do" list. Now if it had been a secular concert I would have jumped at the chance. I had often worked a second job as concert security for a company in Los Angeles, CA, and the best thing about the job was that it gave me the opportunity to see some great groups like Chicago, The Eagles, Ike and Tina Turner, among others, without having to pay. Most of the guys who worked these gigs were huge football players from the University of California, Los Angeles and the University of Southern California with arms the size of my legs so I usually stayed close to one of them if there was going to be trouble.

For some reason, on this weekly drive back to hell raise with the boys, I was drawn to make the slight diversion and stop in at the Calvary Chapel Saturday night event. I sat down in the very back and listened to a guy by the name of Keith Green play the piano and sing. He was really talented. After an hour or so of music a guy named Jimmy Kempner came up on the stage and gave a short message. He explained how we are all sinners and the purpose of Jesus's life and death was to redeem us from the just punishment for those sins. The Lord had prepared my heart for that night and my decision to take Jesus as my Savior.

Before continuing further I must first flashback to a time when I was younger in order to give this story some depth. I was raised by an intransigent single mom. All six of us kids went to a Catholic grammar school some 2½ miles from our little farm. Believe me, I remember the distance well, because we walked it often. We turned those jaunts into something fun for, between my brother and I it became an ongoing battle to see who could bounce a pebble off the roof of a passing car without them stopping to chase us down. Few ever stopped and those that did had no chance to catch us for we disappeared into the shrubbery knowing every deer trail like the back of our hand. We never broke any car windows that I know of and I begrudgingly must admit that it was probably my brother who achieved the higher score, for he went on to become a high school All American forward in water polo, while I drowned in the deep end trying to block his shots as a goalie. I personally credit those rock-throwing contests for his high scoring prowess. I went on to attend an all-boys Catholic high school in San Pedro, CA (Fermin Lasuen) for a year before we moved up to Santa Barbara, CA, where I finished high school. Looking back now, I am glad for both of those parochial schooling opportunities since without a doubt I received a much better education as a result, although I still do harbor bitterness toward the nuns who took away my precious slingshot in grammar school. It left a big hole in my heart, since their "theft" retired my ability to shoot all the cute girls in the butt when they weren't looking. Always have been a sucker for pretty gals. The highlight of my grammar school days was when I had to give a city kid a licking because he smashed my sandwich in the door on purpose. Some city kids just don't like us farm boys. My mom with no money to pay for private schooling had petitioned the monsignor in charge of the grammar school for a show of kindness and somehow we kids were allowed to attend at a drastically discounted rate. In any case, while I served as an altar boy and participated in all the other trappings of the Catholic Church, it certainly wasn't by choice. I just went through the motions. In those days, you did what you were told or you got your butt whupped. At home, our mom's favorite instrument of pain was a wide leather belt, while at school they preferred a sawed off canoe paddle. We need a return to corporate punishment nowadays – never seen such an unruly bunch of kids. Anyway, as a young boy, this Catholic religion stuff made no sense at all. What in the hell was the purpose of Jesus coming as Savior on Christmas if you still had to do more good things than bad to get to heaven. If you did three mortal sins it was all over baby, as they could not be overcome by any amount of vainly repeated rosaries. Kind of like baseball – 3 strikes and you are out. It was eternal damnation forever. Anyway, it wasn't long until I had moved out of the house and I didn't have to attend any more services where the congregation chanted stuff in Latin. What was the problem with English? I suppose it wasn't as holy as Latin.

When I headed back down to Southern California to attend the Orange Coast College (OCC) construction program, I met up with my dad. I had not seen him since I was five years old. This had not been by his choice, but my mom did not want him anywhere around or for him to have any part of our lives. I learned many years later that he felt we kids would suffer less at her angry hands if he became invisible. I liked my dad immediately and grew to love him deeply over the time I spent in Los Angeles area through the 1970s. He gave me a room in his house for a couple months until I had found an apartment to rent with some other guys who were also attending OCC. While he was a busy man, he always found time to sit down and talk to me. It was from these talks that I began to question many of the things I had been taught through public high school. I remember telling him about the evolution theory of creation that I had learned at school. He then astutely asked me questions designed to illuminate the major flaws of this theory. He asked me that if this theory's evidence is based on fossils why hadn't a single transitional form ever been found fossilized in rocks. He asked me if I knew anything of the second law of thermal dynamics which of course I didn't, then he went on to explain it. He showed me how this law puts a huge damper on the evolution theory because it demonstrates that all matter is winding down in concentration or diffusing, which is the direct opposite to the evolution theory which depends on matter and energy winding up in concentration in order to advance a life form. My dad also shared how it would be plain impossible for the eye to evolve. Now you must recognize that my dad was one really smart dude. He was the "go to" guy that North American Aviation sent to Congress from among all their talented staff to make presentations in front of the Armed Services Committee. He would report on the progress in the development of various aviation weapon systems and provide counsel in advance of a new program approval. He was chief of the flight dynamics division that designed the flight systems for the space shuttle and was instrumental in developing the modern day VTOL (vertical takeoff and landing) systems that are used in aircraft like the Harrier jet. So when he shared some scientific stuff it was probably a darn good idea to listen up, so I did. **(fig 12-1)**

My dad being a strong Christian was a Sunday school teacher for 8- to 10-year-old kids at a local Presbyterian Church and he invited me to sit in on a class one Sunday. I accepted the invitation and was amazed at how well these kids knew the stories of the Bible. I felt pretty ashamed for here I was a grown man but knew so little of God's word that an 8-year-old kid could easily run circles around me. I went a few more times as a guest hoping to

learn a bit more on the sly. Once I got busy at OCC, I never went again, but the Lord had planted some seeds.

While at OCC I was part of the crew team and we lifted weights at a place called SCAR (Sports Conditioning and Rehabilitation) in Orange, CA. They had designed a special workout routine just for us. It was murderous but it worked to get us in fantastic shape. We moved through a 21-machine circuit and did one set to muscle failure at each weight station. The weight on each machine was set so we would fail between 8 and 10 repetitions, except for the quadriceps, which were set to fail at 15 repetitions. You did the circuit with a helper who preset the machines so you could move at lightning speed from one machine to the next, all the while maxing out on each machine. There was no stopping until you finished some 15 to 20 minutes later. When you did finish, you were so wiped out that all you could do was just sit still for 5 to 10 minutes until your muscle coordination returned. Your hands were shaking so much that you couldn't even grab a shower knob to turn the water on or undo the laces on your shoes. Now, talk about coincidences, the Athletes in Action wrestling team also worked out at the same training center and once they found out I had been a wrestler through high school, one of the guys would always sit down by my side during these shaking recovery times and talk. They may have had a captive audience, but I enjoyed talking with them. Not only did we talk about wrestling a bunch, but they would share a bit about Jesus. For this they used a little booklet entitled "The Four Spiritual Laws" to help illustrate God's plan of salvation. These talks threw a bit of water on the spiritual seeds that had been planted by my father.

I did very well in crew at OCC and was invited to the US Olympic development camp in 1975 and was chosen to be a member of our collegiate team that went to race in the Henley Royal Regatta on the Thames River, England, also in 1975. I enjoyed crew and my body type fit the sport well. I had little chance to make the 1976 US Olympic team since the eight-man shell had pretty much been set after they won the world championship in 1974, so I didn't even try. Coach Allen Rosenberg planned to keep that group together. What I did decide to do was to transfer to a four-year university so I could row my last two years of college eligibility and see where it went from there. OCC was only a two-year junior college, so I had three years in which to complete my remaining two years of eligibility. Since my only reason for attending a university was to row, I chose the school that had the best heavyweight men's crew in those days – Harvard University. I spent the first year of my eligibility framing in the Los Angeles, CA, housing tracts in order to save up some funds, and then drove out to Boston, MA. I had gotten fairly good grades through my time at OCC, so I figured I could make it through if I hung with one of the easier majors. Although in those days Harvard cost less than $5000 a year in tuition/fees to attend, it would still be quite the challenge for me financially. Since I already knew how to live on pennies, having done so all my life, I wasn't really worried, plus I planned on framing as much as I could during the school year to keep the green coming in. I already knew the men's heavyweight coach, Harry Parker, so he was expecting me, but his hands were tied to help me with admission. Unlike many other schools where sports coaches can help an athlete get admitted, admission to Harvard was based on the student's academic merit alone (I say "was" because this was before affirmative action). No sweat, I thought. When I arrived in Boston, MA, in July of 1977, I immediately got a job with a local framer and began to train with the varsity crew several weeks before school started in anticipation of being admitted. At the last minute I was not accepted for transfer admission because I had too many credits. I couldn't believe it! Since I always enjoy taking evening classes in subjects of interest I had taken a few during the year that I was working to save up funds to attend Harvard. These same classes threw me over the maximum allowable transferable credit amount of 60 units. I asked the admissions department if they could just drop these classes to lessen my total, but that was not permitted. As my heart sank deep I packed up my belongings and made the long drive back to Los Angeles, CA, where the top plates awaited me.

Back in the Los Angeles housing tracts, I was working from 6 a.m. to 6 p.m., six days a week. It was nothing more than work, eat, sleep, work, day in and day out. Since I worked solo, I had lots of time to think about things. I began to ask myself questions like: What is the purpose of life? Is this all there is to it? Why am I here? Where was I going with my life? I had just gone through a huge letdown and it had taken a toll on my spirit. I went from being a well-known and liked OCC "Athlete of the Year" with a promising future in crew at Harvard, back to being a lonely framer that nobody even knew existed out on some dusty housing tract in the East Los Angeles basin. It was a very humbling and discouraging time, but it served a specific purpose that God had ordained before time. It caused me to look up. I was doing some heavy-duty soul searching but could not find a single answer to any of it. So, as I drove down Highway 57 to meet up with some friends in Costa Mesa, CA, the Holy Spirit moved me to swing by Calvary Chapel that Saturday night early September 1977 and get some answers.

Now that I have returned full circle to where I left you hanging at the beginning of this chapter, I continue on. Hearing Pastor Kempner speak, I felt like he was talking directly to me. He strolled with us down the "Roman Road" as many call it. The first step of that walk is where an individual recognize that they are a sinner (*Romans* 3:23). The second step is a recognition that, because we are sinners, we are separated from God (*Romans* 6:23). And the third step is recognizing that God provided a way out from under this curse of separation if we will only confess with our mouth that Jesus is Lord and believe that God raised Him from the grave (*Romans* 10:9–10). I sure knew I was a sinner and feared the penalty I would need to pay. I had been quite a hell raiser at OCC and my behavior had been far from exemplary. When Jesus was offered as the remedy for my sin, I immediately humbly accepted His gift of salvation and forgiveness. They made an altar call but I was dressed so shabbily in my dirty work shorts, etc., that I felt I couldn't possibly go up front so I didn't. I had accepted Jesus as my Savior and felt relief beyond belief. From that day forward I knew where I was going (heaven) no matter what else happened in my life. My guilty status had been reversed. This was a promise made by the One who cannot break promises. Salvation could not be lost. It cannot be rescinded. What comfort. This was really good news for me, since I just naturally screw up more than 10 other people combined. As with any gift that is offered to someone, they must accept it otherwise it just sits on the counter unopened and it does them no good. Salvation is this way. It is offered to all, but it will only benefit those who accept it. I had taken that step and accepted it. The gist of the Bible can be found in a single verse in *John* 3:16. "For God so loved the world that he gave His only begotten Son, so that whosoever believes in Him shall not perish but have eternal life." This was the very first Bible verse that I ever memorized.

A simple little story that I was to hear years later helped cement in my mind how God's perfect justice and mercy are combined in Jesus's salvation plan. In this story, let's say that you/I are a criminal that has committed some crime and are being brought before the judge for sentencing. Let's say the crime was that you/I killed someone. Now this judge (God the Father) is only able to administer perfect judgment, meaning that if the penalty for killing someone is to lose your own life He must give you/me this penalty. He cannot do anything less. Now, as He names the just penalty to you/me, someone in the audience stands up and petitions to address the judge. The gentleman is recognized and He (Jesus) offers to suffer that penalty for you/me. He offers to be a substitute and receive the just penalty due for the crime. The Judge OK's the offer, since the penalty remains intact and is not diminished but, by allowing a substitute to serve in your/my place, He has also shown mercy to the criminal. Now the convicted criminal has a decision to make. You/I can accept that offer of Jesus taking upon Himself our penalty and go free or you/I can reject His offer and personally serve out the penalty by the loss of our life. In other words, the gift is there for the taking, but it will not be forced on anyone. It can just as easily sit on the table unclaimed. While the gift of salvation is offered to us free, it most certainly wasn't free for the One who provided it – it cost His life. "Greater love has no one than this, that a man lay down his life for his friends." (*John* 15:13).

Living the Christian life after salvation requires a daily humbling of oneself before a holy God. Putting His desires before our own. Obedience is not a requirement for salvation since salvation is a free gift that cannot be earned in any way. Obedience, simply put, is the suggested way to live in order to have the closest fellowship with God. We do this as a response to His love, not to earn His love. Do we not think of the needs of our wife and kids before our own? Do we not want to behave in a certain way so that we can have the closest relationship with them? That is all obedience is – a desire to have a close relationship with God. The reason He suggests a certain behavior is not for His sake but for ours. He made us and as a result knows what would provide us with the most fulfilling life. Who knows a Ford truck better than the designer, Ford Motor Company? If you want your Ford truck to work well and last, it would be wise to follow the approved company maintenance manual. You could use the manual from some other truck manufacturer or just do what you think is best, but, in either case, things won't work out as well as if you had stuck to the instructions of the Ford truck manual.

Many create a works or obedience environment in order to receive or keep salvation. This is nothing more than a slap to the face of Jesus. It exhibits unbelief in His finished work. It shows that we won't accept it as He said unless we also throw something into the pot. It is an attempt to participate in our own salvation. "For by grace are you saved through faith; and that not of yourselves; it is a gift of God: Not of works, lest any man should boast." (*Ephesians* 2:8–9)

After my salvation experience I made a 180° turn. I stopped all obvious sins and cleaned up my foul mouth instantaneously. I now knew that I had a purpose in my life – to bring glory to the Lord in all that I do. This is what

I needed – a purpose to live for. I was a roof guy, so I would glorify Him by being the best roof cutter and stacker I could possibly be. "The most important days in your life are the day you were born and the day you find out why" – Mark Twain.

I returned to Calvary Chapel the following Saturday night after my initial conversion to attend the concert again and this time I went forward at the altar call, since I had prepared beforehand by throwing on some better clothes before heading inside to enjoy the music. A group by the name of Gentle Faith was performing that night and the lead vocalist, Darrell Mansfield, was killer on the harmonica. After I made my public acknowledgment of having placed my faith in Jesus Christ, the concert staff gave me a copy of the book of *John* to read. I also started attending Sunday morning worship services where I listened to Pastor Chuck Smith share insights into God's Word. Thus began my never-ending journey of learning to represent the Lord as a chosen son. I will never forget that beautiful song that I learned when I took the Lord Jesus as my Savior *"I have decided to follow Jesus (3 times), ... no turning back (2 times), ... the cross before me the world behind me (3 times), ... no turning back (2 times), ...though none go with me still I will follow (3 times), ... no turning back (2 times)."*

It wasn't long after this time that I left the Los Angeles area for the central coast of California. Roof trusses had begun to invade the tracts and I certainly wasn't going to let all my roof cutting and stacking skills go to waste by sticking around to roll trusses. They were still doing cut-and-stack roofs in Lompoc, CA, so I worked there briefly before ending up in the custom home building market of Santa Barbara, CA. Soon after arriving in Santa Barbara, CA, I was baptized in a little church's indoor pool. As time went on, I realized that the Lord did indeed have a plan for my life. It was nothing like I had anticipated, that is for sure, and for His plan I would need to rely on all His strength, courage, and wisdom to carry me through. In 1987, I blew out my low back on the job and was basically bed ridden for eight months of treatment during which time I put together *A Roof Cutter's Secrets*. Even for a dense-headed idiot like me, it was obvious that the Lord wanted me to write a book on roof framing. Looking back now with perfect 20/20 hindsight it is so clear that up to that point He had been guiding me through one facet after another of roof framing so that I could put all the knowledge I had gained down on paper for others to benefit from. At one point, several contractors had even pulled me aside and shared their belief that I had a responsibility to pass along what I had been so fortunate to learn. If I hadn't got hurt when I did, it is highly unlikely that *A Roof Cutter's Secrets* would have ever been written. I was always going 100 mph and only rarely did I stop long enough to breathe. It was as if after the Lord had taught me what he wanted me to learn, He even made me stop long enough to write it all down. With the publication of *A Roof Cutter's Secrets* in 1988, I met up with Clayton DeKorne at *The Journal of Light Construction* and soon he had me teaching seminars and workshops on roof framing. What a great opportunity that was and throughout the 1990s into the early 2000s, I had a blast sharing with folks at *JLC* Live conferences.

As a result of my back injury, and upon recommendation of the doctors, I began to look for a new career and decided to give my childhood dream of being a bush pilot a try. After getting my commercial pilot and instructor certificates, I was able to pick up weekend jobs flying skydivers and giving flight instruction. In 1989, I was hired by my first Alaskan Air Taxi for the summer season. After that, my summers belonged to the skies over Alaska. I made flying a summertime affair, so that during the fall/winter/spring I could continue to cut roofs for folks but quickly found myself back running framing crews. I now had two busy careers and I loved them both. It felt good to be swamped. In reality, adding a second career to my life made me much better in both and was a good move. When summer came along I was overjoyed to get away from framing for a 3- to 4-month hiatus in Alaska. Then again, by the time summer was over, I was burned out from the 14-hour days and looking forward to being back up on the top plates. Each season reignited the passion for the following work activity whether it was flying or framing. My mind was fresh and rested, chomping on the bit for a new challenge whether it came as some cool custom home roof or landing on some unknown beach/gravel bar. Two careers broke the monotony of doing the same thing over and over, decade after decade. Many folks probably do this by taking vacations but I have never done that. I suppose it is just my mental makeup, but I have always felt the need to be productive somehow even at rest. Certainly this character trait played a role in keeping me going for so long as a framer. "To understand one's world, one must sometimes turn away from it! To serve better, one must briefly hold it at a distance. Where can the necessary solitude be found, the long breathing space in which mind gathers its strength and takes stock of its courage." – Albert Camus

As a pilot, I came to realize that the Lord had gifted me with good bush flying skills and I longed to find a way that I could use these skills to benefit others if possible. I had heard that at times missionary groups needed pilots so I began to investigate this and contacted several. In 1990, I went down to Redlands, CA, to do a check ride with the newly created offshoot of Mission Aviation Fellowship (MAF) called AirServ. AirServ had been organized after the disastrous Ethiopian famine of 1983 to 1985 to help speed the delivery of UN emergency food during future famines of this type throughout Eastern Africa. Their representative put me through the wringer in one of their Cessna 206s and, when we were finished, he gave me very high marks, saying that to his knowledge only a couple other guys had come through the evaluation process who could handle the plane like I did that day. I was jazzed to have done so well and considered it a confirmation that the Lord wanted me

12-2 Eddie Schertz spent 10 years flying the jungles of Peru and 25 years in the Wings of Hope hanger (photo 2003)

to continue down that path. AirServ put me on their list for future openings. Some six months later they did contact me with an opportunity to go to Africa but unfortunately I was tied up on a job and couldn't go. Since then I have kicked myself many times for passing up on the opportunity (it would never come up again) but I had made a promise to help spot swordfish for a fishing group out of Santa Barbara, CA, so I couldn't just run off like an immature brat and leave them stranded. Being responsible and faithful does hurt at times.

Most missionary groups only accept pilot trainees who are also certified aircraft mechanics. I was not one of these, so I started to work on getting this certificate. I began to volunteer at aviation repair facilities to gain the required "hands on" experience, all the while hitting the books to gain the technical knowledge that an A&P (airframe and powerplant) mechanic must have to past the written and practical examinations. Fitting all this in as part time took a while to complete but eventually I got the certificate. I believe it was in 1990 that I started volunteering for Wings of Hope (WoH) in Chester-field, MO. I would save up a little money so I could take a few weeks off to go out to Missouri and help out in their hanger. I learned a great deal from the guys there, especially Ed Schertz. **(fig 12-2)** Ed took me under his wing and I became his special little project. Not only did he teach me mechanical skills, but he also taught me to fly an aircraft to the edge of its STOL (short takeoff and landing) performance envelope in a bush environment. After a year or so of being associated with WoH and, even though I didn't have my A&P certificate yet, Ed felt comfortable enough with my mechanical skills that

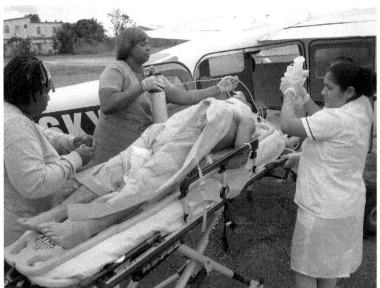

12-3 Transporting a patient from Punta Gorda to Belize City by air saved 12 hours by road in the early 1990s

WoH sent me down to Belize several times to serve as volunteer pilot in their humanitarian aid air ambulance operation. **(fig 12-3)** I enjoyed the people of Belize to no end, and grew so close to many that we were all in tears when my time was up and I had to head back to the States. I found that the Lord had given me the unique ability to fit into foreign cultures with relative ease. In no time at all, the locals had accepted me as one of their own. I took this as a second confirmation that the Lord did indeed want to use me in a foreign field.

Not wanting to break any more hearts on short-term humanitarian aid stints, I settled on the idea that it would be best if I looked for a long-term project somewhere in a Third World country. In some country where I could not only serve as a volunteer pilot/mechanic, but where I might also be able to teach rough carpentry skills to the locals. While a minimal cost air ambulance service does help many poor folks through a onetime medical emergency, it does nothing to help them in their daily ongoing struggle to escape poverty. Undoubtedly, many of you have heard the axiom from Maimonides "Give a man a fish and you feed him for a day; teach a man to fish and you feed him for a lifetime." I have seen it played out in real life over and over again. If a poor unskilled man had such good luck as to even have a job, he might be able to earn the equivalent of $5 US a day on and off cutting weeds with a machete. Now consider that even with minimal construction skills he could almost triple that daily income and have steady employment. The effect of this increase in funds for his family would be immense. Even with just a little extra money he could supplement his family's rice and beans diet with a chicken and/or some vegetables. With a few more pennies he could buy some cheap ½-inch PVC pipe to bring water from a nearby stream to outside his dirt-floor shanty. He might even be able to buy a few sheets of zinc roofing to toss up on top of that branch-framed thatched shanty and finally keep the torrential rains at bay. A few more pennies might allow him the opportunity to buy a small butane stove so his family as a troop no longer have to walk for hours each morning, going farther and farther away, trying to collect enough firewood for their typical campfire cooking arrangement. Or maybe even funds for a mosquito net to help his family avoid Dengue fever. He would not even consider the luxury of toilet paper that we all accept as an absolute necessity.

Most people, including even the poor in advanced Western-type societies have little understanding of extreme poverty. I have seen it first-hand, but still cannot fathom how they can live on less than $1.25 day per person (definition of extreme poverty: US $1.25 day in 2008) much less the $1 day per **family** that many must survive on. To see this with one's own eyes does two things: first, it moves one's heart to be full of gratitude for that which we do have; and second, it motivates one to do and give what we can to help. I feel it would be a useful experience if everybody was to spend some time helping out in a Third World country. It would sure help to grow their empathy toward and their understanding of extreme poverty. While poverty is something that will never be completely destroyed, we can still do much to help with its decline (*Mark* 14:7). It is nothing for many of us to give up a few things and live a simpler life in order to be able to share with others. Actually, worldwide extreme poverty has decreased much over the past 30 years, from 50% in 1981 to 22% in 2010 despite a 59% increase in the populations of the developing countries (James Rodgers – *What's Behind the Stunning Decrease in Global Poverty*). A good portion of this decrease has resulted from the increased proliferation of the free market system throughout the world in addition to technological advances in production, but let us not forget the value of the donations in time, money, and training that have been provided by individuals, churches, and corporations. After my father's death, my stepmom told me a bit about my father and his love for the Lord. Evidently, as a young man he had decided to give everything above what he needed for a very modest lifestyle to the Lord. He always drove an old car and lived in a simple little tract house. Everything above what was needed to support this went to charity. He had no fancy or expensive toys. He had no profundity of possessions choking his garage, just a few tools to help him with the upkeep of his home and auto. A vacation for him was a simple backpacking trip through the Sierra Nevada Mountains of California, certainly not some expensive beach front jaunt to Cancun, Mexico, or the like. Other than having been sent to Europe as an emissary for his employer in the 1960s or being part of some overseas military deployment, my father never traveled the world, although he certainly could have done so if he had kept back a bit of the money he gave to the Lord. He had a heart of gold and hearing all of this years after he went to be with the Lord helped me organize my priorities as a young Christian. My father figured that helping the Lord and the poor was the best use of his abundance.

"The ground of a certain rich man yielded an abundant harvest. He thought to himself, 'What shall I do? I have no place to store my crops.' Then he said, 'This is what I'll do. I will tear down my barns and build bigger ones, and there I will store my surplus grain. And I'll say to myself, You have plenty of grain laid up for many years. Take life easy; eat, drink and be merry.' But God said to him, 'You fool! This very night your life will be demanded from you. Then who will get what you have prepared for yourself?' This is how it will be with whoever stores up things for themselves but is not rich toward God." (*Luke* 12:16–21).

Too many folks fill their theoretical "barns" here on earth with little consideration of how close eternity is.

For a long time I wrestled with the theodicy of "how a loving God can allow so much miserable poverty and suffering on earth." It is a complicated subject that I confess is way over my head, but this I do know – God is in control and His plan for earth's redemption will be completed. As Max Lucado said "God is God. He knows what he is doing. When you can't trace his hand, trust his heart." Just look to the cross if you want to know His heart. The many physical needs that exist all around us allow each of us an opportunity to show our love for Christ in a real-life manner. If poverty and other physical needs did not exist, we would have much fewer opportunities in which to show our love for Him. If you love someone you do what you can to help them and make sure they are taken care of, being fed, clothed, etc. "Truly I tell you, whatever you did for one of the least of these brothers and sisters of mine, you did for me." (*Matthew* 25:40).

It was in 2002 when a friend of mine in the Peace Corps knowing that I was associated with Wings of Hope, told me of an area along the Gulfo de los Mosquitos (Gulf of the Mosquitos) in Panama that was in desperate need of some type of humanitarian aid air service. After discussing the situation with the director of WoH, I made an exploratory trip to this area to check things out and was given the green light to proceed. Upon returning to the USA, I stuck my old pickup in storage, packed a few duffel bags and headed back south to spearhead a humanitarian aid project whose goal was to bring air transportation into the Gulf of the Mosquitos region. Central America would become my second home for many years. Because WoH is a straight "volunteer" organization, I would return to the USA each year to frame a bit in California and then fly a bit in Alaska to generate my personal overseas support.

Not being a fan of hot muggy climates, I knew I wouldn't last long unless I could find some place to escape the steam bath heat. Thank God there were mountains around where the temperatures were a good 15° cooler than at sea level, so I headed straight for them. While the humidity was still intense up there, at least the cooler temperature made it survivable. I have noticed over the past 15 years that my body has grown more and more incapable of handling hot humidity. Now, as an old man, I break out in heat rash blisters after only a day in the sweltering sea level temperatures. Air conditioning is the only cure – another "thank you" to Our Lord. Dry heat, while uncomfortable, doesn't affect me like hot humidity does. I seem to be able to tolerate summer in the high desert or Rocky Mountain plateaus without incident.

I found many communities of poor Ngäbe-Buglé Indians living along the lonely 200-mile stretch of the Golfo de los Mosquitos coast. These indigenous folks were so isolated from medical help that it was a 2- to 3-day hike up and over the "Cordillera de Talamanca" mountain range to even arrive at the country's road system and, from there, nearly a day by ground transportation to a government hospital for medical attention. The zone was also known for its abundance of rain – some **22 feet** a year – so the foot trails were nothing more than troughs of mud a good part of the year. If you were sick or injured, you certainly would not be making this type of hike, so many times simple medical issues turned into life-threatening events. Dengue fever and malaria were rampant, while easily treatable snake bites killed people just because they couldn't get to the antivenom in time. It sure seemed like a place for an air ambulance, if we could only find some places to land the aircraft close to the communities. I approached the government's health department with the idea of a joint project and found that they were more than happy to team up because they too were looking to find a better way to access the area. Small Boston whaler-type boats were the current method of transportation into this area and their use was limited in certain periods of the year due to weather conditions. It was lucky if the communities along this stretch of the Gulf saw one boat a week during the dry season. Commercial marine transportation companies shied away from providing service to the area since no one there had any money to pay a fare. The Department of Education also wanted in on our air transportation project. They needed a way to get teachers in/out of the little community schools that had been started deep in this area. Overall, the government more or less just overlooked the area because it provided no tax revenue due to its poverty. I suppose they felt they couldn't justify the expenditure when there were millions of other needy folks in parts where at least some tax revenue could be collected. I won't get into the politics of it all, but the bottom line is that there are some hefty mineral deposits in the indigenous area that could have been developed and would have provided some huge sums of money to better folk's lives. The government sought to bring in outside mining companies who had the expertise and funding to develop these areas in conjunction with the locals, but this was flatly rejected by the Ngäbe-Buglé leadership. Their decision was the direct result of the meddling of various

12-4 Flying salmon off the beaches of Alaska's Kvichak Bay during the 1990s and early 2000s

outside environmental groups. So in the end, the government just washed their hands. Yes, stupid decisions had been made by the native leadership but still, innocent people were suffering and it was these folks whom we wanted to help if at all possible. Most of these folks were just struggling to put food in the mouths of their kids and had no understanding of what they as a people had or the politics of what even went on. I have seen the same stupidity in other countries. You have an extremely poor people sitting on top of a pile of gold (or another mineral of value), but because of outside environmental wacko influence, they decide not to touch it. If it had been mined, there would have been work for their men, electricity in their communities, medical clinics constructed, dirt roads paved, schools built. But no – it is so much better to leave the gold in the ground and condemn the people to a life of misery than put a couple little holes in the forest.

I originally figured that we might be able to use the beaches adjacent to the little communities as our runways but unfortunately this idea was dropped after we did a "kick the sand" inspection and found them way too soft to operate a light aircraft even with super-wide sand-capable tires. It was my error to assume that the beaches facing the Caribbean Sea would be hard packed like the ones I worked in Alaska. **(fig 12-4)** Without a big tide and heavy wave action they did not get the tamping required to produce a firm surface. Hoping to find some alternative options, we looked at areas that had been used as landing strips by Manuel Noriega during his drug-running days but found by aerial survey that the jungle had long since reclaimed them. It would require major bulldozer work to make any of them flyable

12-5 The jungle reclaimed all the old bush strips that Noriega carved out along the Gulf of Mosquitoes

12-6 Panama has no river bars like this one that I worked along the Holitna River in the Alaska Interior

again and there certainly wasn't money or time in the project framework for this. **(fig 12-5)** On top of that, I really had no hankering for the international environmental scandal the wackos would create if we knocked down a few trees in order to build a few dirt airstrips, so I switched over to searching for useable gravel bars along some of the rivers as landing sites. **(fig 12-6)** These we used often in the Alaska interior as drop off and pick up locations for hunters and fishermen, but unfortunately nothing workable was located, so at this point we counseled the government that the best option to access the area would be by using helicopters. Every little community always had some clearing hacked out of the jungle where they could play soccer and this area could easily double as a landing zone for a helicopter (see upper right

12-7 Wood frame projects provided an opportunity to teach men Western style framing in Central America

hand corner **fig 12-5**). It all made perfect sense, especially considering that the government had a few Vietnam era Hueys sitting around. Anyhow, some four years after I began work on the project, the area finally had an emergency medical air ambulance service. I suspect that some twenty years or so in the future, the government will most likely cut a road down the coast to open up the area, but, until that happens, at least now folks had a way out in an emergency. Concurrent with the WoH air transportation project, I began to provide rough carpentry skill training. When various wood frame projects presented themselves, I used them as an opportunity to train men in Western framing techniques. **(fig 12-7)**

The indigenous Ngäbé are physically amazing people. Short, stocky, powerful folks that historically were never defeated by the Spanish Conquistadors or anyone else for that matter. I once saw a young 12-year-old boy walking along a mountain trail carrying a 10-inch-diameter log some 8 feet long on one shoulder – something I could never even imagine doing when I was in my prime. Another time, when we were hiking into the jungle to examine various river bars for possible aircraft landing sites, a 14-year-old Ngäbé girl passed us like a flash of light. She was carrying a small child up front on her chest together with a huge canvas bag on her back (most likely food provisions for her family). She had no fancy backpack with padded shoulder straps or a hip belt that we might consider essential if we were to carry what appeared to be nearly 70 lbs. She wore a nagua (Ngäbé tribal dress) and

12-8 A typical Ngäbé Indian family that inhabits western Panama

had a pair of cheap rubber rain boots on her feet as she plowed thru the mud and rivers. I tried for a while to keep up with her but she just left me in the dust (better said mud). Another time, a Ngäbé friend of mine named Ernesto helped me move some heavy Guayacan beams. I was totally astounded by his strength. What two regular guys my size would have had trouble moving, he handled by himself with total ease. He was not huge like these weightlifter types, but I feel confident he could have easily out-lifted most.

These people are mentally tough. The hard lives they live have made them people of true grit. They are courageous and self-reliant. Because of their cultural norms, they tend to avoid contact with outsiders so it takes a long time to develop a relationship with a Ngäbé person and win his/her trust. In the isolated mountain regions, the girls are "married" by the time they are 14 years old and a year later along comes their first child, followed quickly by a procession of 6 to 8 others. **(fig 12-8)** Unfortunately, while the parents are loyal and caring, to have such a string of new responsibilities only sinks them further into the mire of extreme poverty. They do their best to scratch out a living by cultivating a small parcel of land, and many supplement this by seasonal work hand harvesting coffee beans from December to March. The lucky few get a job providing labor to some of the huge agricultural companies.

It was my hope to befriend some of the Ngäbé people to the point that I could share the idea of maybe waiting until they are 20 to 21 years old to have their first child after they had built up some financial resources and developed an agricultural area large enough to support the growing family. After that I hoped to suggest that they slow down on the number of kids they had so as to have the funds to send their kids through school. This action alone would end poverty in their lineage. The standard custom of creating large families when the parents themselves are only barely surviving ends up condemning their kids to the same cycle. I know it is a hard sell, but it was something I wanted to try. Usually it was many years too late for the parents, but my hope was that their children might follow this new and different path.

The decline in my ability to teach due to increasing physical difficulties has coincided with the disappearance of wood as a building material in Central America, so we will have to wait and see what and where the Lord may want us next. I certainly can still fly OK, so maybe He will have me focus more on that in some lonely "not too hot" place on the globe.

One thing I have noticed each time I return to the USA is how expensive things have gotten. It may not be as visible to folks who live stateside continually, but for me, who returns after being outside a long time, I definitely face some heavy-duty culture shock. Remember the frog in the pan of water analogy. If the temperature of the water is heated slowly the frog doesn't feel the change, but he sure does if you try to toss him in a pan of steaming water. I feel kind of like the poor frog who gets tossed into the steaming water.

When I made my decision to help out overseas in 2002 as a volunteer I did not grasp how big a decision it really was, nor the profound effect it would have on my life. While most of the folks my age would continue to move forward financially until sometime in their 60s, I, from my decision date onward, would only move backward. Over time, an immense economic chasm has grown between me and my peers. Many of them have a difficult time understanding why I don't have the funds to participate in the things they do. Not that money matters, except that it sure does help to have a little when you get old and are no longer able to work physically. It is impossible for me to try and recapture the time that I have spent as a volunteer. Even if that could miraculously happen, my body's deteriorated condition would never allow me to take advantage of it. It is just part of the sacrifice long-term missionaries and volunteers make. Not only is being a missionary or volunteer an end to all financial advancement, but it is a donation of the very years of your life. Not that I would do anything differently now, having 20/20 hindsight, it is just that at the time I made the decision I did not see all the real-life ramifications that went with that decision. I bet that few do. It has certainly helped to increase my appreciation for the huge sacrifices that many folks have made throughout history by donating their lives to help the poor or share the Gospel. When I headed overseas as a volunteer I was counting on the earnings I would make from working stateside each summer plus any royalties that might dribble in from the republication of *A*

Roof Cutter's Secrets (2002), to allow me to live at the basic economic level of nationals in a Third World country. Mission Aviation Fellowship had counseled me that I was way underfunded, which was probably true, but so was the apostle Paul who supported his ministry as a tent maker. "You yourselves know that these hands of mine have supplied my own needs and the needs of my companions." (*Acts* 20:34). Unfortunately, unforeseen medical issues put a real kink in my plans (but certainly not God's plan). Before, when things were tight, I just worked longer hours and more days to raise my income, but that is no longer a viable option. I have had to learn humility and to truly trust the Lord "day by day." This lesson is never easy and, in truth, it has been a very difficult one for me. It comes from that self-reliant spirit that has always driven my life. I have had to come to the end of myself and it is only by Him that I now go forth.

"Therefore do not worry, saying, 'What shall we eat?' or 'What shall we drink?' or 'What shall we wear?' For the pagans pursue all these things, and your Heavenly Father knows that you need them. But seek first the kingdom of God and His righteousness, and all these things will be added unto you." (*Matthew* 6:31–33)

Now some 40 years later as supposedly a "mature" Christian, I still screw-up way too often, but I keep getting up each time after I fall off the horse. That is really what counts. Confess and try again. "If we confess our sins, He is faithful and just to forgive us our sins and to cleanse us from all unrighteousness." (1 *John* 1:9).

The Lord used Christian rock music as a powerful evangelical tool in my life. What started as a little movement in Costa Mesa, CA, in the early 1970s has spread worldwide. Today there are literally hundreds of terrific Christian bands and individuals out there singing praise to the Lord. While I don't play a musical instrument, I do love to listen to bands like Hillsong United or Elevation Worship. I guess that means I am still a hippie at heart.

I challenge each of you who do not know the Lord as your Savior to check it out. Earnestly ask the Lord to open doors that will make His truth clear to you. Take a read through the book of *John*. If you have doubts, realize that it's OK, so did the Apostles Peter, Paul, and Thomas (myself included) at various times in their lives. Bear in mind that some of these folks spent three years at our Lord's side and saw Him do miracle after miracle, yet they still had doubts. Take the step and your faith with grow. If you are a thinker read C.S. Lewis's book *Mere Christianity* or Lee Stobles's *A Case for Christ* (also a 2017 film). *Revelation* 3:20 says, "Behold, I stand at the door, and knock: if any man hears my voice and opens the door, I will come in to him, and will sup with him, and he with me." Jesus will never reject your prayer for salvation no matter what type of life you have lived. He is there right now waiting for you. Only by accepting our Lord Jesus as your Savior can you be saved. "Salvation is found in no one else, for there is no other name under heaven given to mankind by which we must be saved." (*Acts* 4:12). What do you have to lose? "Give Jesus a chance." As C.S. Lewis said, "If Christianity is false, it's of zero importance. But if it's true, there's nothing more important in the entire universe."

For those of you who are my Christian brothers and sisters already, please join me as we pray for those in the framing trade who have yet to accept the sacrifice that Jesus made on the cross to wash away the consequence of their sin so they can share eternity with us in heaven. Carpenters will always have that very special bond of the trade and I feel a special pride to know that our Savior was also one of us in that sense – a simple carpenter who worked with His hands. Never forget that. He could have chosen any level of society through which to arrive here on this earth to bring His message, but He chose to identify with us "nail pounders." Pretty cool – the most important person to visit this planet was a carpenter. For sure we will have lots to talk about in heaven and I definitely look forward to sharing those roof situations that have always stumped me with the perfect Carpenter Himself. Just think He chose us to be part of His team.

But those who hope in the LORD will renew their strength.
They will soar on wings like eagles; they will run
and not grow weary, they will walk and not be faint.

(Isaiah 40:31)

13

Train to Survive the Battle

Preparation for tomorrow is hard work today. – Bruce Lee

I worked flying Sockeye salmon off the beaches in Bristol Bay, AK, for some twelve summer seasons (1990s to early 2000s). One of the set-net fishermen I worked for was a gentleman named William Crawford "Winky." At 58 he was still as strong as an ox and one day I asked him what was the key to his physical work longevity. He replied "hard work and young women." His current wife was 33 years old and an absolute jewel from Indonesia. After I thought about it a while, what he said made sense. Exercise has always been the closest thing to the fountain of youth we will see on this planet and, with a young gal as a wife, one is put to the task just to keep up. Now I am not suggesting anyone exchange their current wife for a younger model, but his point was that younger gals carry a lot of excitement for life just built in. They are always moving, they want to go see this, or do that, so if you are together with them their energy just gets passed along to you by osmosis. Winky died a few years later in his early 60s due to heart issues, so I wonder if there was a flaw somewhere in his theory. Anyway, I will always miss him, he taught me much about using a Cessna 206 to work the beach. I do hope to make it to Indonesia some day before I die so I can say hi to his bride Augustine who must be my age now. Boy, does time fly!

I have always been an athlete since as far back as I can remember. In grammar school, it was baseball. In high school, it was football, wrestling, water polo, and track. In college, it was rowing. While competition in sports helps develop character, it is also one of the best training fields for a production framer since so much athleticism is required. Sports help you develop the strength, stamina, balance, coordination, and team spirit that will carry you through your career. Other than professional sports or the military's elite Special Forces, I can think of no other type of work that uses the body to the same level of intensity on a daily basis as roof framing does. So if we conclude that what we do is similar to a competitive athletic activity, why would we not train for it in the same manner. Not only would it better our jobsite performance, but it would also fortify our body against injury.

While I had run 3 miles and did calisthenics (push-ups, pull-ups, sit-ups, etc.) 4 times a week ever since my high school sports days, after my low back injury in 1987, physical therapy/training took on a new meaning. Now, not only would I have to do certain exercises throughout my life to stay out of a wheelchair, but this injury motivated me to develop an exercise program that could help protect my other "as of yet" uninjured body parts from damage. So, for the past 30+ years I have been assembling a list of exercises geared specifically to help us framers survive the physical abuse our career will dump on us. I always strive to find exercises that are effective yet simple. I am a "keep it simple, stupid" (KISS) type of guy – what else can I say.

A few years after my spine injury in the late 1980s, I was blessed to receive some excellent training from a physical therapist who worked with Spine Care Medical Group in Daly City, CA, by the name of Bruce. He had been a former pro athlete (football, I think it was) who when injured in competition decided to become a physical therapist. His focus was mainly directed toward helping guys who worked with their bodies like us framers to cope with sudden life-changing injuries. Bruce taught me that with proper body mechanics and avoiding certain activities or movements I would be able to live a near-normal life. I learned that I should never again rotate at the waist. Hips, shoulders, and knees must stay in the same plane at all times. For example, if a normal person wanted to see something to the side, they would rotate their head until their neck's rotational limit was reached and if after that they still needed more angle they would rotate at the waist. I on the other hand, must spin my whole body like a solid plank by stepping backward if I needed more angle once my neck's rotational limit was reached. So sports like golf, boxing, baseball, kayaking would be good example of the ones in which I should never again participate since they all incorporate twisting motions at the waist. I also had to nix jumping activities like basketball and volleyball, or running downhill, etc., that could shock load the spinal disks.

Paramount in low back injury survivability is a three-part exercise plan. The first part is to strengthen your stomach and back muscles (core) in order to brace or stabilize the spine. The second part is to develop strong legs and good hamstring flexibility in order to perform the correct squatted lifting technique to pick up items on the ground. Weak thighs and/or bad knees present a strong temptation to use your back to help in a lift. The third part is to strengthen your upper body so that when you are lifting something from waist high it can be accomplished easily without any temptation to incorporate your back in the lift. I have also come to learn the importance of just everyday walking for a healthy low back. Many times, a good hour-long walk combined with a heating pad and NSAIDs (nonsteroidal anti-inflammatory drugs), did wonders to lessen my back pain episodes. Somehow, walking helps relax the muscle spasms that accompany most low back injuries.

I cannot overemphasize the need to build a strong core. The stomach muscles are strengthened to provide a powerful short-term protective contraction during a movement, while the back muscles are strengthened for muscular endurance. A good analogy would be to equate your spine to the mast of a sailboat. Alone, the mast is fragile, but when reinforced by rigging it becomes nearly unbreakable. Without those guy-wire cables running to the front, to the back, and to each side, the mast would snap right off at the deck in the first gale she faced. Our spine is basically the same. Without the muscles of our cores to serve as rigging, the spine has little strength. Therefore, it would only make sense that we want some strong "guy-lines" (core muscles) to support our mast (spine) when it has to sustain some fierce winds (lifting loads). Front versus back has the abdominal muscles in tension against the back muscles and glutes (buttocks), while the muscles along the side of stomach (obliques) coupled with the hip flexors are in tension side-to-side. The taller the mast or the longer the spine, the more stress is placed on it by winds or lifted loads on account of leverage. This is the reason that we tall skinny guys are more inclined to end up with back injuries in construction – simple physics. Short stocky folks will always have an advantage over us when it comes to lifting weight. If unconvinced, just think of all the amazing Chinese weightlifters or the huge powerful Samoans. Of course, any spine, no matter how genetically blessed, can get damaged, so it goes without saying that anyone involved in construction labor should strive to maintain a very strong core.

One general rule to keep in mind when exercising any muscle group is to be sure to give equal time to the opposing muscle group. So if you do 4 stomach-strengthening exercises, compliment them with 4 back-strengthening exercises. That way, you are developing each side of the guy-wire setup equally. You must stay physically balanced or you risk injury. Same goes for strengthening your legs, arms, whatever. If you do 3 quadriceps-strengthening exercises like squats, do 3 hamstring- and glute-strengthening exercises as well. If you do 3 pull-down arm exercises, do 3 push overhead arm exercises, etc.

So while there are all kinds of exercises available that one can do, let me share some of the exercises that I believe will help any rough framer resist the physical onslaughts of our merciless trade. These same exercises have helped me stay on top of my game as a roof framer much longer than most and, when I did get injured, they helped me return to the jobsite in the least amount of time possible. Lifting weights is a great method to strengthen body parts and various medical reports also give this type of strength training high grades to help keep the mind sharp and avoid Alzheimer's disease. I don't like the hassle or lost time traveling to/from a weight-lifting gym, so I have never used one unless I happened to be staying at some hotel that had a gym. I do all the same stuff at home with body weight type exercises and often add extra loose weights strapped around my waist. Not only do I eliminate travel time by working out at home, but I forgo the monthly membership fee. One thing is certain – never succumb to the type of thinking that says "I did enough physical labor and exercise on the jobsite so there is no need to do exercise at home." While I will never downplay the amount of heavy labor we do on the jobsite, it can in no way be considered a balanced exercise program nor does it give your cardiovascular system the workout it needs to stay healthy.

As I have shared elsewhere, consider daily exercise a part of your job. You may do 8 hours on the jobsite, but your day is not done until you take care of your equipment (the body). While I have listed a bunch of exercises to follow for each part of the body, choose just a few at random out of the list for each body section to be worked. If an area is injured, you may want to put more focus on this area to help it recover, but don't shy away from exercising that part because of the pain, just do it more gently. If you avoid exercising a painful area, the muscles that serve as protection will atrophy and you will end up more likely to reinjure it. When done correctly it might take 30 to 45 minutes to do your strengthening exercises and they should be alternated every other day with +/–30 minutes of some type of aerobic exercise (running, rowing, biking, swimming, soccer, etc.) to keep your cardiovascular system healthy. If you are able, ride your bike to/from work occasionally. It is one of the best ways to warm up for the job in the morning and unwind at the end of the day (only works if you have tool storage on the jobsite). Little things, like always take the stairs instead of using an escalator or running to the corner store for groceries, are simple ways to make training an integral part of your daily life. While most folks might not train on Sunday, I almost always did. It was typically my one day off so I was able to do even more. Not only did exercise help protect me in a brutal job, but I know of no better stress reliever or calming mental therapy. Often after church on Sunday I would go on a long run up in the hills of Santa Barbara or Berkeley, CA. Sometimes I would pedal over to a nearby community swimming pool for a few laps in mini triathlon style. If you want to get the heart pumping – run hills – I love 'em. I would also do a fair amount of backward running since it produces between 4 and 8 times the benefit of forward running for a given distance. And as everyone knows, it is always about time efficiency for me.

All that is in the past now. Today, with all my physical deficiencies, I do 1½ hours of physical therapy (PT) daily just to be able to move around the house. I do a core and leg series 4 times a week and an arm and shoulder series 2 times a week. Getting a good cardiovascular workout is near impossible since I am very limited in what I can do. Surprising my resting heart rate is still somehow in the low 50s. I do my best to get in a few short walks a couple times a week. I can't go far, because my knees swell up and force me to stop. A vertical-position stationary bike works OK, but to get out in the street on a regular bike where I would rather be is tough. Even with beach cruiser handlebars, my damaged neck goes bonkers after a short ride because I can't get it vertical enough. I really should have someone bend a special pair of handlebars for me. Swimming is another great exercise for us folks with disabilities, but with both shoulders separated I can only do it briefly before the joint pain is too much. I make do the best I can but certainly can't enjoy these activities like I once did.

Skipping rope was another activity I loved and was fairly good at it. I do miss it, but various knee surgeries put it off limits many years back. It, as well as running are two of the many things I look forward to doing again in heaven. Skipping rope was such a quick, clean way to get a super cardiovascular workout, all the while building balance and agility. I had a routine that mixed in all kinds of different skips.

1. *The boxer* (2 jumps left foot – 2 jumps right foot)
2. *The Irish jig* (1 leg triangular pattern – front/side/back)
3. *The skier* (2 leg X pattern)
4. *The Russian dancer* (skipping rope in a 2-leg full squatted position)
5. *The compass* (25 reps single foot front/back, 25 reps single foot side/side)
6. *Continuous double jumps* with occasional "triple jump" tossed in.

When I couldn't get outside to run because the weather was lousy, I spent 20 minutes with the jump rope. Rowing a Concept 2 ergometer is very close to a perfect exercise format. You get both cardiovascular (cardio) and near-full-body strength training in one vehicle. If you decide to pick up rowing, but have never done it before, I suggest you find an expert to help you get the correct technique down. That way you won't develop bad habits. Many times I have passed gyms that have rowing machines only to cringe when I see the miserable technique of the users. I suppose I notice it more as a result of my crew background. There are some good YouTube videos demonstrating correct form as well.

WARM-UP

I start my exercise routine with a series of joint rotations: basically making circles with every joint from the neck down to the ankles, clockwise then counterclockwise. Then, I move on to gently get the blood flowing and the muscles warm. I found that burpees along with some skipping rope to be the quickest warm-up exercises. Unfortunately, I can't do either of these anymore due to my back and knee injuries so I have had to substitute a minute or two of push-up position running in place instead (also known

13-1 Atomic situps

13-2 Hands between knees crunches

13-3 Knees to elbow with a twist crunches

13-4 Alternating straight leg raised crunches

as "mountain climbers"). When warm and a little out of breath, I head into my strengthening exercises.

CORE

Our first line of protection against back injuries is a rock-solid core. My stomach exercises are fairly straightforward and simple. I perform exercises that keep my back on or near the ground so as to protect my damaged spine. I target the lower portion of my abdominals by incorporating crunches with some type of leg lift. I loved to do vertical sit-ups from my personal invented extreme slant board, but no more. Another favorite that I had to retire from the exercise list was "V" sit-ups. In these, you raise your feet and chest simultaneously to form a "V" and then touch your toes with your hands. You balance on your butt. On all the following exercises, except for the atomic or regular sit-ups, I start from a face-up, flat-on-my-back, floor position. On all crunch-type exercises, your shoulder blades should come off the floor. Always look straight up at the ceiling. In the crunch, try to raise your face and touch it flat against the ceiling (off course you can't – but try), rather than cranking your chin toward your chest, which is hard on your neck. What is paramount in all "back on floor" stomach exercises is that you always keep the small of your back pressed firmly against the floor. Never, never, never, let it

rise. With stomach exercises do enough reps to get a good burn and then do 10 to 15 more. For me that works out to be about 50 repetitions (reps) for most exercises. I also move from one exercise to the next with little rest in between.

My abdominal exercises include:

1. *Atomic sit-ups.* Hold your legs airborne by 6-inches and move your knees in (bend them) and out (straighten them) to counterbalance a partial sit-up. **(fig 13-1)**
2. *Hands between bent-knees crunches or toe-touch crunches with legs vertical in air* (set of 50 reps). **(fig 13-2)**
3. *Bent-knee half sit-ups.* In a very quick moment tighten your stomach and lift your upper body off the floor like a straight board only enough to clear the spine all the way to the tail bone. This usually only takes a few inches at shoulder level.
4. *Knees-to-elbow crunches.* Lying on your back with knees bent, feet flat on floor positioned near your buttocks. Lift both knees simultaneously and bring them toward your upper body to meet up with an upward crunch of the chest. In the chest up "crunched" position make a quick side-to-side elbow to opposite knee double twist. **(fig 13-3)**
5. *Alternating straight-leg-raised crunches.* Both legs remain straight throughout this exercise. Start with your left leg raised 6 inches above the ground and your right leg raised to the vertical position. Now crunch your chest toward your right leg. Lower this leg while raising the left leg and crunch your chest toward your left leg. Some folks may call this giant flutter kicks with a sequential crunch. **(fig 13-4)**
6. *Dying bug.* Start by lying face up on the floor. Extend your right hand horizontally straight overhead keeping it slightly off the ground while simultaneously extending your right leg horizontally straight and holding it slightly off the ground as well. On the left side bend your knee and bring it toward your chest to just past vertical and touch it with your left hand. Now alternately swap these left and right positions by swing your right hand to

touch your right knee as it comes up to your chest while the left side arm and knee are moving to the laid out horizontal position. **(fig 13-5)**

7. *Regular sit-ups with feet unsupported* (not held by anything). Keep your heels planted on the ground and touch your elbows to your knees. I limit the range of my spinal movement to 20° short of vertical on account of my low back issues.

When training any part of the body constantly change the tempo of the exercises (slow/fast) between sessions or mix in variations in order to confuse the muscle. There really is only so much one can do with this methodology, but the muscles do find a way to skate through an exercise if you always only do the same thing over and over again in the same manner and order. A little variety also helps to keep the training interesting and more challenging. CrossFit is a big proponent of this style of training. Too bad it came along when I was an old man, I would have loved to have competed in it when younger. By mixing up the speed at which you perform the repetitions of an exercise develops your muscles in two distinct forms. If you do slow repetitions you will build strength. whereas if you do fast explosive repetitions you will build speed or power. Everyone is better at one or the other. I, for example, do better with fast explosive repetitions. Also bear in mind that it is imperative to breathe correctly during the exercise's repetitions themselves. On the exertion stroke of an exercise you should be forcibly exhaling, while on the recovery stroke you should be inhaling. For example, when doing a simple push-up – exhale as you push up and inhale as you lower your body back down to the ground.

My back exercises incorporate both facedown and faceup positions. Facedown include:

1. *Superman.* The exerciser assumes a static Clark Kent flying position on his belly. His arms and legs should be straight out and airborne. This static position is held for 3 minutes (count to 200). I can't do "superman" with my arms stretched overhead anymore due to my shoulder injuries, so I either hold them lifted up straight along my legs in dive-bomber position or in the bent arm position straight out from my shoulders like a skydiver. **(fig 13-6)**
2. *Hunting dog.* From a hands and knees crawling position, raise the right arm and left leg straight out horizontally and hold this position for 2 minutes (count 100), then swap over to raise the opposite arm and leg for the same time. **(fig 13-7)**

My faceup back exercises are all different variations of hip thrusts (also known as back bridges) and are accomplished from a position where you are lying on the ground knees bent with your feet tucked up close to your butt. During these exercises the hips are raised so only your shoulders and feet are left touching the ground.

13-6 Superman

13-7 Hunting dog

13-8 Single-leg hip thrusts

My faceup exercises include:

1. *Single-leg hip thrusts.* Begin with one leg extended straight out at +/−30° from horizontal while you raise and lower your hips slowly using the other leg. Do 20 reps, then switch and do 20 reps using the other leg. The straight leg should parallel the bent leg's thigh when the hips are in the up position – no higher. Make sure you really push your hips up good so the only two points touching the ground at the top of the movement are shoulders and the foot. Your torso and thigh should form a straight line at the top of the movement. **(fig 13-8)**

2. *Double-leg hip thrusts.* These are done in the same manner as the single-leg hip thrusts, except that both feet are planted on the ground. To add an extra punch to this exercise, add an exercise band around your knees.

When at the top of the "hips up" thrust position, pause for a second, squeeze the cheeks of your glutes together, and open your knees against the resistance of the band. Do 30 slow reps. **(fig 13-9)**

3. *Hip thrust static position hold* is an alternate variation of either the single- or double-leg hip thrust exercise where, instead of raising and lowering the hips, the hip are raised 1 time to their highest position and held there. Hold this position for about 2 minutes (count 100) on the single-leg static hip thrust or 3 minutes (count 200) on the double-leg static hip thrust.

Static position type exercises help to develop back muscle endurance. Make sure, once again, that when you do single-leg static hip thrusts that your uplifted leg stays in line with the working thigh. A common error when doing the single-leg static hip thrusts is to let the raised leg drift upward where the exercise is easier to do. Fight the body's natural inclination to do this and keep the uplifted leg angle at 30° from horizontal.

All the named back-strengthening exercises also incorporate your glutes (buttocks). At first, you will find that your hamstrings also want to be involved in the exercise since your back and glutes (gluteal muscles) are weak but, as both of these areas strengthen, you should find that your hamstrings become less involved. You can check this when you are in the "hips up" position by grabbing your hamstrings to see if they are loose. Strong glutes are paramount in protecting your low back from injury, so strengthening them should be a major focus in any back injury recuperation. You definitely want to develop a standing posture where your hips are rolled forward and under by contracting your glutes while simultaneously pressing your stomach muscles

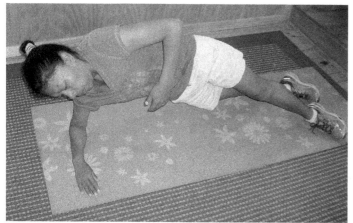

13-10 Side planks

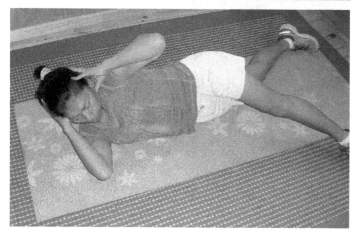

13-11 Side situps

flat against your spine and lifting your chest to push back your shoulders. That same at "attention" position they taught you in boot camp does have a purpose. Keep it and you will go a long way to protect your back.

For the obliques on each side (the guy wires that stabilize the spine side-to-side), I do:

1. *Side planks.* On one elbow. (count 100) **(fig 13-10)**
2. *Side sit-ups.* To stabilize on your body on its side, set the top leg forward and the bottom leg behind. (30 reps) **(fig 13-11)**
3. *Side plank Stars.* While holding in the side plank position raise the topside arm and leg to form an "X" when viewed from the side. (count 50) **(fig 13-12)**

There are other good oblique exercises but most involve some type of rotational spine motion which of course I am unable to do, so I stick to these three.

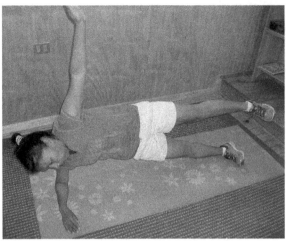

13-12 Side plank "Stars"

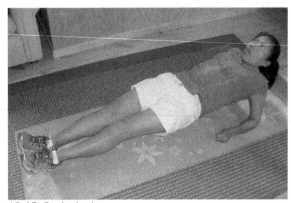

13-13 Back plank

Speaking of "planks," I also do a set for both my stomach and my back. For the stomach plank I am face-down supported on both of my elbows and the toes of one foot. The other foot is held straight legged 5 to 6 inches above the ground for 2 minutes (100 count) and then switch feet. A one-foot stomach plank is a taste more difficult than the standard two-foot stomach plank version and works the glutes at the same time. A more extreme version of this one leg raised stomach plank, is to bend the knee of the raised leg to 90° and lift the sole of that foot towards the ceiling. Folks with low back issues should avoid this version though, since it does torque the low back a bit. For the back plank, I am faceup on my elbows and heels with my hips thrust upward to their highest position and static hold this position for 2 minutes (count 100). **(fig 13-13)** The back plank is more difficult if you raise up one heel while in the plank position but it is too much torque for my lower spine so I stick to the two-heel on the ground version.

LEGS

The second part of our back protection plan is strong legs. For the quadriceps (quads), I work different variations of double-leg and single-leg body weight squats, then finish up with wall sits. In any squatting exercise, make sure you are looking straight ahead, your back is straight, and your heels stay on the ground. At the lowest part of a full squat, your hips should be level with your knees so that both thighs are parallel to the floor. No need to go any lower as it will only stress out your knees. You can do fast-paced half-squats where you only lower until your thighs are at 45° to the floor instead of parallel with

it. For these, you need to up the repetitions considerably (150 to 200 reps). For slow squats, take 3 seconds to lower to the full squat position and then pause in this lowered position for 3 seconds isometrically before returning to the standing position. I alternate a quadriceps exercise with a hamstring exercise and keep alternating until I have completed the number of exercises that I had planned to do. I usually do 2 quadriceps and 2 hamstrings exercises. While one could do all the exercises of one type together you should give 30 to 60 seconds between sets, so, by working the hamstrings while the quads are resting, I finish the whole routine up a bit quicker and may have even held my heart rate up better for some cardiovascular benefit. All leg exercises except static holds and fast half-squats are done in 2 to 3 sets of 20 reps.

Quadriceps
My favorite quadriceps exercises include:

1. *Regular squats.* Squat down to touch the floor between your spread feet. **(fig 13-14)**
2. *Invisible chair squats.* With your feet normal width apart, lower your butt in a manner that mimics sitting down in a chair. I extend my hands to the front as needed for counterbalance.
3. *Bench slide squats.* Squat down and then, while in the squatted sitting position, step side-to-side like you are sliding back/forth to each end of a park bench.
4. *Single-leg and two-leg wall sits.* Sit against the wall and hold these isometric positions for 2 minutes (count 100). **(fig 13-15)**
5. *Single leg step-downs.* From the height of an upside down 5-gallon paint bucket step down to the side with one foot. Keep the toes lifted on the

13-15 Two-leg wall sit

13-16 Reverse lunges

nonworking foot and lower with the working leg to just barely touch the nonworking leg's heel to the ground before driving back up with the working leg.

6. *Reverse lunges.* You can do either forward or reverse but with the knee issues I find reverse a bit more accommodating. I also need something like a chair or a wall situated to one side to hold on to. It would be better if I didn't use one, but such is life. When doing lunges, take a large enough step forward or reverse so your shin never passes vertical. It would be best if it was 5° to 10° short of vertical angling back toward your hips. **(fig 13-16)**

Another good thigh exercise, which I can't do anymore because of my condition, is jumping up onto a higher surface. I liked to do stadium bleachers in this manner. I would jump from one row of bleacher seats to the next higher level in rapid fire succession until I reached the top. Killer workout.

Hamstrings/Buttocks

While most quadriceps exercises do work the hamstrings and glutes, to some degree, I like to target them with additional specific exercises due to their importance in low spine stabilization. I use two exercises that I find super isolates their movement. One I named "big steps," while the other is a calisthenic version of the typical weight room "hamstring curls." "Big steps" are done using either a padded chair or a bed. You will also need something to the side to help you balance. This can be a chair, a dresser, a desk, or a wall.

1. *Big steps.* Stand on both feet about 2 feet from the edge of the bed facing away, then grab your support to the side and step forward an additional 2 feet with your right foot. Extend your left foot rearward to place the top of your foot (dorsal) in a bent knee position on the edge of the bed. You will be pretty stretched out with the right foot well in front of the adjoining knee. From this position, flex and extend your front leg. The knee of the rear leg that is supported on the edge of the bed or chair should nearly touch the floor when you lower the front leg. In the down position, the top of your extended thigh should be level with the floor and the front knee no farther forward than above the heel of the front foot. If needed, move the front foot farther forward until this can be achieved. **(fig 13-17)**

2. *Hamstring curls.* Sit on the floor facing a desk or bar stool as high as your shoulders. Place both hands on the floor slightly behind your back and brace your torso in a near-vertical position while you place the heels of both feet on the desk/stool with your legs straight. You may need to move toward or away from the desk/stool until your find the position that has the correct feel. From this position, do a two-legged hamstring curl by bending your knees and pulling your buttocks toward the heels of your feet. You want the angle between your heels and buttocks to be as small

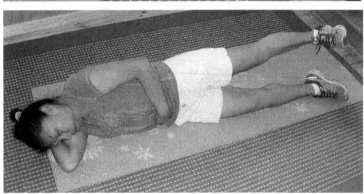

13-18 Hamstring curls

13-19 Top and bottom straight-leg side raises (top leg raise shown)

as you can get it. Gently lower your butt to just skim the floor and repeat. If your hamstrings are weak, you may need to start at a lower level like a chair or bed and work up to shoulder height. **(fig 13-18)**

Running or walking (as is the case of us folks with disabilities) stadium stairs taking the risers several steps at a time or running the bleachers is a great exercise to strengthen your hamstrings and glutes. Having to step up 18 to 22 inches requires the legs to push down and behind. It is that "behind" movement that really incorporates these two muscle groups. When I rowed crew, sprinting up stadium bleachers was perhaps our best land-based leg training exercise. Another good one is running sand hills. Remember that Walter Payton, the famous Chicago Bears running back, built his powerful legs by running sand hills. Lacking access to any stadium stairs,

13-20 Clam shell knee opens

bleachers, or sand hills, go find the steepest hill or trail around and take huge forward steps while running or walking uphill.

Hip Flexors

I do a variety of leg lifts from the side-lying position to exercise the hip flexors. These exercises along with some hip stretches go a long way to prevent hip bursitis or to aid in recuperating from this painful ailment.

1. *Top and bottom straight-leg side raises in the side-lying position.* Be sure your hips are vertical (not inclined either forward or backward) and that the leg you are raising is straight in line with your body. The unused leg is positioned forward as a stabilizer for both lifts. When you do side leg raises correctly, it is difficult to see the leg being raised because it is behind your hip. I have found that if you position your hips vertically and then jam the leg you will be raising as far rearward as possible, you will be in the correct position. These are short lifts of 6 to 8 inches. Do 50 reps with 5-lbs ankle weights and then roll over to the opposite side and repeat with both legs. Without ankle weights, add more reps or double up the sets. **(fig 13-19)**

2. *Clam-shell knee opens.* With a resistance band loop positioned around your knee joints, lie on your side and bring both your knees up together toward your chest so they are 90° to your torso. Now open and close your knees while keeping both feet together. The band should be tight enough so that you can only spread your knees 5 to 6 inches. Do two sets of 15 reps. If you don't have an exercise band available, set a couple ankle weights or some other type of weight on the topside knee joint to provide resistance and do "mini" clam-shell opens (open the knees 2 inches) but triple the number of repetitions. If all else fails and you have nothing at all for weight, use your hand from the topside shoulder to provide downward pressure on the topside knee joint. **(fig 13-20)** When finished with one side, roll over and do the same on the other side. If you have a

resistance band, finish up by rolling to your back and doing some "clam-shell opens" from a knees bent position. This position is identical to the start position for double-leg hip thrusts.

3. *Circular knee opens.* These are done in the same side-lying knees at 90° to torso position as used in "clam-shell knee opens." Raise the top leg 2 inches and do small clockwise and counterclockwise circles. Do these with a couple ankle weights set on the topside knee joint. I alternate 10 clockwise circles with 10 counterclockwise circles until I reach 100, then roll to the opposite side and do the same.

13-21 Toe raisers

Miscellaneous Leg Exercises

Another important exercise for your legs would be sets of "toe raisers" done on a stairway or some other type of drop off so you can get a full range of up and down motion (2 sets of 20). **(fig 13-21)** On my exercise walks, I also spend some time walking on my heels and on my toes. Both of these exercises were assigned to do after my knee replacement, but I have incorporated them into my ongoing exercise routine because of their benefits. I also like to walk (run in younger days) backwards and sideways. Both of these help to develop areas of the leg that many times are skipped over. You may remember sideways running from your grammar school days – the trailing leg alternately crosses in front and behind of the leading leg's step. I would definitely recommend fitting it into your running regime as a prophylaxis to avoid hip joint issues and help strengthen those hip flexors.

UPPER BODY

The third part of the back protection plan requires us to have a strong upper body in order to lift things from waist level on up without incorporating the back in the lifting movement. The upper body is easily strengthened with push-ups, pull-ups, and bar dips of which there are a wide variety of types. I personally cycle through a list of some twenty different push-ups and nearly the same number of pull-ups. Varying the speed, placing your feet on a chair for push-ups, using push-up stands, and/or adding weight can really confuse the muscle. Slow repetitions taking 2 seconds up/down build strength, while fast repetitions develop explosive power. Do both. The number of desired repetitions on upper body exercises will vary between individuals, as well as the exercise itself, so you will have to figure that out yourself. Intensity is the trick to achieving good benefit, so, in whatever you do – push it. Most of the time I do repetitions to muscle failure or thereabouts. In the regular push-up position, your arms will see 64% of your body weight but, with your feet on a surface 2 feet higher than your hand position, they will see 74% of your body weight. Whenever possible I do push-ups on my fists. Not only does it allow a bit more range of motion (ROM), but helps strengthen your wrists. Rest 30 to 60 seconds between arm exercise sets.

Here are 10 of my favorite push-ups:

1. *Normal style push-up variations.* Standard shoulder width, super wide width, hands along your sides at the level of your **xiphoid process**, one hand on a soccer ball with the other on the floor, or mountain climber style where you raise one knee toward the elbow on the same side in as you lower.
2. *Triceps push-ups* (index and thumb of both hands touching to form triangle). Standard or on a soccer ball.
3. *Reverse hand push-ups* (fingers pointed toward feet). These sure help strengthen the front part of the rotator cuff.
4. *Side-to-side jumping push-ups.* In this exercise it helps to have some type of a body length straight line marked on the floor. It can be a row of tile or a specific floor board. Start in the regular push-up position with your feet on the line and your upper body on the left side of the line, then do an explosive push-up to throw the upper body so it lands on the right side of the line. This is followed by another explosive push-up from the right side of the line to return to the start position on the left side of the line. It is basically another version of the hand-clap style push-up, except here you are moving right/left instead of shooting straight up with a hand clap. Feet stay in one position, and only the upper body moves right/left on explosion.
5. *Walking forward and reverse push-ups.* Start in the regular push-up position. Lift and move your right hand forward one palm length, do a push-up. Lift and move your left hand so it is now one palm length ahead of your right hand, do a push-up. Do repetitions, moving forward in this manner, then do the same number of repetitions moving backward to finish where you started.
6. *Walking side-to-side push-ups.* Start in the standard push-up position and do a push-up. When back up in the top raised position, lift your left hand and set it next to your right hand while simultaneously lifting your right foot and moving it to the right the same distance your left hand just moved. Now, lift your right hand and move it to the right the same distance you just moved your left hand while simultaneously lifting your left leg and moving it over to be next to your right foot. Think of it as parallel walking your body sideways to a new push-up position some 18 inches to the right of the original start position. Do another regular push-up. At the top raised position, after that push-up, reverse the sideways walking movement to return your body to the original start position and do another push-up. Continue moving back and forth sideways doing a push-up at each position until you have completed the desired number of repetitions.

7. *Overhead push-ups.* Place your hands together in the triceps push-up fashion above your head. You are almost in the prone superman flying position. Push down and raise your body. In the up position, your arms will have about a 45° angle from the floor to your shoulder. These push-ups are difficult.

8. *Shoulder push-ups.* In a regular push-up position, walk your hands toward your feet until your buttocks are high in the air and from the side you have the outline of a steep mountain (45° hands to butt, 45° feet to butt). Do a push-up but follow the 45° angle of your arms as you go up/down. When this is done correctly, you will touch the top of your head to the floor.

9. *Feet on wall push-ups.* Position yourself close to and perpendicular to a wall. Get in the lowered push-up position and set your right foot against the wall. Raise your left foot so its toes are level with the heel of your right foot (12 inches above floor). Keeping pressure against the wall, raise your right foot even with the left. Now you are in the start position. Do regular push-ups with as much range of motion as you can without your feet coming unglued from the wall.

10. *Dive bomber push-ups.* You may have seen the military do this type. Start position is similar to that of shoulder push-ups, except that your feet are spread wide. Your butt is up the air in stink bug fashion. Lower your upper body following the angle of your arms until your body parallels the ground and your chest is just forward of your hands. At this point, keeping your butt down, push your chest up as if you were pulling out of a dive-bombing run. You will end up in an off-the-ground cobra or lizard stretch position with your feet wide. From this position, reverse the movement following the same curved route until you are back to the starting position.

Here are a half-dozen or so of my favorite pull-up exercises:

1. *Regular style pull-up variations*: standard width, extra wide width, narrow width (hand touching).
2. *Chin-up style variations*: standard width, narrow width (hands touching).
3. *Behind the neck pull-ups.*
4. *Michael Jai White pull-ups.* Start from the regular pull-up hanging position. Pull up and, while in the up position, move your whole body sideways to the left so it is centered behind your left fist. From here move back horizontally to the right until you are centered behind your right fist then return to the middle. From this regular pull-up top position, push straight back away from the bar 12 inches, then pull back in and finally lower to the hanging position. That was one rep.
5. *Front/back pull-ups.* Do pull-ups with one hand in a chin-up grip and the other hand in a regular pull-up grip. On the second set, switch the hand positions around. Another somewhat tougher option is to loop a hand towel around the bar and grab it right below the bar with the chin up hand instead of the bar itself. Makes it tougher and really works the grip.
6. *Neutral pull-ups.* These are done from two shoulder width overhead parallel bars, so your fists are facing each other.
7. *Rowing pull-ups.* These can either be done at an elementary school monkey bar setup (looks like a ladder positioned flat horizontally), a pair of rings hung from a normal pull-up bar, or using the seat of a swing-set as if it were a low horizontal bar. **(fig 13-22)** Think of this exercise kind of like an upside-down push-up. Instead of pushing up from the ground with the body positioned horizontally, you are pulling up with the body hanging horizontally. At a school's monkey bar setup grab somewhere in the middle of the run and kick your feet up to hook one of the crossbars or something so you are stretched out hanging in an upside down push-up position. You can do repetitions with either your hands grabbing a crossbar or the two long outside support bars. If you hang rings from your pull-up bar, set your feet on a tall stool or something so that your body is at least level in the up position of the pull cycle.

Since both my shoulders are separated I have to stick to either neutral pull-ups, rowing pull-ups, or narrow grip pull-ups and chin-ups. If I go with a normal or wide grip, my bicep tendon subluxes out of its groove on the head of the humerus. This holds true if I lower to a lockout hanging pull-up position. Behind-the-neck pull-ups were always my favorite style through-out life, but I have had to give them up, at least until someone surgically fixes both my shoulders. Hanging 20 to 30 lbs from your waist is an excellent way to up your nonweighted reps. I find that discarded oil or coolant gallon containers filled with water make excellent low-cost weights for things like this. Every month I like to do a max test in push-ups and pull-ups. That way,

13-23 Use two chairs to do bar dips when no bars are available

I can keep track of any improvement. If I ever spot a climbing rope or climbing pole somewhere I always stop and give it a try. I can still make it up, but not in the fancy gymnast's "L-lever" style (legs held horizontal straight at 90° to torso) that we would do when I raced crew. I haven't seen a pegboard in many decades, but they give you one hell of an upper body workout.

A few bar dip varieties one can do:

1. *Regular dips done from two parallel bars* – with or without weights hung from your waist.
2. *Muscle up dips.* Basically the upper half of a regular "muscle up" done from a single chest high kid's pull-up bar. These are done in the same fashion as a regular dip, but your hand grip is in line. Lower yourself until your chest touches the bar.
3. *Chair dips.* Position two sturdy chairs facing each other about 3 feet apart. Sit on one of these chairs and grab the seat's edge to each side of your exiting legs with both hands. Next place the heels of both feet on the opposing chair seat, then slide your butt forward off the chair until your body is supported only by your hands and heels. Lower yourself as if you were doing regular parallel bar dips.

If you don't have access to parallel dip bars, two chairs can be substituted instead. **(fig 13-23)** That is what I do most of the time, unless I pass a school on my way home from work that has some jungle gym equipment. If you need a pull-up bar try looking for one of these doorway-mounted versions at a thrift store before you buy new, I always see them there. Of course, on the jobsite, there is always all kinds of situations where you can do both pull-ups and bar dips. I would use CJs many times to do my pull-up sets. Sure, it is not as comfortable for the hands as a smooth round bar, but the important thing is to get them done. If you like to exercise outdoors, maybe you have two trees in your yard that are close enough together so that you can create a pull-up bar by setting a sturdy pole or pipe between a couple of branch saddles. Many times, while traveling, I find some part of a building where I can at least hook my fingers tips and do rock climber style pull-ups. Exposed fire sprinkler pipes are a great find since their hanging system is usually designed to carry lots of weight. Just use your head and look it over well so you don't pull the whole mess down.

I strive to do 3 sets of pull exercises (pull-ups) and 3 sets of push exercises (push-up/bar dips). I always work at the highest intensity and go to muscle failure on each set whether it is slow or fast repetitions. Since each person is different physically, the number of reps I may do will be different than what might work for you so I won't suggest a number, but as always give it your best shot. I normally finish the pull-up, push-up, and bar dip module of my upper body workout with some static isometric holds. I have three types I like. I consider them my fourth set.

1. *Static hold.* At mid-range of a pull-up, push-up, or bar dip hold for 1 minute (count 80).
2. *Elevator pull-ups, push-ups, or bar dips.* Start in the up position for push exercises or the hanging bottom position for pull exercises. Next, lower yourself to mid-range for push exercises or raise yourself to mid-range position for pull exercises and hold there for a count of 10. Now lower yourself to the lowest position for push exercises or raise yourself to the highest position for pull exercises and hold there for a count of 10. That is followed by pushing up to the mid-range position for push exercises or lower yourself to the mid-range position for pull exercises and again hold there for a count to 10. Last, return to the full up position for push exercises or the lowest bottom position for pull exercises and hold there for a count of 10. That is one rep. Usually 5 to 6 reps will work for most folks. Do more reps or add weight if it gets easy. Think of the exercise like the movement an elevator in a three-story building that stops at each floor level on the way up and down.
3. *10-second repetitions.* These very simply are pull-ups, push-ups, or bar dips done super super slow. It should take to a count of 10 to complete each leg of the exercise. 10 seconds up and 10 seconds down. Do 4 to 5 reps or more if able. These are tough.

One upper body exercise regime I like to cycle into my routine on an irregular basis is what I call "endurance reps." I do 4 pull-ups every 20 seconds for 8 minutes (96 total) followed immediately by 10 push-ups every 20 seconds for 8 minutes (240 total). I use triceps push-ups for the push-up series, but I rotate through various types of pull-ups in the pull-up series to be kinder on my damaged shoulders. During the last minute of each series it should be a struggle to finish the repetitions; if it wasn't a struggle, then raise the number of reps the next time you do the regime. For the first few minutes of each series, it is a breeze, but as the muscles get tired, the repetitions get increasingly harder to complete.

I nicknamed another fun repetition regime that I occasionally do "pyramid reps." I start out with a large first set of a push-up or pull-up exercises, let's say 12 pull-ups. That is my pyramid base. Then I subtract 1 repetition on each of the following sets until I zero out. So my second set is 11 pull-ups, my third set is 10 pull-ups, and so on. You can lessen each successive set by a different number, say 3 repetitions if you start with a very high base number like 30 push-ups. "Pyramid reps" can be done in an inverted format as well, starting from 1 repetition on the first set of pull-ups and then adding an additional repetition on successive sets until you reach your desired maximum reps, say 12 pull-ups. Whether you do regular or inverted "pyramid reps," you want to be really struggling to finish the last set, otherwise you need to up the reps.

SHOULDER – ROTATOR CUFF

Since we framers use our shoulders a great deal (even more before the pneumatic nail gun days), I added a series of resistance band exercises that specifically target the rotator cuff area to my exercise routine. Resistance bands allow you to work movements that are hard to address in weight training or calisthenics. While the major upper body exercises like push-ups, pull-ups, and bar dips do help strengthen this area in a bulk sense, they lack any rotational aspect. I was taught a couple handfuls of rotator cuff exercises years ago in order to strengthen an injured shoulder. They were so beneficial that even after my shoulder had improved, I kept right on doing them figuring that they were probably the best way to prevent another injury. Some folks don't like using exercise bands because the resistance varies so much through an exercise's range of motion. It starts off light but ends super hard. This is very true if one uses short bands, since the percentage of band elongation during the exercise is very high. But when you use a long band, the percentage of elongation is insignificant and the resistance stays more or less constant throughout the exercise. In my band exercise series, I use a very long band. I purchase a 6-yard roll (18 feet) and, because all my band exercises are two handed, I double it in half with big overhand knot thus creating a small loop. This small loop works perfect for resistance on double-leg hip thrusts or "clam-shell opens" and serves as the point of attachment when needed. I always get the heaviest grade band a manufacturer has to offer. By stretching a 9-foot band to 11 feet during an exercise causes an elongation of about 20%, which results in only a minimum variation of resistance through the exercise. You will need a good 12- to 14-foot-long area to use the band following my methodology. An exercise band will generally last

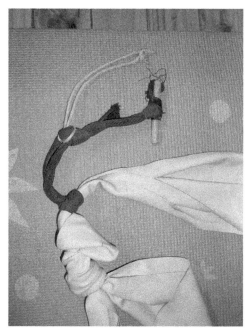

13-24 A short loop of line encircling the far side of a door knob places an exercise band at mid-height

for about a year. For most horizontal pull-type exercises, I anchor the knotted loop of the band to a doorway at door knob height. There are several ways to do this. One way is to attach a thin piece of webbing having a knot near the exercise band's loop, open a door, fit the webbing and knot through the door crack on the hinged side, then close the door. Another option is to attach a short loop of parachute line near the band's loop and then use this to encircle the far side of the door knob and close the door. **(fig 13-24)** A third option is to screw in a small drinking cup hanging hook into the door frame at belly button height to serve as an anchor point for the parachute cord loop. On the two loose ends of the band, I install some short carpenter pencils or their equivalents as hand grips.

With the band attached to a doorway and gripping a loose end of the band in each hand, I would step away until I have stretched the band enough to produce the desired resistance, then perform the exercise. When the hand grip is grasped in your hand, run the band through the gap between the index and middle finger. I typically run a loop of the band around the palm of my hand and then let it exit between those two fingers to better distribute the load. On all these resistance band exercises, I do 4 sets of 10 reps.

Here is a list of the exercises I do with the band anchored at or near door knob height:

1. *The "wrestler" in two distinct versions.* In the first version, stand facing the anchor point while gripping a loose end of the band in each hand. Turn sideways between your hands to the right. Your right hand will now be in front of your stomach bent at 90° while your left hand will be behind your back bent at 90° with your left side facing the anchor point. Move sideways away from the anchor point, stretching the band until the desired exercise tension is achieved. In part one of this exercise, lift both bent elbows to the side as far as you can. The right arm, which is farthest from the anchor point, will be stretching the band while the left arm that is closest the anchor point will be relaxing the band. **(fig 13-25)**

13-25 The "wrestler" rotator cuff exercise done facing towards the anchor point and turned sideways

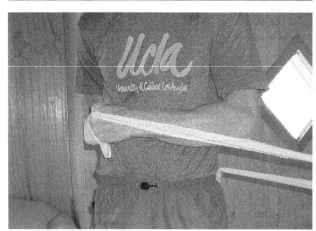

13-26 The "wrestler" rotator cuff exercise done facing away from the anchor point turned sideways

Part two is to reverse this motion. The left arm that is behind your back will pull until its physical limit is reached while the right arm in front of your stomach relaxes the band stretch. That was one rep. After doing the desired number of repetitions, turn back to face the anchor point and then turn sideways to the left to repeat the exercise with the arms in reversed positions with your right side facing the anchor point. The second version of this exercise is done similarly, except this time you start with your back toward the anchor point, arms at your sides while gripping a loose end of the band in each hand and then turn sideways. **(fig 13-26)** In this version, the band applies resistance in the opposite direction of the first version. Movements are the same in and out with 90° bent elbows.

2. *Forward and reverse muscle man poise rotations at shoulder level.* For reverse rotations, face the anchor point while gripping a loose end of the band in each hand. Raise your right arm to your side so that your upper

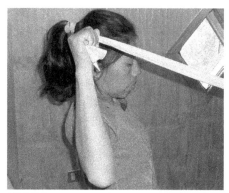

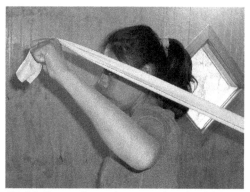

13-27 Reverse muscle man poise shoulder rotation

13-28 Forward muscle man poise shoulder rotation

arm is level with your shoulder and your foreman is bent upward at 90°. This will be similar to the muscle man front single-bicep pose position. Back away from the anchor point to develop the desired exercise tension in the band. Now keeping the upper arm fixed in this muscle man position both up/down and front/back, radially rotate your right fist to the front until your forearm is horizontal. This is the start position. From here radially rotate the forearm against the band's resistance up through the vertical position as far as possible and then relax to return the forearm back to the horizontal start position. That was one rep. **(fig 13-27)** After doing the desired repetitions on the right arm, raise your left arm and do the same. For forward rotations, position yourself in the same muscle man single-bicep pose position, except this time your back is facing the band's anchor point. The start position on forward rotations is the vertical muscle man pose position. Now, keeping the upper arm fixed up/down and front/back as before, radially rotate your fist to the front of your body against the band resistance until it reaches the horizontal position and then return it back up to the vertical muscle man pose position. **(fig 13-28)** That was one rep. It is kind of like a wrist wrestler's arm rotation done straight out to the side of your body. Switch hands when you have done the desired reps.

3. *Internal and external shoulder rotations at stomach level.* We will start with external rotations first. Stand facing the anchor point while gripping a loose end of the band in each hand. In a car driver's double-handed steering position with your upper arms locked tight against your sides and both forearms level,turn sideways to the right. Step sideways away from the anchor point to develop the desired exercise tension in the band. With your right elbow glued to your side, rotate the right forearm internally (medial) until it is up against your stomach. This is the start position. From here rotate externally (lateral) against the band's resistance to its maximum limit. Your forearm should be nearly straight out from your side at the full extent of

13-29 External shoulder rotations at stomach level – start position

13-30 External shoulder rotations at stomach level – finish position

the rotation. Release the pressure and return the forearm to the start position. That was one rep. **(figs 13-29, 13-30)** When the desired number of repetitions have been completed, switch to the left hand that has been patiently waiting for its turn to participate. Keeping your left elbow glued to your side, rotate the left forearm externally until it is in its maximum position. This would be releasing pressure on the band. In this position, you may need to shuffle away from the anchor point to increase the tension on the band. This "straight out to the side" forearm position that was the pull limitation for the external rotations is the start position for internal rotations. From here, rotate internally against the band's resistance until your forearm is up against your stomach, then release the pressure and return the forearm to the start position. That was one rep. **(figs 13-31, 13-32)** When the desired number of repetitions have been completed, return to the car driver's double-handed steering position and turn 180° to your left so that your right side is now facing the band's anchor point. In this position, you will do external rotations with the left arm and internal rotations with the right arm.

4. *Straight arm front/rear flexions.* Face the anchor point and straighten both arms at your sides, palms facing rear while gripping a loose end of the band in each hand. Back away from the anchor point to develop the desired exercise tension in the band. In this straight-arm-locked position, move your left hand against the band's resistance, as far as possible to the rear, while moving your right arm in the straight-arm-locked position to the front by releasing the band's tension. This is the start position. Now "walk" your hands thru one cycle where your left hand goes forward and back while your right hand does the opposite going back and then forward. That was one rep. **(fig 13-33)** When the desired number of repetitions have been completed, spin around so your back is now facing the anchor point and do the exact same exercise in this reversed position.

13-31 Internal shoulder rotations at stomach level – start position

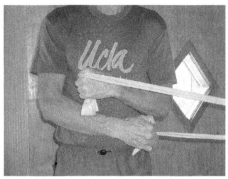

13-32 Internal shoulder rotations at stomach level – finish position

13-33 Straight arm flexions done both facing toward and facing away from the anchor point

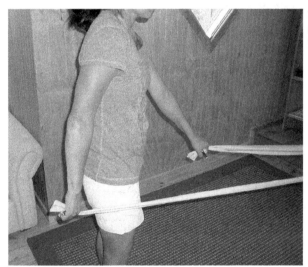

5. *Boxer's hooking punches.* Stand facing the anchor point while gripping a loose end of the band in each hand. In car driver's double-handed steering position, with your upper arms locked tight against your sides and both forearms level, turn sideways to the left so your right side is facing the anchor point. Move sideways away from the anchor point to develop the desired exercise tension in the band. Now raise your right elbow straight up on your side with the elbow bent at 90° until it is level with your shoulder and then move your fist keeping the boxer's hooking position to the right until your arm reaches its outside limit to the side. This is the start position. From here throw a wide right hook across the front of your body against the band's resistance keeping the whole arm in the 90° bent hooking position and level with the shoulder. After reaching

13-34 Boxer's hook and Karate's back fist shoulder height punches (right back fist punch shown)

its inside limit, return the hooked arm to its start position. That was one rep. After completing the desired number of repetitions on the right arm, switch over to the left arm, staying in the same sideways to band anchor position. The left arm will now do a boxer's wide hook in reverse motion or maybe a better description is that you are throwing a bent arm back fist to the side. Start by raising your bent left elbow straight up on your side until it is level with your shoulder and then move it across your chest to the right until it reaches its limit. This is the start position. From here throw a slow bent arm back fist to the left against the tension of the band. You may have to move toward the anchor point slightly to find a tension that is correct. After the left has reached its farthest outward limit, return it to the start point. That was one rep. When you have completed the desired number of repetitions, spin your body 180° to the right and do shoulder-height wide hooks to the front and back fists to the side with your left side facing the band's anchor point. **(fig 13-34)**

I finish off the band workout for my shoulders with a handful of exercises where I am in a standing position with the resistance band looped under the heels of my feet. Gripping a loose end of the band in each hand, I position my hands even with the middle of my hips and then step on each band so my heels are in the center of the band and the band heads upward from behind them. If you need more tension for the exercises, simply shorten the band length by lowering your hands when you step on it. In the floor-anchored position a few exercises include:

1. *Simultaneous two-handed shoulder press.*

13-35 Alternating uppercut punches that reach past the top of one's head

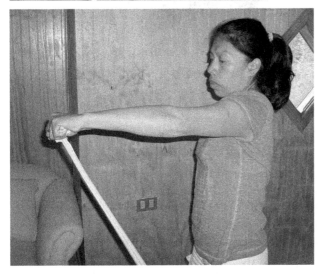

13-36 Alternating palm down straight arm raises to the front

2. *Alternating hand uppercut punches* that reach past the top of one's head. **(fig 13-35)**
3. *Alternating palm-down, straight-arm raises to the front.* Top limit is head height. **(fig 13-36)**
4. *Simultaneous two-handed palm-up or palm-down arm raises to the side.* Top limit is head height and each elbow has a slight bend.
5. *Simultaneous two-handed "behind the head" triceps extensions.* **(fig 13-37)**
6. *Simultaneous two-handed palm-up arm curls.* **(fig 13-38)**

Before we leave the shoulder section, I want to mention that swimming is one of the best exercises someone can do to strengthen their shoulders. In my own life, I have seen how, with time, it can do near miracles to help heal injured shoulders.

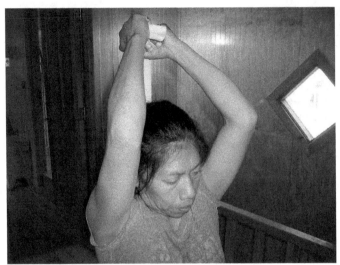

13-37 Simultaneous two-handed "behind the head" triceps extensions

HANDS

A framer's handshake is kind of like his signature. It does not go unnoticed. His hands are calloused and his handshake is firm. One doesn't spend 8 to 12 hours a day swinging a hammer and hauling lumber without having some effect on these two incredible extremities. The human hand has always amazed me in both its dexterity and strength. I remember as a young man easily punishing anyone who wanted to compete in a hand-squeezing challenge. I never lost a hand-squeeze challenge until I was working a weekend night security job at a recording studio in Hollywood, CA. The shift supervisor was a retired Canadian league football lineman who had hands so large that a 50 cent piece could easily pass through his wedding ring. To be truthful, I forfeited the match-up. If I had gone against him, it was likely he would have broken every bone in my hand. There are just some guys that one should never tangle with, and he was one of those guys. For all I know, he probably grew up wrestling grizzly bears in Montana. Anyway, for us framers, our hands are pretty darn important.

While doing pull-ups on different-size bars will help strengthen your hands, it wasn't enough to stop me from getting both lateral and medial tendonitis (tennis elbow and golfer's elbow) at various times in my career, so I decided to add some hand exercises and stretches to keep these injuries at bay. My favorite hand exercise for many years was to simply grab a piece of newspaper by one corner and crumple it up into a ball using only the fingers of that hand. Unfortunately, with Internet news nowadays, few people get the printed newspaper delivered anymore, so I have had to replace that simple newspaper-crumpling exercise with some resistance band exercises.

13-38 Simultaneous two-handed palm-up arm curls

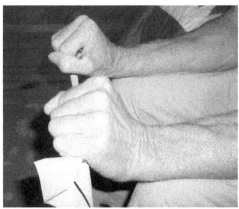

13-39 Palm-down wrist curls

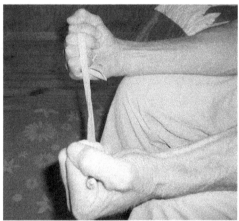

13-40 External wrist rotations

They are all done in the seated position with the band looped under the heels of your feet like was done for the standing shoulder band exercises with each hand grasping a loose end of the band. Your arms are resting on top of your thighs with your fists extended past the knee so you have full range of motion downward. These exercises can also be done with a set of dumbbells if you have some. See how 15 to 20 lbs feel and work up from there. Do 4 sets of 10 reps on all these exercises.

1. *Palm-up curls*
2. *Palm-down curls* **(fig 13-39)**
3. *External wrist rotations.* From the palm down fist position rotate your fists outward to a palm up position. If the band is positioned in your hands so it leaves the grips between your index and middle finger, the band will stretch over the three lower finger middle phalanges (second bone in from fingertip). You should feel the workout on the outside of your forearm close to the elbow. **(fig 13-40)**

Two more hand exercises that I like to do are hand closures against a flexible foam ball and finger extensions against a rubber band looped around the first digits of my five fingers. **(fig 13-41)** It's hard to find a good rubber band that will last very long or provides adequate resistance, so many times I just substitute the fingers of my free hand outside of the exercising fingers to provide resistance. Another good substitute for the foam ball is a ball of pliable

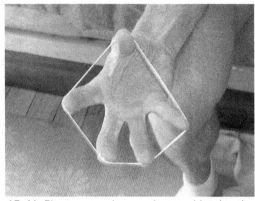

13-41 Finger extensions against a rubber band

wax or clay to work in your hand. In the 1972 film *The Mechanic*, Charles Bronson, who played the part of a paid assassin, kept his hands strong by constantly massaging a ball of wax he carried in his pocket.

NECK

Many folks take their necks for granted, but when your neck has issues, it can sure make life miserable. It is bad enough that our poor necks must carry around an 11-lbs dead weight all day (average head weight) but we crazy framers only compound its normal balancing act by all the strange gyrations that are a part of our job tasks. Your head may spend the day anywhere from hanging down while framing walls to being bent backward while working overhead. When I was on the high school wrestling team, our necks played an important role in the sport and we did all kinds of exercises to strengthen our neck muscles. I wouldn't try to do any of them today because I would probably end up paralyzed from the neck down, but, thankfully, there are kinder exercises that one can do to help the neck survive the rigors of rough carpentry. It was at the 30-year mark in my framing career when I first developed cervical disc issues. It was payback time for all the overhead framing with my neck crooked backward. The physical therapists gave me an exercise regime that included resistance exercises and traction to combat my disc issues. The exercises have gone a long way to subdue the pain and keep my neck functioning. I can't twist my neck very far to either side, but I am OK most of the time if I just avoid positions that put my neck in a bind like lying face down or looking at the stars from a standing position.

While an individual can lay supine on the floor, lift their head, and do four-point circular head rotations to the right followed by the same to the left and then combine these with vertical up and down repetitions to strengthen our neck muscles, I prefer to do a combination of concentric and eccentric

13-42 Side-to-side horizontal neck rotations

13-43 Side-to-side vertical neck rotations

repetitions using my hand/hands to provide the needed resistance. I do these exercises when I am seated on the ground with my legs spread as wide as I can.

1. *Horizontal side-to-side neck rotations.* Looking to the right, place the heel of your left hand on the left side of your chin so that your thumb follows along the jawbone. Your fingers will be pointed up toward the top of your head with the index finger positioned along the joint between the side of your nose with the cheek. Now turn your head to the left resisting the turn with your left hand. The turn should take 1 to 2 seconds. When reaching your maximum limit to the left, push your head all the way back to the right in a reverse course against the force of the neck muscles who are striving to keep your head at the far left turn limit. This return movement should take about 1 to 2 seconds as well. When back to the starting position you have completed one rep. Do 20 repetitions to the left and then switch to do 20 repetitions to the right using the right hand as resistance. **(fig 13-42)**

2. *Vertical side-to-side neck rotations* exercise the muscles along each side of the neck. Start by trying to place your right ear on your right shoulder. In this tilted right position place the heel of your left hand just above your left ear in the temple area. Now rotate your head from this position through the normal head vertical position and attempt to place your left ear on your left shoulder all the while resisting with your left hand. This shoulder-to-shoulder rotation should take 1 to 2 seconds. When the maximum limit to the left has been reached, push your head through the vertical upright position and back to the right tilted start position against the force of the neck muscles that are striving to keep your head in the left-tilted position. This return movement should take about 1 to 2 seconds as well. When back to the starting position you have completed one rep. Do 20 repetitions to the left and then switch to do 20 repetitions to the right using the right hand as resistance. **(fig 13-43)**

3. *Vertical front-to-back and back-to-front neck rotations* exercise the muscles on the front and back of the neck. Roll your head forward and try to place

your chin against your chest. In this head forward tilted position, lace the fingers of both hands together and place them behind your head similar to the hand placement for sit-ups. Now roll your head backward through the normal upright position and to the rear as far as possible while providing resistance with your finger-laced hands. This front-to-back movement should take 1 to 2 seconds. When you have reached your maximum rear tilt limit, push your head back forward through upright to the front tilted start position against the force of the neck muscles that are fighting to keep your head in the full back-tilted position. This return

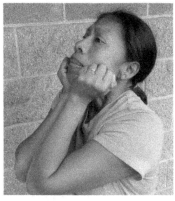

13-44 Front-to-back and back-to-front vertical neck rotations (back-to-front rotations shown)

movement should take about 1 to 2 seconds as well. When back to the start position you have completed one rep. Do 20 repetitions of front-to-back rotations, then switch over to do 20 repetitions of back-to-front rotations. Back-to-front repetitions are done similarly except resistance is applied to the forward-roll movement. Start with your head fully tilted back and place the heels of both hands butted together under your chin. I like to make a partial fist with each hand to roll my fingers down, but your fingers can stay extended if you prefer. Roll your head through upright into the front tilted position while resisting with both hands. This forward head roll should take 1 to 2 seconds. When you have reached the maximum forward tilt limit, push your head back to the rear tilt position against the force of the neck muscles who are fighting to keep your head in the full forward tilt position. This return trip should take about 1 to 2 seconds, just as on all the other neck exercises. **(fig 13-44)**

STRETCHING

In General

Most people know how important stretching is for range of motion and joint health but few of us really put the effort into it that it deserves. Whenever you exercise some muscle group, be sure to stretch it soon afterward while the muscles are still warm. While there are many people who like to stretch before exercising, I find this practice questionable, especially for older folks. It is easier to pull a cold muscle than a warm one. In all stretches, apply pressure only up to the point you begin to feel some slight pain. Every person must learn the difference between good pain and bad pain in order to stretch effectively. Good stretch pain might be compared to a little child complaining about eating some green beans on his/her plate which we all know is nutri-

13-45 Stretch the stomach muscles with a press-up back bridge

tionally beneficial. Too much stretch pain will cause the muscle to tighten up as a protective mechanism, which is counterproductive. One or two stretch repetitions of 15- to 30-second duration works well for all the stretches I will share. They should be done in a gentle, firm, and constant manner – no bouncing. During each stretch, you should find that the muscle will relax a bit, enabling you to apply more pressure and move the joint farther through the ROM. What follows are the stretches I like to do and, in many cases, the only way I am able to do them because of my back and other injuries.

Stomach

1. *Faceup back bridge stretch* is probably the best stomach stretch. Start by lying supine on your back, then place the palm of each hand on the floor just above its corresponding shoulder with your fingers pointing toward your feet. Your elbows will be aimed towards the ceiling. Next, walk your feet up so each heel is nearly touching its corresponding buttocks cheek. It may help to do a hip thrust so you can get your feet even closer. Now press up from your hands and feet and attempt to touch your belly button to the ceiling. You will feel a good stretch through your stomach. Hold your maximum height position steady for 15 to 30 seconds. One or two reps is good. **(fig 13-45)**
2. *Lizard stretch* or *Cobra stretch* as some folks call it, is another favorite stomach stretch. It is done from the facedown prone position. From this position, bring your hands up to standard push-up position under your shoulders and then press up while keeping your pelvis firmly planted on

the ground. This is an excellent stretch to help with low back pain and, in that case, should be done several times a day. **(fig 13-46)**

Back

An easy way to stretch your back begins by sitting on the floor and placing the soles of your feet together so your knees point out to each side. From here, slide your "praying feet" toward your crotch as much as possible and then grab them with your hands. Finally gently pull your upper body toward your feet. You should feel a good stretch all the way down your spine. **(fig 13-47)** Unfortunately, with my back condition I can't do this stretch anymore so I just hang from a pull-up bar to unload the spine. When there is no pull-up bar available, I do what I call the "old football huddle position stretch." From standing, I take my hands and place them right above my knees with my elbows locked straight and then try to sit down. You will only be able to achieve a quarter squat position because of the geometry involved in this movement, but it will give the lower back a nice unloading stretch. **(fig 13-48)**

Groin

For those of you who have no problem doing the "praying feet" back stretch, work right into a groin stretch from that position by sliding your hands off your feet to each side and grab each ankle; then press down simultaneously with each elbow on your bent knees. **(fig 13-49)** For us folks with back issues, this same stretch is best done from a supine position with your "praying feet" and knees in the air. Another super groin stretch is to sit on the floor with your feet spread as wide open as you can get them and gently lean forward. I used to be able to place my face on the ground, but after back surgery I am now happy if I can just get my torso to the forward side of vertical.

13-47 Yoga style back stretch

13-48 Football huddle low back unloading stretch

13-49 Sitting position groin stretch

Legs

Most everyone has some favorite hamstring, glute, and quadriceps stretches, and there are many good ones that can be done from a standing position, but these types torque the low back, so I do nearly all my leg stretches from a supine position to help stabilize the lumbar spine region. I follow a simple routine that does a fairly good job of stretching all the major leg/hip muscle groups. I will run through it for you.

1. *Glute stretch.* Laying on my back, I bend my right knee and raise it toward my right shoulder. From there I grab the knee just below the top to the tibia (lower leg bone) with both hands and gently pull this knee diagonally

13-50 Supine cross-body glute stretch

13-51 Hip rotation stretch

across my torso to the left and then inward toward my chest. You should feel a stretch along the outside of your right leg's gluteus maximus muscle. Your pelvis should stay pegged to the floor throughout the stretch. When done with the right-sided glute stretch, switch over to the left leg and stretch the left side glute in the same manner. **(fig 13-50)**

2. *Hip rotation stretch.* When finished with the left glute stretch, release the grip on your left knee and, keeping your knee bent and in the up position, grab your left ankle with both hands side-by-side. In order to accomplish this, your leg must swing out to the side in a yoga-like position. Now, place your left elbow inside your bent left knee and brace it from moving while simultaneously pulling on your ankle with both hands in a rowing type movement. This will produce a levered stretch that you will feel in the glute and hip area. Like always, when done stretching one side, switch over and do the same stretch on the other side. **(fig 13-51)**

3. *Hamstring stretch.* From the supine position, simply do a straight leg raise as far toward your face as you can, and then grab behind mid-calf with both hands and pull toward your chest. During this stretch, make sure your leg stays straight and that your torso stays flat on the ground. Stretch

13-52 Supine hamstring stretch

13-53 Side-lying quadriceps stretch

one leg, then switch over to work the other. **(fig 13-52)**

4. *Quadriceps stretch.* From a floor position, roll over onto your left side, kick your left leg forward (bottom leg) for balance then bend your right knee and bring your right leg toward your face until you can reach down with your right hand and grab the top of your foot (dorsal). From there pull your foot back around behind your buttocks towards your belt line. To stabilize your pelvis in a vertical position throughout the stretch I have found that it is best to grab the crook behind your left knee with your left hand. With it positioned there, you will be able counter the force of the right hand's pull. Roll to the right to stretch the left leg. **(fig 13-53)**

5. *Iliotibial (IT) stretch.* About 10 years back, I stumbled upon a stretch that just about performs a miracle to help lessen the pain for acute hip bursitis.

It focuses on the IT band and associated muscles. This stretch is done from the one knee down "wedding proposal" or football player's "take a knee" position. In this position, kick your front foot forward 18 inches or so and then lean way forward over this leg until the thigh of the kneeling knee is in line with your torso. You will need to stabilize yourself with both hands placed on the ground to each side of your torso. The front leg should be at least vertical in this position. If it isn't, move your foot farther forward until this is achieved. Now roll the knee of your forward leg out to the side (laterally) and onto the side of your forward foot. You should feel a good stretch down the outside of that leg. Stretch one side and then reverse the leg positions to stretch the other side. **(fig 13-54)**

6. *Calf muscle stretch.* To stretch the back side of my lower legs, I like to alternately just drop the heel of one foot over a stair step after I am done doing my "toe raiser" reps and let my body weight apply the needed pressure. When done with one calf, I switch to the other foot. **(fig 13-21)**

Upper Body
When I swam or played water polo in high school, we always did several upper body stretches before we got into the pool, and, like many things I learned in competitive sports, I carried them forward into my life as a rough carpenter. Not only does keeping your shoulders super limber with good ROM help protect against jobsite injuries, but it is a major focus of physical therapy after a shoulder injury and surgery. I do a seven-stretch series that really limbers up those tight shoulder and arm muscles. I invented the sixth and seventh upper body stretches that I describe and as of yet have never seen anyone demonstrate them, although without a doubt someone somewhere has probably stumbled across them as well. Both do a killer job of stretching the rotator cuff and they came about as I was trying to nurse

13-55 Swimmer's pectoral/bicep stretch

one shoulder back to health after a SLAP lesion (superior labral tear from anterior to posterior) surgical repair. All the following stretches are done from a standing position.

1. *Pectoral/bicep stretch.* Grab an exercise band in front of your body, waist high, palms facing down, as if it were a motorcycle handlebar showing +/–24 inches of band between your fists. A towel will work in a pinch but I prefer a band better because it applies some gentle pressure. Next raise the band straight overhead and then lower it with your arms straight in a circular arc behind your head until it is about 45° off vertical. If you can't make it to that 45° position, widen the grip on your band or towel until you can. You should feel a good stretch on the front of your shoulders, across your chest, and down your bicep muscles. In swimming, we did this stretch with a partner directly behind us who grabbed the wrists of our straight arms just below shoulder height and gently applied some pressure in an attempt to bring them together. **(fig 13-55)**

2. *Hands clasped diagnally behind the upper back shoulder stretch.* For this stretch, place your left hand behind your back with its palm facing away from the body, then reach up as if trying to touch the shoulder blade of the opposite shoulder with the back of this hand. Now, extend your right hand straight overhead and bend it at the elbow so your forearm is hanging down, then try to touch the middle of your back with the palm of this hand. If your rotator cuffs are flexible, you should be able to grab the fingertips of your left hand with the fingertips of your right hand and pull the two together to lock fists for the allotted stretch time. You should feel a good stretch all through the rotator cuff. If your hands are too far apart to clasp fingertips, use a towel or something similar spanning between both hands as an aid to draw the lower arm up higher so you

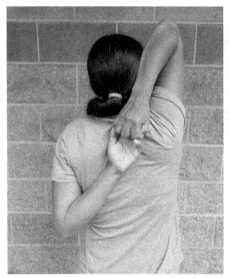

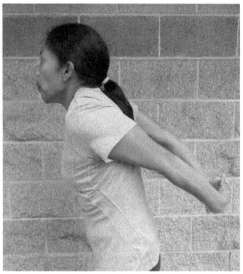

13-56 Hands clasped diagonally behind the upper back, shoulder stretch

13-57 Praying hands behind the back, shoulder stretch

can now reach it with your upper hand. If your rotator cuffs are super stiff or you are recovering from shoulder surgery, this stretch will be near impossible to accomplish, but keep after it and in time you will get there if you are diligent. I personally like to use the exercise band that is already in my hands from the pectoral/bicep stretch as my stretch assistant for these rotator cuff stretches and, for this reason, this stretch is second in my sequence. When you are done stretching one side, reverse your hand positions so the right arm is coming up from below, while the left arm is coming down from above to stretch the other side. **(fig 13-56)**

3. *Praying hands behind the back, shoulder stretch.* Place your hands behind your back as if you were being hand cuffed and interlace the fingers from both hands in the praying hand configuration with both palms facing one another. Now straighten and lock your elbows and then slowly raise both arms up to horizontal or as high as you can lift them. You should feel a good stretch somewhat similar to the pectoral/bicep stretch. **(fig 13-57)** To apply a little extra upward pressure, do this stretch facing away from a bar height surface onto which you can rest your praying hands and then squat down.

4. *Arm across chest shoulder stretch.* Take your right arm and reach across your body at shoulder level as far as possible. Then using your left arm bent 90° at the elbow like a wrist wrestler, reach over and hook the right arm just above the elbow using the 90° cleft of the bent left elbow. Gripped in such a fashion, simply tighten up the left arm's 90° angle by doing a vertical wrist curl, to apply some stretching pressure to the right

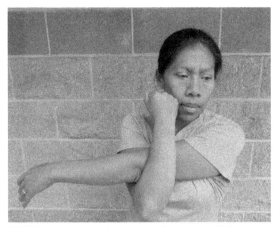

13-58 Arm across chest shoulder stretch (left shoulder stretch shown)

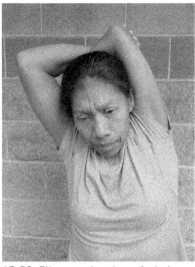

13-59 Elbow to sky triceps/latissimus dorsi stretch (left side stretch shown)

shoulder. When done stretching the right arm switch everything around and stretch the left shoulder. **(fig 13-58)**

5. *Elbow to sky triceps/latissimus dorsi stretch.* Start with your right hand in the same upper position of the earlier rotator cuff stretch where you were trying to touch the middle of your back by reaching down from above. Its elbow should be pointing skyward and located behind your head. Now, with your left hand, reach up behind your head and grab your right elbow. With firm pressure, pull this elbow a taste further behind your head and then lean your upper body to the left to get a good stretch from your right elbow all the way down your right side latissimus dorsi. When done stretching the right arm, switch over and do the same to the left arm. **(fig 13-59)**

6. *Interior rotation shoulder stretch.* Position yourself at a doorway, a post, or an outside wall corner. What you need is a 90° corner against which to place the inside of your elbow with open space to the side so you can stand. Begin by making a fist with your right hand and place the back of this fist behind the center of your spine at the low lumbar region. Now is when the 90° corner surface comes into play. What you must do is back up to that surface and place the inside 3 to 4 inches of your right elbow on that surface and then roll and push your right hip into your forearm. It is almost like you are turning your body to the right but you are stopped by the elbow on this surface. The fist at the center of your spine will raise up as your elbow rolls forward pivoting on the wing of the hip bone. Believe me, if you are doing this correctly, you will feel a great stretch through the shoulder. When

13-60 Interior rotation shoulder stretch in a doorway (left shoulder stretch shown)

finished stretching the right side, do the same with the left side. **(fig 13-60)**

7. *Arm wrestler's shoulder stretch.* Take your right arm and position it in front of your chest at 90° like you are getting ready to have an imaginary wrist wrestling match with someone. Now take your left arm and reach under your right arm to touch the outside of your right shoulder with your palm. This puts you in the correct position to now spin your palm to face away from that shoulder and grab your right wrist. From this position simply use your left arm to lever your right arm down and away. During this stretch your right hand never loses its 90° position while it is being forced to rotate outward to a horizontal position. It sure gives the rotator cuff a good stretch. Like always, when finished with one arm, reverse the setup and stretch the other arm. **(fig 13-61)**

Hand

Last but not least, let's not forget to stretch out our hands or, more specifically, the muscles of our forearms that move our fingers and wrists. This is actually easy to do. With the palm of one hand facing up, you only have to pull the fingers on this hand back slightly to stretch the flexors (anterior of the forearm) or by making a fist and then pushing that fist over in the opposite direction to stretch the extensors (posterior of the forearm). There are lots of positions in which to do these two stretches but if you stick the elbow of one arm in your stomach and keep the fingers of your hand pointed away for both stretches you can't go wrong. **(fig 13-62)** These stretches are an important part of avoiding tendonitis problems. Maybe you remember doing these same stretches in Martial Arts classes. Anyhow, I do them every day rain or shine.

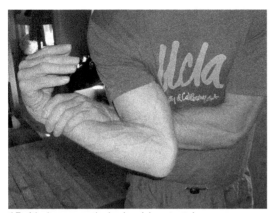

13-61 Arm wrestler's shoulder stretch

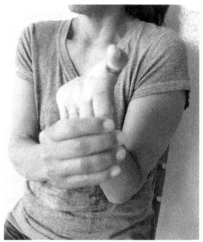

13-62 Palm forward forearm muscle stretch

BALANCE

One of the most important assets for a roof stacker is good balance. I loved to hire guys who were good up high because if one specialized in framing homes with complicated roofs it sure helped to have folks who could move around up top comfortably. I remember framing a three-story commercial building in downtown Santa Barbara, CA, sometime in the mid-1980s. The top floor of this building had a beautiful exposed beam Hip/Gable combo roof design with T&G decking above. To handle the job I decided to beef up my normal crew with two more guys for the high work. I chose two guys who were both Wallendas. One I had gotten to know while working for Ventura framing contractor Jim Martin on a job or two. That was Frank Yacovelli. The other was a guy named Al who had thoroughly impressed me with his up-high abilities on another job. To set the stage for this story, realize we had just finished standing all the walls on the top floor and were prepping to plumb-and-line by tying all the double plates together and positioning liner braces, etc. This work is typically done by one or two guys running around the wobbly double plates and nailing the corners, intersections, etc. Anyhow, Frank was up top on an outside rake wall doing something, I can't remember exactly what, but he was puffing away on a cigarette in his mouth (had a nicotine habit) while bent over. Unfortunately, some of the cigarette's ashes fell on his shoe and it caught on fire. Evidently there was some left over floor glue (highly flammable) on his shoe from when we had sheathed the top floor. Anyhow, I look up and there is Frank jumping up and down on this rake wall trying to smoother his shoe fire. Bear in mind it was a +35-foot vertical drop to the street below. Simply amazing balance. I do miss old Frank – and yes he put the flame out all the while making a joke of it. Years later in the 1990s, while framing a big custom home in the Bay Area, the crew was up on the top plates jockeying a long beam or something into position with a crane. Somehow Dave Sylvester (the cat) accidentally got nudged off the top plates by the hanging beam and took a tumble. I looked over to see Dave contorting himself into position for a soft landing all the while grabbing for his cell phone which was in free fall near him (he got it). When he jumped right back up on the top plates after that 10-foot fall we all agreed he was down to "eight lives." And we wouldn't let him give us this "a good carpenter always beats his hammer to the ground" excuse either since we saw that his hammer had never left his bags. I suppose that had it been a couple decades later, I would have been obliged to razz him about the dangers of texting while walking plate.

While I was never as good as the previously mentioned Wallendas up high I could hold my own especially if it was the typical West Coast single-story home. As we age, our balance goes downhill, but I found that by doing a few simple balance exercises on a regular basis, one can slow that natural decline or even plateau it. I incorporated three easy balance exercises into my PT regime when I was about 40 years old, and they must have worked for I can still walk plates with no sweat if I can somehow just get up there. All three of these exercises are done with your **eyes closed** so be sure you are in an area where, if you stumble, you won't hurt yourself. The first exercise is to walk heel to toe going forward (remember eyes closed). Strive to get to where you can do 30 or more steps in this direction. Then do the same stepping backward toe to heel (eyes closed). Once again strive for 30 or more steps. My second balance exercise is to stand on one foot and balance (eyes closed). The foot on which you are standing cannot move at all. I do this with my hands to the side to use as a balance pole. Shoot for 60 seconds (count to 100) on each foot. **(fig 13-63)** The last exercise is a modified version of that same single-foot stand, only this time, instead of standing motionless on one foot, you do single-leg quarter squats (eyes closed). This makes it a bit harder since your body has to adjust to the constantly shifting weight. Shoot for 6 to 10 slow quarter squats per leg. By doing any of these on uneven surfaces or gusty conditions will up the degree of difficulty. I suppose another really cool practice technique would be to walk one of these webbing straps that are strung between two trees, but I never have had the chance to try. The three exercises I list take only a few minutes to do and work great to improve or keep your balance sharp.

THE THREE LEGGED-STOOL

Good physical training is an important aspect of framing career survival and, while I have emphasized exercise in this chapter, don't forget about the other two legs of the three-legged health stool – nutrition and rest. Personally, I am always amazed at how many people are totally clueless about good eating habits when there is so much information available. The US Department

13-63 One legged, eyes closed balance practice

of Agriculture (USDA) has been publishing food guidelines since 1917. My favorite reference was the "Food Pyramid Guidelines" that came out in 1992. I suppose I like it because I am a visual learner. It was so ingeniously simple that even a youngster of 5 years old could understand it. In 2010, the USDA updated the pyramid to "My Plate" in a modern-day interactive information webpage format. It seems to make it more complicated, but that is our government at work for us. I have always been interested in nutrition reaching back to my crew racing days at Orange Coast College. In an attempt to better my rowing performance I would spend nights at the University of California, Irvine, medical library pouring over everything I could find on applying nutrition to competition. Basically I found that you can't go wrong with the good old food pyramid, but I would add that it is best if one eats foods taken from as close to "the ground" as possible. By "the ground" I mean: fresh from harvest with little or no processing; no added junk like hormones, antibiotics, etc.; animals that have been raised in a cage-free environment – grazing on grass or whatever it is they eat in a natural way. If one stays away from sweets, sodas, alcohol, processed foods, white breads, white sugar, corn syrup, hydrogenated oils, saturated fats, etc., and drinks lots and lots of water, he/she will have few food-related health issues. If you can't understand any item in the list of ingredients for a food product, put it back on the store shelf. One of my heroes, Jack Lalanne, once said that "if it tastes good – spit it out." The reasoning behind his words is that whatever tastes good to the human pallet is always stuff that is bad for us like fats and sugars. I personally have developed such a fine-tuned digestive system that if I eat anything bad for me, I usually get sick to my stomach. And of course the biggie for many people – eat less. There is no need for the amount of food most people put down. Eat a meal the size of your fist and replace all your dinner plates with smaller ones that hold less food so you will not be tempted to pile on the plate more than you should be eating. Never ask for a second helping. The only way one can get fat is to shovel more calories in your mouth than your body needs. Jack Lalanne suggested that an individual eat only until they are about 3/4 satisfied.

Following these simple ideas one should have little problem staying at a decent weight all his/her life with a low body fat content. Strive to keep the thickness of a folded pinch of skin at the side of your belly button added together to the thickness of a pinch of folded skin from the back of your upper arm at less than or equal to 3/4 inch combined. Make it a lifelong goal to stay within 8 lbs of what weight you were as a senior in high school. That seemed to be the time when most people from my day were in their best shape physically. I suppose I haven't done too bad since I now weigh about the same as when I wrestled back in high school. I did bulk up a bit when I rowed at OCC but lost it all as soon as I was back framing full time. Pulling on an oar rowing required a different body mass composition as compared to running around the top plates all day under the hot Los Angeles, CA, summer sun. The weight loss was nothing more than unnecessary muscle mass sloughing off, so I could be more efficient under a different set of physical demands. What an amazing body the Lord has given us in that it can so easily adapt to life's changes.

I don't believe in fad diets, many are plain bad for your health since they are so out of balance. Just use common sense and control your desires. Addicting elements like sugar and coffee, I won't even touch. I am not suggesting that anyone become a nutrition "loco" like me but do be careful with what and how much you put into your fine-tuned "engine." After all is said and done, "we are what we eat." If you want to be a cream puff then by all means go right ahead and chug them down, but if you want to be a "lean, mean, fighting machine" – eat that way.

Water intake is of paramount importance to good health. On the construction jobsite, or any outside work for that matter, the medical experts say to sip water throughout the day. While that may work for some people I am more of a binge style water drinker sucking down a large volume of liquid at one time. I suppose this habit started in the housing tracts when I was a piecemeal stacker. Once I went up on the top plates I would not come down until I finished stacking any particular roof and I worked straight through without breaks. This took some preplanning. I trained my digestive system so that I had a bowel movement before I left for the job in the morning and if I needed to urinate during the day I would fire hose off the top plates rather dropping down to dirt level and use the jobsite portable toilet which might have been a few houses away. In reality I sweated out so much water that urinating was only seldom required. I typically brought three quarts of cold/frozen water plus 4 to 5 quarts of Gatorade up to the roof level with me in a hand cooler. The cooler I stashed by the keg of 16d sinkers and, when I would return to refill my nail bags, I also chugged down some Gatorade or water. Since my 444X nail bag could hold a large amount of nails this wasn't really that often. I believe half of my frigid water got poured over my face and head just to cool off. Each night my routine was to fill three quart-sized plastic bottles ¾ with water and stick them in the freezer. In the morning when they were frozen I would top them off with tap water. They would serve as ice for the bottles of Gatorade and provided some killer cold water when needed. During the summer, the east Los Angeles basin hovered around 100° so the work days could be brutal. This may have been nothing compared to other parts of the country like Las Vegas, NV, or Phoenix, AZ, but it was still damn hot. I was blessed to have a very efficient body-cooling system when younger and therefore handled the dry California heat fairly well. I was skinny with lots of surface area to act as a radiator and disperse my internal body heat. Stockier folks definitely have a tougher time and are built more for the cold. I never ate much during the day, maybe just a handful of mixed nuts or gorp now and then. Big meals slowed me down, and who wanted to eat anyway when it was that hot. Gatorade was my daily staple. I should have bought stock in the company considering how much I patronized their products. In the afternoon when I came down off the roof, the first thing I did was down another quart or so of cold water. I would continue to super-hydrate until I went to bed. When I switched over to framing custom homes we would take two breaks during the work day and these times became my Gatorade/water binge opportunities. In everyday family-style living consider taking two big glasses of water at every meal. Jack Lalanne preached that when you sit down to eat, down the first glass of water you put to your lips in its entirety, while the second glass is there to drink casually with your meal.

As far as physical rest is concerned, medical researchers have found that 8 hours is a good amount of sleep for the "normal person" to aim for. But since "we" framers are far from normal people, I believe 9 hours of sleep is needed to recharge our fatigued body's batteries after a long day of hard manual labor. Therefore, all through my career I would discipline myself to hit the hay early enough so I could get 9 hours of sleep, whether I had a long list of "must do" things awaiting me at home or not. Nothing on that home "to do" list was more important than my health and having a sharp mind on the jobsite. For the sake of my crew I had the responsibility to not only be in the best physical shape possible but to be clear minded. How easy it is for a simple lack of sufficient rest to degrade our thinking process or slow our reactions. So do yourself a favor – keep to a good daily routine and get to bed early.

> Physical fitness is not only one of the most important keys to a healthy body, it is the basis of dynamic and creative intellectual activity.
>
> – John F. Kennedy

Acknowledgments

Muchísimas gracias (much thanks) to all the folks who helped make this book a reality. Here is a list of who they are and what they did. First and foremost would be Rick Tyrell. Rick took it upon himself to keep me motivated and focused on the task. Not only is Rick a truly amazing carpenter and a very dear friend but he is also an English major and seasoned writer, so I laid on him the daunting task of proof reading everything. He never flinched. Beloved Christian pastors, George Castillo and Alan Haitt, both did secondary proof reads on chapter 12, "Teaming up with the Perfect Carpenter." Personal trainer, Maya Andrade, modeled the exercises in chapter 13, "Train to Survive the Battle." My former boss at National Lumber, Dave Saunders, supplied several photos that I was lacking in chapter 3, "The Minimalist," and chapter 7, "Smiles and Frowns." Dave Sylvester, Kathy Curtiss, and Shone Freeman, all went through their old photo albums to come up with some prints from the 1980s and early 1990s, so I could fill various holes in chapter 5, "The Making of a Framing Crew." Jim Goold, who played a major role in the 2002 revised version of *A Roof Cutter's Secrets*, did the new technical drawings that I included in chapter 7, "Smiles and Frowns." Nancy Wachter (CPS Media), was the book's editor. It was she who had to correct all my bad grammar. Annie Clark, did the book's layout, assembly, and cover design. I had had the pleasure of working with Annie on Hanley Wood's 2002 edition of *A Roof Cutter's Secrets*, so it was a real treat to be able to work with her again on this book. Last but certainly not least, Shone Freeman, Dave Sylvester, Davido Biesinger, Thad Connolly, Nick Ridge, and Chuck Cline all volunteered to spot check various chapters or sections to make sure my memory stayed on course.

Glossary/Abbreviations

A/C = air conditioning
ACL = anterior cruciate ligament
amp = ampere

CA valley jacks = California valley jacks
CAD = computer-aided design
Cat = Caterpillar Inc.
CG = center of gravity
cid = cubic inch displacement
CJ = ceiling joists
CM calculator = Construction Master calculator
Com LL = common rafter line length
CPR = cardiopulmonary resuscitation
CSM = circulation, sensation, and motion

DDD = degenerative disc disease

EMT = emergency medical technician

FAA = Federal Aviation Administration
FJ = floor joists
FOHC = "Free of heart center" or lumber void of the tree's pith

GC = general contractor

HAP = height above plate
HD = heavy duty
hp = horsepower
HP = high performance
H/V LL = hip/valley line length

ICP = Intracranial pressure

JLC Live = *Journal of Light Construction* Live

KISS = Keep it simple, stupid.

Lb/s = pounds by weight
LL = line length
LP = long point
LSL = laminated strand lumber

LVL = laminated veneer lumber

mpg = miles per gallon
MRI = magnetic resonance imaging

OB = Outward Bound School
OC = on center spacing
OCC = Orange Coast College
ops = military type operation usually consisting of a strike or raid
OSB = oriented strand board
OSHA = Occupational Safety and Health Administration
OSL = oriented strand lumber

PRP = platelet-rich plasma
PSL = parallel strand lumber
PT = physical therapy

RCS = The 2002+ version of Will Holladay's book *A Roof Cutter's Secrets*
rep/s = repetitions
ROM = range of motion
rpm = revolutions per minute
RR = roof rise

SDS screws = self-drilling screw (high tensile strength)
SIPs = structural insulated panels
SLAP lesion = superior labral tear from anterior to posterior
s/n = serial number
SOP = standard operating procedure
SP = short point

T&G = tongue and groove
TKA = total knee arthroplasty or total knee replacement
TJI = Trus Joist I-Joist

UBC = Uniform Building Code
USPTO = US Patent and Trademark Office

WC = Workers' Compensation
WFR = Wilderness First Responder
wh = Will Holladay
WMA = Wilderness Medical Associates
WMI = Wilderness Medical Institute